Butterworths
Security
Dictionary
Terms and Concepts

Butterworths
Security
Dictionary
Terms and Concepts

John J. Fay

Butterworths
Boston London Durban Singapore Sydney Toronto Wellington

**Library of Congress Cataloging-in-
Publication Data**

Fay, John J. (John Joseph), 1934–
    Butterworths security dictionary.

    Bibliography: p.
    Includes index.
    1. Security systems—Dictionaries.
I. Title.
TH9705.F39   1987   621.389′2   87–
6409
ISBN 0–409–90033–8

Butterworth Publishers
80 Montvale Avenue
Stoneham, MA 02180

10 9 8 7 6 5 4 3 2 1

Printed in the United States of America

TABLE OF CONTENTS

PREFACE

As is the case in so many fields, the security field has a language of its own. Because security reaches into nearly every human activity, its language is extensive and diverse. The language of security contains a common core of terms descended from criminal law, business management, psychology, physics, and other disciplines. It has also borrowed from the numerous industries supported and serviced by security. The experienced security practitioner will be comfortably familiar with many of the core terms, but will have a lesser facility with terms that lie outside his particular industry. A security manager in banking, for example, will use in his everyday working vocabulary terms that are likely to be unknown by his counterpart at a manufacturing plant.

For someone just entering security, learning the idioms of the job can be frustrating and time-consuming. As the beginner moves into the journeyman level, he will discover that a wealth of security-related phrases exist outside of his immediate job or specialty. He will see a larger part of security's total field and will observe changes constantly taking place—changes that are driven by new ideas, new processes, new techniques, and new technologies. He will also note that each change is brimming over with new terms to be mastered and added to his professional vocabulary. The security industry is becoming increasingly sophisticated and interdependent. It is no longer enough to merely know the language of a single specialty or one segment of the field.

Whether technician or generalist, subordinate or supervisor, the security practitioner seeking to excel has a need to communicate. The communication process is enhanced when the practitioner has some knowledge of syntax and grammar, but it is absolutely critical for him to know the basic terms of reference. The basic terms are the building blocks; the rules of speaking and writing are the cement that holds them in place.

This book is more than a dictionary or glossary. The major effort has been to explain and describe rather than to simply define. Examples have been liberally provided where they seemed to be needed. In the three Concepts sections, the effort has been to gather into one readily accessible source a collection of generic ideas broadly applicable to the field. They are arranged in three categories: procedural, organizational (managerial), and legal.

A publication of this type is not a one-time project. It is undertaken with an expectation of later editions. The continued rapid growth of the security field certainly suggests the need for periodic updating. A reader who may be disappointed at not finding a particular term or who may disagree with any provided is encouraged to send comments to me or the publisher. If worthy, they will appear as corrections or additions in the next edition. This is one way in which the language of our profession can be clarified and refreshed.

I have drawn heavily from many references, most of which are identified in the Bibliography. Additionally, I have had the good fortune of being able to call upon many friends whose collective knowledge and experiences contributed to the writing and editing process. Those contributors are identified in the Acknowledgments.

I make no pretension or claim that this work is the final authority on any of the entries contained in it. The language of security is developmental and in constant flux. Definitions change with time and custom. My aim has been to report the most common usage of a term at the time it was chosen for inclusion.

John J. Fay

ACKNOWLEDGMENTS

The author gratefully acknowledges the help given by the following persons and organizations.

Gary Adamson, Barbara Bomar, Boyd Burdett, Sam Daskam, Ron Decker, Sarah Dowdy, Calvina Fay, Larry Fennelly, Carole Hardy, Carol Johnson, Fred Link, Leon Mathieu, Tom McGreevy, Ron Perry, and Tracy Weaver.

American Society for Industrial Security, Conoco, Drug Enforcement Administration, Georgia Crime Information Center, Georgia Peace Officer Standards and Training Council, Houston Police Department, Information Security Associates, Interrotec Associates, National Crime Prevention Institute, Petroleum Industry Security Council, Standard Oil Company of Ohio, U.S. Air Force Security Police, U.S. Army Military Police School, and the U.S. Department of State.

A

abandonment. the act of deserting a pregnant or dependent wife or dependent children without providing proper support; the relinquishment of a legal claim, privilege, or right; the discontinuation of a planned and intended crime before its commission.

abatement. a suspension of a legal proceeding.

ABC Method. a surveillance technique which utilizes a trailing vehicle behind the subject, and a vehicle on each of the parallel streets. It allows pickup if the subject turns right or left.

abduct. to restrain a person by using or threatening to use deadly physical force with intent to prevent his liberation by either secreting or holding him in a place where he is not likely to be found.

abduction. the carrying away or detaining of a person by force; the unlawful taking or detention of any female for purposes of marriage, concubinage, or prostitution.

aberration. a visual discrepancy between the image of an object produced by an optical lens or cathode ray tube and the object itself.

abet. to aid, encourage or incite another person to commit a crime.

ab initio. a legal term meaning "from the beginning"; null and void because of fatal defects at the time an agreement was made, as in an illegal plea bargain.

A-bomb. a marihuana cigarette laced with heroin or opium.

abort button. a human-operated device that disconnects an automatically programmed response action. It is frequently used in computer rooms to prevent triggering of halon or water sprinklers after human observation has confirmed that fire is not present. The automatic discharge is interrupted if the abort button is pressed within a pre-set number of seconds after the fire alarm signal has sounded.

abortion. the unlawful destruction or bringing forth, prematurely, of the human fetus before the natural time of its birth.

abrasion collar. a narrow ring around the entry of a bullet hole in the skin of a victim. The skin, being resistant and elastic, will be stretched by the impacting bullet. A narrow ring around the bullet hole is formed by the abrasive action of the bullet. The ring may also contain residues from the surface of the bullet.

abrasion tool mark. a mark made when a tool cuts into or slides against a surface. Abrasion marks are caused by pliers, bolt cutters, knives and axes.

abrogate. to abolish or nullify; to set aside.

abscond. to go away secretly or hide in order to avoid legal proceedings, as to jump bail; to flee with the property of another, as when a cashier absconds with entrusted money.

absolute liability. a type of liability that arises from extremely dangerous operations. For example, a highway construction contractor could be held liable for damages caused by the use of explosives. A claimant would not have to prove that the use of explosives is inherently dangerous.

absolute privilege. a prohibition against prosecution for criminal libel, regardless of malice, generally limited to official participation in the governmental process. This prohibition is based on the belief that the public benefits by having officials at liberty to exercise their functions with independence and without fear of litigation.

absolute zero. a hypothetical temperature at which there is a total absence of heat.

absolve. to free from an accusation or from guilt.

absorption-elution. a common test method used in a crime lab to determine blood groups.

abstinence syndrome. the group of physical symptoms experienced by an addict when the addictive drug is withdrawn. The syndrome varies according to the drug abused. In narcotics abuse, the symptoms include watery eyes, runny nose, yawning, and perspiration from 8 to 12 hours after the previous dose. This is followed by restlessness, irritability, loss of appetite, insomnia, goose flesh, tremors, and finally yawning and severe sneezing. These symptoms peak at 48 to 72 hours, and are followed by nausea, vomiting, weakness, stomach cramps, and possibly diarrhea. Heart rate and blood pressure are elevated. Chills alternating with flushing and excessive sweating are characteristic. Pains in the bones and muscles of the back and extremities occur as do muscle spasms and kicking movements. Suicide is a possibility, and without treatment the symptoms may continue for 7 to 10 days. Also called the withdrawal syndrome.

Acapulco gold. marihuana grown around Acapulco, Mexico. It is high-grade and golden brown in color.

accelerant. any highly flammable substance used by an arsonist to start a fire. Commonly used accelerants are gasoline, kerosene, naphtha, and jet fuel. Also called accelerator.

accelerated depreciation. a method of depreciation used in the computation of income

1

taxes. It speeds up the write-off of value at a rate greater than normal depreciation.

acceleration clause. a clause in contracts evidencing a debt, such as mortgages and installment contracts, that results in the entire debt becoming immediately due and payable when a condition of the contract is breached. Without an acceleration clause, the mortgagee or seller would have to sue for the amount of each payment as it became due, or would have to wait until the entire debt matured.

acceleration scuff. in traffic accident investigation, a scuffmark made when power is applied to the driving wheels with sufficient force to cause at least one of the wheels to spin on the road surface.

access. the ability and opportunity to obtain knowledge of classified information.

access code. symbolic data or an equipment mode that allows authorized entry into a controlled area or into a computer file without causing an alarm condition or deactivating sensors.

access control. control of persons, vehicles and materials through entrances and exits of a protected area; an aspect of security that utilizes hardware systems and specialized procedures to control and monitor movements into, out of, or within a protected area. Access to various areas may be a function of authorization level or time, or a combination of both. Some access control systems feature historical data bases for reference.

access control card. a card containing coded information. It is placed in or near a card reader nearby an entry point. The card is read by the reader and access is granted if the information on the card is valid for that specific time, day, and entry point.

access list. a list of persons having authority, usually on a temporary basis, to enter a protected area.

access mode. a feature of an alarm monitoring system which allows sensors to be shunted by automatic or manual command. An alarm signal is silenced when a protected area is in the access mode. However, if the system is tampered with during the access mode, an alarm would be annunciated.

access parameters. specifications programmed or entered into a central controller which define system variables such as authorization levels, entry times, and identification codes.

accessory. a person who was not present when a crime was committed, but who was involved as a guilty party either before or after the crime.

accessory after the fact. a person who, knowing that another has committed a felony, subsequently aids the felon to escape or pre-vents the felon's arrest and prosecution. An accessory after the fact must have an intention to assist and must actually do so.

accessory before the fact. a person who, before the time a crime is committed, knows of the particular crime contemplated, assents to or approves of it, and expresses a view of it in a form which operates to encourage the principal to perform the act. An accessory before the fact is similar to a principal in the second degree. The difference relates to where the accessory was at the time the act was committed.

accident. as used in connection with motor vehicles, any situation wherein one so operates a motor vehicle as to cause injury to the person or property of another, or to himself.

accidental whorl. a fingerprint pattern consisting of a combination of two different types of patterns, with the exception of the plain arch, with two or more deltas; or a pattern which has some of the requirements for two or more different types; or a pattern which conforms to none of the definitions.

accident analysis. a critical examination of facts developed in an accident investigation for the purpose of identifying causal factors and prescribing measures designed to prevent recurrence.

accident proneness. a personal trait or predisposition, as opposed to some characteristic of the environment, that leads some persons to have more accidents than others within a given time period and under conditions where all face the same risks.

Accident Response Group. a team of scientific, medical and technical persons who with specialized equipment carry out the Department of Energy's accident response operations upon notification of a peacetime nuclear accident.

accident severity. a measure of the severity or seriousness of losses, rather than the number of losses. It is measured in terms of time lost from work rather than the number of individual accidents.

accommodation endorsement. an endorsement made for the purpose of lending the endorser's credit to a party to the instrument. A regular endorsement transfers title to the instrument, whereas an accommodation endorsement is for additional security only. An accommodation endorser is never the maker, drawer, acceptor, payee, or holder of the instrument he endorses.

accomplice. a person who helps another person commit a crime.

accordian load. hose loaded into a hose compartment by folding it back and forth accordian-style.

accountability. the state of being responsible and punishable for a criminal act. This responsibility is reduced or abolished in certain instances because of age, mental defect, or other reason.

account executive. a pimp or procurer of high-priced prostitutes.

accumulator circuit. a circuit that initiates an alarm signal as a function of accumulated information. For example, a circuit programmed to send a signal when a door remains unclosed after a specified number of seconds, or when a specified number of sensors activate in one zone within a given period of time.

accusation. a formal charge made to a competent authority against someone who allegedly has committed a crime.

ace lock. a type of pin tumbler lock in which the pins are installed in a circle around the axis of the cylinder, and move perpendicularly to the face of the cylinder. The shear line of the driver and bottom tumblers is a plane parallel to the face of the cylinder. This type of lock is operated with a push key.

acetorphine. an opium derivative classified as a Schedule I Controlled Substance.

acetyldihydrocodeine. an opium derivative classified as a Schedule I Controlled Substance.

acetylmethadol. an opiate classified as a Schedule I Controlled Substance.

acid. LSD.

acid head. a user of hallucinogenic drugs such as LSD.

acid phosphatase. an enzyme which is found in large quantities in the seminal fluid of man and ape. There are also small quantities of acid-reacting phosphatase in vaginal fluid, fecal material, red blood cells, and rarely in saliva. Differentiation between the various types of phosphatase may be done by using multiple laboratory tests, quantification of amount present, or separation by electrophoresis.

acid phosphatase reaction test. a crime laboratory test which determines the presence of semen in a suspect stain or substance. The test provides a positive chemical reaction for semen and is considered specific.

acid test for silver content. an investigator's test in which a solution of silver nitrate, nitrate acid, and water is applied to a silver coin to determine if it is counterfeit.

acid test ratio. cash plus other assets that can be immediately converted to cash divided by current liabilities. Because it indicates the abilities of a business enterprise to meet its current obligations, the acid test ratio is one of the most important credit barometers used by lending institutions.

ack-ack. to dip the end of a cigarette in heroin powder, light it, and smoke it.

acknowledge. to verify receipt of an alarm condition by responding in some way such as to depress a special function key or throw a switch. It is an operation required in some alarm monitoring systems as a means of ensuring that the alarm condition has been acknowledged.

AC line carrier. a system that transmits signals over standard AC power lines. The signals can be alarm signals or data that activate other devices on the AC power lines.

acoustic fuse. a bomb sensitive to minute sonic or subsonic variations. The fuse operates from an influence exerted by the target on a sensitive detecting device within the fuse itself.

acoustic pickup. a conventional or a specially designed microphone used for the detection of sounds.

acoustic room. in electronic countermeasures, an area shielded acoustically against eavesdropping.

AC power supply. a power supply source that serves as a source of one or more alternating-current output voltages. The supply may be an AC generator, transformer, or inverter.

AC ripple. fluctuations in the output of a rectifier or power supply.

acquisition. purchase or takeover of another organization.

acquisitive vandalism. a legal term for damage to property accompanied by a larceny such as the looting of vending machines or the taking of plants and shrubs.

acquit. to set free, release, or discharge as from an accusation of crime.

acquittal. a judgment of a court, based either on the verdict of a jury or a judicial officer, that the defendant is not guilty of the offense for which tried.

action. gambling play, as in betting or wagering.

action ex contractu. an action at law to recover damages for the breach of a duty arising out of a contract.

action ex delicto. an action at law to recover damages for the breach of a duty existing by reason of a general law. An action to recover damages for an injury caused by the negligent use of an automobile is an ex delicto action. Tort or wrong is the basis of the action.

action steps. activities to be performed within an established time frame to accomplish a given task.

activation analysis. an analysis to determine

chemical elements in a material by bombarding it with neutrons to produce radioactive atoms whose radiations are characteristic of the elements present. The technique has many forensic applications; for example, to determine the presence of lead, antimony and barium in residue taken from the skin of a person believed to have fired a gun. Also called neutron activation analysis.

active card. a type of access card that operates like a miniature transmitter. The card reader provides power to the card and the card emits a readable signal based on binary numbers. It is usually not suitable for security purposes due to cost, bulkiness and interference with other transmitters or receivers which may be nearby.

active imaging. forming a visual image on a screen of low light scene by using an infrared illumination source. The technique is not dependent on available light energy to electronically form the image.

active leaf. the leaf of a double door that must be opened first and which is used in normal pedestrian traffic. This leaf is usually the one in which a lock is installed.

active listening. an interviewing technique in which the interviewer listens to both the facts and the feelings of the speaker.

active sensor. a sensor that generates or emits a protection field. Microwave and ultrasonic detectors are examples of active sensors.

Act of God. an accident causal factor generally interpreted as being beyond human control. Examples are lightning, hurricane, flood, tornado and earthquake.

actual cash value. an amount equivalent to the replacement cost of lost or damaged property at the time of the loss less depreciation.

actuating block. that portion of a magnetic contact set containing the magnet. The switching element is housed in the mating piece which is called the contact block.

actuator. any type of sensor or switch in a security system capable of initiating an alarm signal.

actus reus. the criminal act, as contrasted with mens rea, the criminal intent. It is sometimes used to describe the physical or "doing" part of a crime.

acute situational maladjustment. a superficial maladjustment to newly experienced life situations which are especially difficult or trying.

Adamism. a form of exhibitionism in which the male exhibits himself in the nude.

Adamsite. a mob control gas which induces nausea and severe vomiting.

addict. one who has acquired the habit of using narcotics to such an extent that reasonable self-control has been lost.

addict files. files maintained by the Drug Enforcement Administration which identify persons who have been arrested by any federal, state or local law enforcement agency on a charge of illicit drug use.

addiction. a state of periodic or chronic intoxication produced by the repeated consumption of a drug. Addiction characteristics include an overpowering desire or need to continue taking the drug and to obtain it by any means, a tendency to increase the dose, a psychic and generally a physical dependence on the effects of the drug, and an effect detrimental to the individual and to society.

ad hoc. for this; for this special purpose.

ad hoc arbitrator. an arbitrator selected by the parties involved to serve on one case.

Adipex. the trade name for phentermine hydrochloride which is regulated under the Controlled Substances Act as a Schedule IV stimulant.

adipocere. a post mortem condition in which hydrolysis of fatty parts of the body (particularly the cheeks, abdomen wall, and buttocks) turn into fatty acids and soaps. Adipocere is yellowish-white in color, has a greasy feel, and a strong, penetrating, musty odor. The chemical process is induced by enzymes and water in moist anaerobic climates (conditions in which bacteria do not need oxygen to survive). Although adipocere fat may cover wounds, close examination will show the presence of the wounds, even when the process is in an advanced stage.

adjective law. a term relating to the concept that all laws can be organized in two divisions: substantive and adjective. Substantive laws are those that set up rights and duties, and this includes practically all laws except those that are procedural. Adjective law is concerned with the procedure involved in carrying out substantive law, such as the laws of arrest, trial and bail. Also called procedural law.

adjourn. to put off, defer or postpone.

adjudicate. to settle a matter in the exercise of judicial authority.

adjudicatory hearing. the fact finding process wherein a juvenile court determines whether or not there is sufficient evidence to sustain the allegations in a petition.

ad litem. for the suit; for the litigation. A guardian ad litem is a person appointed to prosecute or defend a suit for a person incapacitated by infancy or incompetency.

administrative control. the plan of organization and the procedures and records that are concerned with the decision processes leading to management's authorization of transactions. Such authorization is a management function directly associated with the responsibility for achieving the objectives of the organization and is the starting point for establishing accounting control of transactions.

administrative judge. a judicial officer who supervises administrative functions and performs administrative tasks for a given court, sometimes in addition to performing regular judicial functions.

administrative law. the law concerning the powers and procedures of administrative agencies, including especially the law governing judicial review of administrative action; the rules and regulations framed by an administrative body created by a state legislature or by Congress to carry out a specific statute. For example, the federal income tax law is administered by the Internal Revenue Service. The IRS issues regulations and rules that have the weight of law as long as they keep within the scope of the income tax statute. Frequently such regulations interpret in specific ways the legislature's general intent when it enacted the statute. Thus, administrative bodies that are primarily executive in nature may also have powers that resemble legislative or judicial authority.

admissible. pertinent and proper to be considered in reaching a decision. As applied to evidence, the term means that it is of such character that the court is bound to allow it to be introduced.

admission. a statement of guilt that is less than a full confession; an acknowledgment by either prosecution or defense that a statement of fact made by the opposing side is true; the entry of an offender into the legal jurisdiction of a corrections agency and/or physical custody of a correctional facility.

admission against interest. an admission of a fact which, though short of a confession, tends to suggest possible guilt; for example, that the subject had a motive or opportunity to commit the crime.

admonition. a reprimand from a judge to a person accused, upon being discharged, warning him of the consequences of his conduct, and intimating to him that a repetition of the offense will bring more severe punishment. Also, any authoritative oral communication or statement by way of advice or caution by the court.

ADP system. an assembly of computer hardware, software, facilities, persons and procedures configured for the purpose of computing, sequencing, storing, retrieving or otherwise manipulating data and information with a minimum of human intervention.

ADP system security. a level of protection for classified information related to hardware/software functions, characteristics and features of such functions, operation and accountability procedures, and access controls at central, remote and terminal computer facilities.

ad quod damnum. to what damage; what injury. It is a phrase used to describe the plaintiff's money loss or the damages he claims.

adrenal exhaustion. physical exhaustion brought on by extended or acute fear or other emotional stress. It is an important factor in polygraphy.

adultery. an offense committed when one person engages in sexual intercourse with another person at a time when he has a living spouse, or the other person has a living spouse.

ad valorem. according to value.

advance fee scheme. a scheme designed to obtain fees in advance for services the promoter has no intention of providing. Usually the offender will claim to have means of obtaining buyers for one's business, property, securities, or other assets, or to have access to sources of loan financing.

adversary. the opposing party in a civil or criminal action.

adversary system. the Anglo-American system for resolving both civil and criminal disputes. It is characterized by a contest between the initiating party, called the plaintiff in civil proceedings and the prosecutor in criminal proceedings, and the responding party, called the defendant, and presided over by a judge, who adjudicates and renders final judgment for one party or the other, sometimes with the aid of a jury for finding disputed facts, on the basis of evidence presented by the parties in open court, and in light of the applicable law.

adverse action. a personnel action considered unfavorable to an employee, such as a discharge or demotion.

adverse witness. a witness who is biased against or hostile to the party who has called him, and who therefore may be asked leading questions and cross-examined.

aerial measuring system. in nuclear power security, a system that performs aerial measurements of ground and airborne radioactivity over large areas by utilizing instruments that detect and record gamma radiation, both as gross count rates and gamma energy spectra.

affiant. the person who makes and subscribes an affidavit.

affidavit. a written statement which is signed and sworn to under oath before a judge or other official.

affirmant. a person who testifies on affirmation, or one who affirms instead of taking an oath.

affirmation. a solemn declaration made under penalty of perjury.

affirmative action program. a detailed plan of action intended to overcome the causes and effects of discriminatory policies in the hiring, employment and/or training of minority group members.

aforethought. in criminal law, deliberate; planned; premeditated.

a fortiori. a Latin term meaning "by a stronger reason." The phrase is often used in judicial opinions to say that, since specific proven facts lead to a certain conclusion, there are for this reason other facts that logically follow which make stronger the argument for the conclusion.

African black. marihuana grown in Africa.

after-accident situation map. a scale drawing of a traffic accident scene; a graphical summary of results of an accident, usually without indication of assumptions or inferences concerning fault or cause.

aftercare. the status or program membership of a juvenile who has been committed to a treatment or confinement facility, conditionally released from the facility, and placed in a supervisory and/or treatment program.

after image. the retention, usually momentary, of an image on a cathode ray tube screen. When an after image is permanent it is called a burn-in, a condition caused by exposing the sensitive tube to an extremely bright scene for an extended period of time.

Age Discrimination in Employment Act of 1967. a federal law which prohibits discrimination against individuals 40 to 65 years of age. The Act's purpose is to ensure the employment of older persons based on their ability and to prohibit arbitrary age discrimination in employment. The Act is enforced by the Wage and Hour Division of the Department of Labor.

agent of influence. a suborned or ideologically committed individual who occupies a sensitive position in an adversary's opinion-molding institutions or governmental agencies from which he is able to influence public opinion.

agent provocateur. an individual who is specifically hired by an organization to create trouble in a rival organization; an undercover police officer or a person acting on behalf of the police, who surreptitiously seeks to incite others to criminal behavior so that the police may intervene and the offenders may be prosecuted.

agent transmitter. a small radio transmitter concealed on an agent or other person working on behalf of law enforcement. The transmitter is used to surreptitiously capture information from criminals or to give early warning to backup agents if a threat is made against the person wearing the transmitter. Also called a body bug or body wire.

age of consent. the chronological age of a female, usually 16 or 18, after which it is no longer felonious for another to have voluntary sexual relations with her.

aggravated assault. unlawful intentional causing of serious bodily injury with or without a deadly weapon or unlawful intentional attempting or threatening of serious bodily injury or death with a deadly weapon.

aggravating circumstances. circumstances relating to the commission of a crime which cause its gravity to be greater than that of the average instance of the given type of offense.

aggressive patrol. police or security officer saturation of a high-crime area. The patrol officers often employ field inquiries and, where indicated, stop-and-frisk tactics. The objective is to identify offenders, confiscate weapons and stolen property, and generally create difficulties for criminal opportunists.

aggressor. one who first employs hostile force; the party who first offers violence or offense.

aging receivables. a scheduling of accounts receivable according to the length of time they have been outstanding. The schedule will show which accounts are not being paid in a timely manner and may reveal the source of developing cash flow problems.

agitator. one who stirs up, excites, ruffles or perturbs. One who incessantly advocates a social change.

Aguilar v. Texas. a case in which the U.S. Supreme Court ruled that it is not sufficient for a police officer seeking a search warrant to simply tell the issuing judge that an informant, whose information is included in the application for the warrant, has previously proved to be reliable or that the officer knows the informant is reliable.

aid and abet. help, assist, or facilitate the commission of a crime, or encourage, counsel, or incite as to its commission.

aikido. a Japanese art of self-defense employing locks and holds and utilizing the principle of nonresistance to cause an opponent's own momentum to work against him.

Air Force Law Enforcement Terminal System. a U.S. Air Force communications system that allows access to computerized law informant data available through NCIC and the various statewide computerized criminal information systems.

Air Force Radiation Assessment Team. a U.S. Air Force field-qualified team of health physics technicians designated to respond with air transportable equipment to radiation accidents/incidents for the purpose of providing on-site health consultation and instrumentation to detect, identify and quantify radiation hazards.

air gap. a measurement of the maximum distance a magnetic contact switch will operate reliably when not adjacent to metallic objects.

airhead. a drug user who has difficulty thinking or talking.

Air Opium. a nickname given to air operations that transport opium out of areas in Southeast Asia.

air pack. a portable unit, usually worn on the back, typically consisting of an oxygen canister, flow regulator and face mask.

air pressure sensor. a sensor that reacts to changes in air pressure. It is used to protect seldomly used and relatively airtight interior areas.

air transportable radiac package. a collection of radiac equipment, spare parts and trained instrument repair technicians maintained in an alert status by the US Air Force for airlift to the scene of a nuclear weapon accident/incident.

alarm. a warning device triggered by the presence of abnormal conditions in a machine or system; a condition showing a sensor has changed from a secure state.

alarm assessment system. a device or system that allows an operator of an alarm system to evaluate or assess a reported alarm. For example, alarm assessment can be made possible with the use of a CCTV system that permits visual observation at a protected area where a motion sensor has activated.

alarm bypass. a feature of an access control system which shunts the alarm when an authorized card is used for entry.

alarm condition. a threatening condition, such as an intrusion or hold-up, reported by an alarm system.

alarm control unit. that element of an intrusion detection system which provides power, receives and evaluates information from sensors, and transmits signals to the annunciation element.

alarm discriminator. a device that discriminates between genuine alarm stimuli and routine or normal stimuli. For example, an alarm discriminator installed with vibration detectors would discriminate between innocent vibrations caused by passing vehicles

and suspicious vibrations caused by breaking glass.

alarm hold. a means of holding an alarm once sensed. For example, an alarm hold circuit applied to a magnetic contact on a door will continue to indicate an alarm after the door has been closed by the intruder.

alarm indicator. an audible or visual signal used to indicate an alarm condition such as fire or intrusion.

alarming sequential switcher. a video switcher that displays views from several cameras in a predetermined cycle. In addition to sequencing, the switcher automatically displays views from a zone that has an alarm signal. The alarm is detected via the CCTV system alarm input for sensors in that zone.

alarm initiator. a device that automatically transmits an alarm signal when a threat event occurs. Examples of alarm initiators are fire and smoke detectors, water flow switches and intrusion detectors.

alarm line. an electrically supervised wire circuit used for the transmission of signals from a protected area to a central receiving point.

alarm receiver. an annunciator with alarm line supervision which may or may not include an audible tone. An alarm receiver may process the signal for display on a separate annunciator. Some receivers have an integral or peripheral hard-copy printer for event-recording purposes.

alarm response time. the elapsed time from the moment an alarm is activated or sounded and a signal transmitted to monitoring stations until firemen or police arrive on the scene.

alarm screen. a window screen, usually laced with fine wire, used as an intrusion detection device. Cutting or breaking the screen causes an open circuit and trips an alarm. Alarm screens are available in many sizes and styles to suit the particular installation.

alarm sensor. that element of an intrusion detection system which senses an existing or changing condition.

alarm shunt. a device which monitors and reports tampering with a switch, such as a doorswitch at a controlled access point.

alarm signal. an audible and/or visual signal indicating an emergency that requires immediate action.

alarm station. a manually operated device or switch that generates an alarm signal. It is used in public areas for reporting emergencies, such as a fire alarm pull station, or in concealed applications, such as a holdup button.

alarm switch monitor. a device which monitors the status of an alarm switch. It can be used to detect intrusion, tampering, failure, fire and similar conditions.

alarm system. a combination of sensors, controls and annunciators arranged to detect and report an intrusion or other emergency.

alarm transmitter. a signaling device reporting sensor or system status to a receiver.

Alco-Analyzer Gas Chromatograph. a breath testing device used by the police to determine alcohol concentrations in the blood of drivers suspected of being under the influence of alcohol.

Alcohol Safety Action Program. a state sponsored effort in cooperation with the National Highway Traffic Safety Administration designed to reduce highway deaths, injuries, and property damage resulting from motor vehicle traffic accidents in which alcohol is a major contributing factor.

Alco-tector. a breath testing device used by the police to determine alcohol concentrations in the blood of drivers suspected of being under the influence of alcohol.

ALGOL. an acronym for algorithmic language, a computer language made up of both algebraic and English components.

algorithm. a simple set of rules arranged in a logical order that will solve all instances of a particular problem. In security applications, combinations of sensor inputs may be categorized into specific sensor patterns which trigger certain annunciation responses as defined by equipment circuitry or software.

alias. a name used for an official purpose that is different from a person's legal name.

alias dictus. otherwise called.

alibi. a defense used by one charged with a crime that he could not have committed the crime because he was elsewhere at the time.

alibi witness. someone testifying in support of a defendant's alibi, usually claiming to have been with or to have observed the defendant in a place other than where the crime was committed at the time of its commission.

alienation. a sense of estrangement or separation from community or society; a lack of cohesion with the surrounding environment, people and social institutions; in law, a transfer of property or of a right to another.

Alien Registration Act of 1940. a US law, also called the Smith Act, that requires the annual registration of aliens. It also prohibits advocating the violent overthrow of the US government.

alien reports file. a file maintained in the district offices and suboffices of the Immigration and Naturalization Service. It is designed mainly as a locator file.

alkaline battery. a battery made of manganese dioxide and alkaline potassium hydroxide in a zinc case. The alkaline battery has an im-

proved shelf life and in lower temperatures operates better than the carbon-zinc battery.

allegation. a statement by a party to a legal proceeding setting out what will be proved.

alleged. a term used to describe someone who has been accused of or is under suspicion for a crime but who has been neither convicted nor exonerated by a trial.

alligator effect. in arson investigations, the checkering of charred wood, giving it the appearance of alligator skin. Large rolling blisters indicate rapid, intense heat, while small, flat alligator marks indicate long, low heat. Alligator marks indicate that the fire was enhanced by an accelerant.

all-out. a signal indicating a fire is out or under control and that all or most of the fire fighting units are ready to resume normal assignments.

all points bulletin. a message sent to all law enforcement agencies within a given communications network. An all points bulletin on LETS, for example, is transmitted nationwide. Also called APB.

all service mask. a canister-type mask which can be used in low concentration of gases or smoke where there is adequate oxygen to support life and permit active fire fighting.

allylprodine. an opiate classified as a Schedule I Controlled Substance.

alphacetylmethadol. an opiate classified as a Schedule I Controlled Substance.

alphameprodine. an opiate classified as a Schedule I Controlled Substance.

alphamethadol. an opiate classified as a Schedule I Controlled Substance.

alphanumeric. a term descriptive of characters consisting of numbers and letters.

alphanumeric character UIC. in computer usage, a format of a user identification code that specifies a user's group and member in alphanumeric form.

alphanumeric key pad. a device similar to a push button telephone dial. The key pad generates a signal (to release a door lock, for example) when the buttons are pressed in a particular coded sequence.

alphaprodine. an opiate classified as a Schedule II Controlled Substance.

Alpha Team. in nuclear weapons security, a US Army team possessing an alpha radiation monitoring capability. The team is usually a component of a Nuclear Accident and Incident Control Team.

alprazolam. the generic name for a barbiturate regulated under the Controlled Substances Act as a Schedule IV depressant. It is sold legally as Xanax.

alternate juror. a person added to a jury panel. The alternate juror is substituted for a juror who, during the trial, dies, becomes ill, or is excused or disqualified by the trial judge. There may be more than one alternate juror in a trial.

alternating current. an electric current that continuously reverses direction. It is usually the primary power source for alarm equipment. Also called AC.

alternating-current alarm system. an alarm transmission system that provides line supervision with an AC balanced resistive-bridge network. An advantage of an AC transmission system is that the signal can be sent via standard voice-grade telephone lines and does not require dedicated DC metallic conductors.

altimeter bomb. a bomb, frequently home-made, which is triggered by the change in atmospheric pressure relative to the altitude and the earth's surface.

AMAC 1. a riot control vehicle which features grenade launchers, a water cannon, an electrified body, CCTV, hermetically sealed air conditioning, firefighting systems, full armor, a built-in drinking water supply and a toilet.

amapola. a Mexican poppy from which opium is extracted.

amateur burglar. a burglar who tends to act on impulse and opportunity. His targets are frequently the more vulnerable buildings, such as schools, churches, and small businesses, and he will generally steal low risk items, such as cash and postage stamps.

ambient light. the light level that is normal for an area without manipulation to alter the level.

ambient temperature. the temperature of the medium by which an object is surrounded.

ambush code. a special code entered on a digital keypad or given verbally to report a duress situation.

ambush evidence. surprise evidence in the course of a trial; last minute secret evidence used to sway the jury with courtroom drama.

A.M. drawing. in a numbers operation, a drawing usually held in the early afternoon to determine that day's winning numbers.

amenable. subject to answer to the law; responsible; liable to punishment.

American Wire Gauge. a standard system for designating wire diameters. Also called the Brown and Sharpe wire gauge.

amicus curiae. a Latin term meaning "friend of the court." An amicus curiae is any person or organization allowed to participate in a lawsuit who would not otherwise have a right to do so.

amindone. a substitute or synthetic narcotic.

amino acid. in forgery detection, the residue left on paper as a result of perspiration when the finger or other parts of the body come into contact with it.

ammonal. a shell bursting charge composed of ammonium nitrate, ammonium powder and TNT.

amnesty. a form of executive clemency, usually extended to a class or group of offenders; for example, draft evaders. In many countries amnesty is extended as a part of national celebrations.

amobarbital. the generic name for a barbiturate regulated under the Controlled Substances Act as a Schedule II drug. The prescription drug called Tuinal contains amobarbital. It is a commonly used barbiturate, usually taken orally or injected. Also called barb, downer, blue, yellow jacket and sleeping pill.

amobarbital sodium. a barbiturate known by the brand name, Amytal (a solid blue capsule). Also known as blue bird, blue devil, blue heaven and blue.

amortization. the return of debt, principal and interest in equal annual installments; the return of invested principal in a sinking fund.

amotivational syndrome. a condition sometimes seen in chronic drug users. It is characterized by a general lack of motivation and loss of personal will, rendering the victim highly susceptible to suggestions and manipulation by other persons.

ampere. a unit of electrical current equivalent to the steady current produced by 1 volt applied across a resistance of 1 ohm.

ampere-hour. a unit of electricity equal to the amount produced in 1 hour by a flow of 1 ampere.

amphetamines. a family of stimulants whose medical use is currently limited to narcolepsy, attention deficit disorders in children, and obesity. The illicit use of amphetamines closely parallels that of cocaine, and despite broad recognition of risks, abuse continues. Vast quantities of amphetamines, such as methamphetamine and dextroamphetamine, are produced in clandestine laboratories. Other names include Biphetamine, Delcobese, Desoxyn, Dexedrine, and Mediatric. Amphetamines appear in the Controlled Substances Act as Schedule II and III stimulants.

amphetamine psychosis. a reaction seen in chronic users of amphetamines. It is characterized by vivid visual, auditory and olfactory hallucinations and delusions.

amphetamine variants. hallucinogens that are chemical variations of amphetamine synthesized in a laboratory. These drugs are numerous and differ from one another in their speed of onset, duration of action, potency, and capacity to modify mood with or without producing hallucinations. They are usually taken orally, sometimes "snorted," and rarely injected. The common variants are DOM, STP, DOB, MDA, TMA, PMA and 2,5-DMA. Amphetamine variants appear in the Controlled Substances Act as Schedule I hallucinogens.

amplifier. a device that creates an enlarged reproduction of the input without drawing power from the input.

amplitude distortion. the difference in the shape of an amplifier's output signal from the shape of the input signal.

amplitude response. the maximum amplitude measurements obtained at selected points on the frequency range for a device operating at rated capacity.

amylase azure test. a crime laboratory test to indicate the presence of saliva. Amylase is an enzyme peculiar to saliva and its detection in or on an object can be significant to an investigation. Amylase, for example, might be found on cigarette butts, envelope flaps, and postage stamps.

anachronism. in forgery detection, something on a suspect document that could not have possibly been present when it had been drawn up at the time indicated.

analog communication. a form of communication consisting of a continuously varying waveform. For example, the electrical signal on a telephone circuit is typically an analog waveform.

analog sensor. a sensor capable of producing a signal that varies over a continuous range. A temperature indicator is an example of an analog sensor.

analog to digital converter. a device that converts analog voltage to binary coded decimal digits.

analysis of variance. a statistical procedure for determining whether the change noted in a variable that has been exposed to other variables exceeds what may be expected by chance.

analytical confirmation. in drug investigations, the confirmation of a field test made of a suspect sample in which the finding was "positive." The field test is analytically confirmed by a second test which uses procedures as sensitive or more sensitive than the field test.

anarchy. action to overthrow an organized government by the use of force or violence or other means.

anchor. a device used to secure a building part or component to adjoining construction or to a supporting member.

anechoic chamber. a sound cavity in a horn or siren that minimizes echoes and vibrations.

ANFO. a low explosive made of ammonium nitrate fertilizer and fuel oil.

angel dust. a form of phencyclidine (PCP) sprayed on marihuana or tobacco for smoking purposes.

angle. the way or manner in which a scheme can be worked; to scheme; personal interest in a crime or racket.

anileridine. an opiate classified as a Schedule II Controlled Substance.

animal. in criminal law, any living creature, except a member of the human race.

animo. with intention, disposition, design, or will.

animo furandi. intent to steal.

ankle belt. a leg-restraining device applied to the ankles of a violent subject. It consists of a braided line passed around each ankle and then secured. A variation of the device allows it to be used while transporting a violent subject in a patrol car.

annealed glass. basic window plate glass not suitable for security applications.

annunciation circuitry. that element of an alarm system's control function which provides the means of conveying information from the control function to the annunciation function.

annunciator. that element of an intrusion detection system which alerts human intelligence to an alarm condition; a visual or audible signaling device which indicates the status of detection sensors.

anomie. a state of normlessness in which there is a breakdown of the rules governing social behavior. It is used to explain some suicides, and to describe the conflict between culturally instilled goals and socially approved means of attaining those goals. The anomie theory suggests that deviance and crime occur when there is an acute gap between cultural norms and goals and the socially structured opportunities for individuals to achieve those goals.

anorectic drug. a drug that causes loss of appetite. Phenmetrazine, benzphetamine, and phendimetrazine are examples of anorectics.

answer. a document which the defendant in a civil lawsuit serves on the plaintiff or his attorney in answer to the summons or complaint.

antenna. a conductor or system of conductors for radiating or receiving electromagnetic waves.

ante mortem. that which proceeds or occurs immediately prior to death.

antemortem wound. a wound inflicted prior to death.

anthropometry. bertillonage; a system of identification using body measurements, e.g., height, length of arms, fingers, feet, and size of skull. The system was created by Alphonse Bertillon.

antibug. a radio noise generator designed to interfere with bugs.

anti-climax dampening effect. in polygraphy, an effect upon a subject being tested in which all questions other than the one feared by the subject will be anti-climactic. Responses to the anti-climactic questions will appear to be dampened in the measurements recorded by the polygraph instrument.

anti-contamination clothing. clothing that provides protection from alpha-beta radiation and which helps to prevent the spread of contamination. A respirator that protects against the inhalation of contaminants is also considered a piece of anti-contamination clothing. Sometimes called anti-C's.

anti-disturbance device. a device built into a homemade bomb that will trigger the bomb if it is jarred, moved or disturbed in any way. Also, any one of various chemical mixtures which when rearranged due to excessive movement or sudden change of temperature will cause an explosive package to detonate.

anti-disturbance fuse. a bomb fuse designed to function upon receipt of some physical disturbance to the explosive ordnance after the fuse is armed. It is employed almost exclusively as an anti-personnel device and may be incorporated as a component of nearly every type of explosive ordnance.

anti-eavesdrop device. a device that scans rf transmission frequencies to detect the presence of covert listening devices.

anti-freeze extinguisher. an extinguisher using calcium chloride solution or a proprietary compound having a low freezing point.

anti-friction latch. a latch bolt that incorporates any device which reduces the closing friction between the latch and the strike.

anti-human test. a crime laboratory test of a suspect stain to determine whether the stain contains blood or other body fluids of human origin. In certain cases where the stain is found not to be human, the exact animal species may be determined.

anti-jam. a feature on some digital communicators and tape dialers that helps prevent incoming telephone calls from interfering with dialouts.

antimony trisulfide vidicon. a CCTV camera designed for daylight or well-illuminated scenes and usually installed indoors. It has a spectral response similar to the human eye.

anti-passback. a feature of an access control system which prevents successive use of one card to pass through any portal in the same direction. To attain this protection, a separate reader is required at each entrance and exit. Anti-passback prevents a card from being passed back to another person for the purpose of gaining unauthorized access.

anti-personnel bomb. a bomb intended to primarily injure or kill people, frequently homemade as in a pipe bomb, and designed to fragment upon explosion.

anti-pick latch. a type of spring latch bolt having an attached parallel bar that prevents a thin-bladed tool from exerting pressure to force open the latch.

Anti-Racketeering Act of 1934. a federal law that, as amended, prohibits the use of extortion or violence that in any way obstructs, delays, or affects interstate commerce. Also called the Hobbs Act.

anti-shim device. a mechanism in a lock which prevents the bolt from being pried back into the door.

antisocial personality. a sociopathic character disorder. It is the cause of criminality in some persons.

Anti-Strikebreaker Act of 1936. a federal statute that prohibits employers from transporting strikebreakers across state lines. As amended in 1938, it also forbids the interstate transportation of persons for the purpose of interfering with peaceful picketing (common carriers excluded). Also called the Byrnes Act.

anti-surveillance equipment. any device or combination of devices designed to detect or prevent the use of electronic surveillance equipment.

antitrust laws. laws designed to prevent restraint of trade, monopoly, and unfair practices in interstate commerce. The antitrust statutes are the Sherman Act (Antitrust Act of 1890), the Clayton Act, the Federal Trade Commission Act, the Robinson-Patman Act, the Miller-Tydings Act, and the Wheeler-Lea Act.

anti-wedge shackle. a padlock shackle having extended shoulders that surround the shackle and thereby protect it from being wedged or cut.

anxiety disorder. a condition in which severe and persistent anxiety interferes with daily functioning.

aortic regurgitation. in polygraphy, an expected and natural phenomenon observed as a dicrotic notch in the cardiosphygmograph tracing. It is caused by blood pressure changes resulting from the expulsion of blood through the semilunar valves in the left ventricle of the heart.

APCO Ten Series. a set of standard radio signals that substitutes numbers for frequently used messages. For example, the signal for "okay" or "acknowledge" is 10-4.

apnea. cessation of breathing; partial asphyxia. In polygraphy, it is a phenomenon frequently observed in the reactions of guilty/deceptive subjects and persons who attempt to distort measurements during testing.

apparatchik. a Russian word for bureaucrat, now used colloquially to refer to any administrative functionary.

appeal. a formal application of one found guilty of a crime by a lower court to have the case sent to a higher court for review.

appeal proceedings. a set of orderly steps by which a court considers the issues and makes a determination in a case before it on appeal.

appearance. the act of coming into a court and submitting to the authority of that court.

appellant. the person who contests the correctness of a court order, judgment, or other decision and who seeks review and relief in a court having appellate jurisdiction, or the person in whose behalf this is done.

appellate court. any court that reviews a trial court's actions, or the decisions of another (but lower-level) appellate court, to determine whether errors have been made and to decide whether to uphold or overturn a verdict.

application. end use of data processing services and facilities. The scope of an application extends to DP services used or invoked, application programs and associated software, input, output, data, procedures, documentation, and responsibility assignments. Payroll and engineering design are examples of applications.

applied stimulus. in polygraphy, an external stimulus applied to an examinee for the purpose of adjusting polygraph instrument controls. An example of an applied stimulus would be to ask the examinee to solve a simple mathematical problem. As the examinee ponders the problem, the polygraphist adjusts the controls.

apprehend. to take, seize or arrest a person.

a priori. from what goes before; from the cause to the effect; a generalization resting on presuppositions and not upon proven facts.

aqueous film forming foam. a fire extinguishing substance consisting of water and a foaming agent.

arbitration. a proceeding established by previous agreement in which both sides to a controversy submit their dispute to persons designated or to be chosen.

arborescent mark. a mark on the body of a lightning victim. It is so-called because of its tree-like shape.

architectural barriers. physical aspects of a building that might hinder or prevent the employment of a physically handicapped person. The lack of a ramp, for example, may prevent a person in a wheelchair from entering a building having only stairways for access.

Architectural Barriers Act of 1968. A federal statute which specifies that buildings and facilities designed, constructed, altered or leased with federal funds are to be usable by and accessible to physically disabled persons.

arch pattern. one of the three basic groups of fingerprint patterns, the other two being the loop and whorl. The arch pattern has two subgroups: the plain arch and tented arch.

area authorization. a feature of an access control system which grants entry through one or more portals into single or multiple areas.

area detection. a technique for detecting an intruder's presence anywhere within a specifically defined area under protection.

area mat. a thin rubber or vinyl mat containing metallic strips, usually concealed under carpets. An alarm is triggered when an intruder steps on the mat.

area protection. the protection of large interior areas with volumetric detection devices such as microwave, passive infrared and ultrasonic sensors.

area sketch. a type of rough sketch which depicts the physical surroundings closest to a crime scene. Area sketches might be made of the house containing a room where a crime occurred, the area immediately surrounding the house, and the neighborhood.

argument of counsel. the final statements given to a court or jury by a prosecutor and defense attorney.

arm. to activate or turn on an alarm system.

armed. the status of a nuclear weapon in which a single signal will initiate detonation.

armed propaganda. a term used by terrorists to describe their acts of violence.

armed robbery. the unlawful taking or attempted taking of property that is in the immediate possession of another, by the use or threatened use of a deadly or dangerous weapon.

armed signal. a signal, transmitted from a protected premises to a central station or other monitoring location, which informs that the alarm system has been armed by an authorized person.

arming station. a switching device from which an alarm system is placed into operation.

armored front. a plate or plates which is secured to the lock front of a mortised lock by machine screws in order to provide protection against tampering with cylinder set screws. Also called armored face plate.

armor piercing bullet. a high-velocity bullet usually jacketed with steel. In larger calibers, armor piercing bullets are manufactured with chemicals that ignite and burn through a target upon impact.

armpit carrying. a shoplifting technique in which the thief places an item, such as a rolled up sweater, under the armpit inside a jacket or coat.

arm's length transaction. a sale involving two parties who are independent of each other.

arraign. to bring an arrested person before the court, where the charge is explained and a plea is taken. If later indicted, the same process is repeated in a higher court.

arrest. the taking of a person into custody to answer for a crime. It may be effected by "an actual restraint of the person or by his submission to custody." Police officers, however, may detain persons for any of several purposes without the detention becoming custodial and thereby an arrest.

arrest rate. the number of arrests as a percentage of the crimes known to the police; the number of arrests as a percentage of the entire population or a cohort thereof, such as arrests of males within the total population or of male juveniles within the male population.

arrest record. a list of a person's arrests and or charges that have been made against him, usually including those that have been dropped and those of which he was found innocent. The arrest record also contains information on dispositions and sentences, where there was adjudication of guilt.

arrest register. a document containing a chronological record of all arrests made by members of a given law enforcement agency, containing the identity of the arrestee, the charges at time of arrest, and the date and time of arrest.

arrival card. a self-addressed card sent by a shipper to a freight agent and designed to be returned to the shipper by the agent when the shipment reaches its destination.

arson. the intentional destruction, by fire or explosive, of the property of another, or of one's own property with the intent to defraud.

arsonist profiling. an investigative technique designed to assist in the identification of an arsonist. A psychological profile is prepared from available clues, such as the ignition device and accelerants used, preparation, methodology, and entry/departure methods and routes.

artillery. paraphernalia for injecting drugs.

Ashuft v. Tennessee. a case in which the U.S. Supreme Court held that the police may not use prolonged and continuous interrogation to obtain a confession.

asportation. the unlawful removing or carry-

ing away of the personal property of another.

assassinate. to kill for hire, or kill a prominent person.

assassin's special. a .22 caliber automatic fitted with a silencer.

assault. unlawful intentional inflicting, or attempted or threatened inflicting, of injury upon another.

assault with a deadly weapon. unlawful intentional inflicting, or attempted or threatened inflicting, of injury or death with the use of a deadly weapon.

assembly language. a computer language that directly interacts with the hardware. It is considered a low-level language, as opposed to high-level languages such as COBOL and FORTRAN.

assets. the valuable resources, or properties and property rights owned by an individual or business enterprise.

assets protection. to shield from danger or harm the money, receivables, information, resources, rights, property and other valuables of an owner.

assignable cause. a causal factor designated as having a relationship to an accident.

assigned counsel. a defense attorney appointed or assigned by the trial judge for an indigent defendant who is not represented by counsel.

assigned risk. a risk which underwriters do not care to insure but which, because of a law or otherwise, must be insured. An example of an assigned risk is a motorist who has repeated convictions for moving violations.

assignment. the transfer of a right or interest in property by one person to another.

Assimilative Crimes Act. an act which provides for the applicability of state criminal statutes to criminal acts committed within federal enclaves but not specifically covered under federal law. The purpose of this statute is to provide for the prosecution in the federal courts of offenses committed within federal enclaves to the degree and extent that such conduct would have been punished had the enclave remained subject to the jurisdiction of the state. Prosecutions under this act are not to enforce the laws of the state, territory, or district, but rather to enforce federal law, the details of which, instead of being delineated by statute, are adopted by reference.

associative evidence. evidence that links a suspect to the crime scene or to the offense. Fingerprints, shoe and tire impressions, and matching hairs, fibers, fragments, and paint chips are examples.

assumed identity. a change of name, address

and/or appearance for the purpose of avoiding detection.

assume the position. an order by a law enforcement officer to a suspect to assume a spread-eagle position preparatory to a search. The term is also used by correctional officers when conducting searches of prisoners.

assumption of risk. a common law defense. For example, a person who rides as a passenger in an automobile has generally "assumed the risk" and therefore has no action against the driver should an accident occur.

asthenic reaction. a psychoneurotic reaction characterized by listlessness, lack of enthusiasm, and physical and mental fatigue.

Astro-Pak. a brand name for a two-part explosive used in blasting. A two-part explosive is composed of two chemicals each of which is not explosive until joined together.

"A" substance. the water soluble substance in body fluids that would be secreted by a person of blood group A or AB.

asylum state. the state or place in which a fugitive from justice seeks refuge.

asynchronous attack. an attack of a computer system which takes advantage of the asynchronous nature of computer operating systems. An attack might be aimed at confusing the queuing of jobs waiting to be performed.

asynchronous communications interface adapter. a device used to interface the parallel data of a computer to a serial synchronous communications link.

atavism. a theory of criminal behavior which postulates that criminality diminishes in the evolutionary development of humanity, and that its appearance as a biological predilection in some persons is a hereditary throwback on the evolutionary scale.

Ativan. the trade name for lorazepam, a depressant drug in the family of benzodiazepines. It is a commonly abused drug and is regulated under the Controlled Substances Act as a Schedule IV depressant.

Atmospheric Release Advisory Capability (ARAC). a capability of the Department of Energy in which a computer model projects the most probable path of radioactive contamination released at a nuclear accident site.

atomic absorption spectrometer. a device that determines a sample's elemental composition by identifying the wavelength of the light that the sample absorbs. It is used in criminal investigations, especially in respect to the evaluation of gunshot residue.

atrocity. the result of conduct that is outrageously or wantonly wicked, criminal, vile, cruel, extremely horrible or shocking.

at ship's tackle. a term used in cargo transactions to indicate the point at which possession changes hands.

attachment. a proceeding by which a person or his property are restrained in accordance with a direction of a civil court to secure payment of a judgment or the presence of the person when the case is being tried.

attachment of property. a writ issued in the course of a lawsuit, directing the sheriff or a law enforcement officer to attach the property of the defendant to satisfy the demands of the plaintiff.

attempt. an act done with intent to commit a crime but falling short of its actual commission. For example, one who aims at a person and pulls the trigger of a non-functioning pistol might be charged with attempted murder.

attempt to commit a crime. a form of conduct, coupled with intent, which tends to effect the commission of a crime.

attenuation. in security communications, a reduction in signal strength.

attenuator. in security communications, a mechanism for reducing signal strength by a known amount.

attestation. the act of signing a written instrument as witness to the signature of a party, at his request. For example, witnessing signatures to a contract or a will.

Attorney General. the chief legal officer of the United States and head of the Department of Justice; the chief legal officer of a state.

Attorney General's list. a document which at one time listed suspected subversive organizations. The document was prepared by the Office of Attorney General of the United States.

attorney in fact. a person who has been appointed by another to transact business for him and in his name. The person does not have to be a lawyer.

attractive nuisance. a dangerous place, object or condition to which children may be attracted. The owner of an attractive nuisance has the legal duty of taking unusual care to prevent injury to those who may be attracted to it. Examples are construction projects, swimming pools and animals.

audible alarm device. a noise-generating device used to call attention to an alarm condition or a change in the mode of operation of a security system.

audio actuator. a sound actuated device used to turn on and off tape recorders or radio transmitters.

audio detection device. any one of a variety of microphones installed in an unoccupied protected area for the purpose of detecting intrusion sounds.

audio discriminator. a sound detection and

evaluation device capable of discriminating between different types of sounds, such as the difference between a passing truck and breaking glass.

audio listen-in. monitoring the sounds at a protected facility to determine when an intrusion occurs and/or to determine the nature of the intrusion after it has been detected by other means.

audio monitoring. an arrangement of microphone, amplifier and receiver that allows a person at a separate location to listen for suspicious sounds.

audio-restore. automatic resetting of an alarm device or system within a specific time period. Also called auto reset.

auditability demonstrability. a term referring to an auditable application whose performance according to specifications and compliance with business control and asset protection requirements can be demonstrated to, or formally tested by, an independent reviewer.

audit trail. a sequential record of system activities sufficient to enable the reconstruction, review, and examination of the sequence of events in the path of a transaction from its inception to final results.

aunt emma. morphine.

authentic act. that which has been executed before a notary public or other public officer, duly authorized, or which is attested by a public seal, or has been rendered public by the authority of a competent magistrate, or which is certified as being a copy of a public register.

authentication server. a device used in conjunction with a password authenticator. The password authenticator is a pocket-sized unit which contains a pre-filed user number and a cryptographic algorithm for calculating a required reply number. In use, a computer network user logs on from a local terminal, utilizing the system's logon routine. At that point an authentication server attached to the host computer displays a challenge number. The user enters the challenge number into the password authenticator which generates a reply number through the terminal. If the reply number is accepted, access is granted.

authorization level. a location or entry point that has a defined security rating. Only individuals having proper clearance and meeting certain identity criteria may enter such an area. In access control systems, authorization levels are the objects of protection.

authorized access control switch. a device for switching a detection system on and off.

authorized person. a person who has a need-to-know for classified information and has been cleared for the receipt of such information.

auto-alarming switcher. a video switcher that has the ability to automatically display a camera view for a zone that has initiated an alarm via the CCTV system. Alarm inputs are located in the field with the CCTV cameras and share the same system for transmitting both the alarm data and video data back to the auto-alarming switcher.

autoclave bomb. a bomb designed to explode when atmospheric conditions change. Also called an altimeter bomb.

autoerotic death. an accidental death, usually by strangling, in which the victim dies performing a bizarre sexual act. The victim, while trying to achieve sexual gratification, will typically use rope or cord to constrict the neck.

Automated Regional Justice Information System. a computerized system that assists law enforcement by providing criminal history information.

Automated Security Clearance Approval System. a computer system used by the US Air Force to transmit and record data pertaining to security clearances and investigations.

automatic calling unit. a dialing device which permits a machine to automatically dial calls over a communication network. The unit is frequently used to summon an emergency response agency (police, fire or medical) in conjunction with an alarm system.

automatic custody transfer. a system for automatically measuring and sampling oil or oil-based products at points of receipt and delivery. Also commonly called a lease automatic custody transfer system or LACT.

automatic data processing security plan. an overall plan that provides security throughout the life cycle of an automated project or program, automated data processing system, or facility. The plan documents the operational requirements; security environment hardware and software configurations and interfaces; security procedures, measures, and features; and, for automatic data processing facilities, the contingency plans for continued support in case of a local disaster.

automatic funds transfer. the transfer of money from one bank account to another without intervening paperwork through direct linking of computers.

automatic iris. in CCTV applications, a feature that causes the aperture of the camera lens to automatically adjust to changing light conditions. Optical adjustment takes place according to a sampling of video signals from the television camera. Compensation is accomplished using a mechanical iris or filters. For example, the automatic iris of a CCTV camera operating in an outdoor parking lot will set the aperture to a relatively large opening in the evening and reduce the aperture during sunlight hours. This reduces damage to the equipment from exposure to extremely bright light.

automatic line disconnect. a feature designed to defeat computer hackers by disconnecting a line after three unsuccessful attempts at a password or ID code.

automatic shutdown. a system in which certain instruments are used to control or maintain the operating conditions of a process. If conditions become abnormal, the automatic shutdown feature stops the process.

automatic smoke control system. a fire suppression system that uses high power fans to draw smoke into ductwork and expel it through exterior vents.

automatic sprinkler system. a fire extinguishment system that activates automatically, usually on a rate-of-rise principle, and which features the release of water through sprinkler heads distributed throughout the protected area.

automation. automatic self-regulating control of equipment, systems or processes.

autonomic nervous system. that division of the human body which regulates the body's internal environment and is generally involuntary. It plays an important part in producing the physiological reactions recorded by the polygraph instrument.

autopsy. the dissection of a dead body and the removal and examination of bone, tissue, organs and/or foreign objects for the purpose of determining the cause and circumstances of death.

autoptic evidence. evidence that results from being seen.

auto-restore. a feature of an alarm system which automatically resets the alarm apparatus within a specified time after receipt of an alarm. Many security monitoring systems will log the original alarm before resetting so as to create a record of alarm events. Also called auto-reset.

auxiliary code. in access control, a secondary control code capable of activating keypad functions. It is often used as a temporary code assignment so that the primary code is not revealed. Also called a secondary code.

auxiliary equipment. equipment subsidiary or supplementary to the main equipment used in an operation.

auxiliary fire alarm system. a system maintained and supervised by a non-governmental entity. The system features alarm devices that when activated cause an alarm to be sent to a municipal fire headquarters or fire station.

auxiliary force. persons, not necessarily security personnel, who supplement the regular security force in emergency situations.

auxiliary lock. a lock installed on a door or window to supplement a previously installed primary lock. Also called a secondary lock. It can be a mortised, bored or rim lock.

available path. the entire area available in a trafficway in which a vehicle may maneuver without interfering with other vehicles. Road space is the area within which a vehicle is legally entitled to travel. Available path is road space plus whatever other space is present for a vehicle to maneuver without causing a hazard.

average footcandles. the average illumination at all points on a lighted surface.

aversive therapy. a form of therapy in which painful effects, such as electric shock or induced nausea, are produced so that they may be associated with a form of addictive, criminal, or otherwise undesirable behavior. The objective is to create in the individual an aversion to that type of activity. Aversive therapy techniques have been applied to homosexuals, child molesters, alcoholics, drug addicts and rapists.

avoidable accident. an accident which could have or can be prevented by proper behavior, or by environmental or equipment modifications or controls. All accidents are theoretically avoidable within the limits of our understanding of scientific and behavioral phenomena. However, not all accidents can be avoided by all individuals.

avoirdupois. a system of weights (16 ounces to the pound) used in weighing articles other than medicines, metals, and precious stones. This system is used in most English speaking countries.

award of contract. the official notice that a contract proposal has been accepted.

Azene. the trade name for a depressant drug in the family of benzodiazepines. It is a commonly abused substance regulated under the Controlled Substances Act as a Schedule IV drug.

B

baby pro. a prostitute under the age of 17.

Bacarate. the trade name for phendimetrazine, an anorectic drug regulated under the Controlled Substances Act as a stimulant.

background investigation. an inquiry into the background of a job applicant. Also, a Department of Defense personnel security investigation consisting of both records reviews and interviews with sources of information.

background noise. a source or combination of sources of interference in a system used for production, detection, measurement or recording of a signal.

backing-up alarm. a device that automatically sounds a continuous or intermittent signal whenever the vehicle is backing up. It is used on some trucks and buses and required on some off-road vehicles.

backlog. the untried cases pending on a court calendar.

back plate. a metal plate on the inside of a door which is used to clamp a pin or disc tumbler rim lock cylinder to the door by means of retaining screws. The tail piece of the cylinder extends through a hole in the back plate.

backstop. to provide appropriate verification and support of cover arrangements for an undercover agent in anticipation of inquiries or other actions which might test the credibility of his or her cover.

backtrack. to pull back the plunger of a hypodermic syringe just before injecting a drug. It is done to facilitate proper insertion of the needle in the vein, and is believed to prolong the drug's effect.

backups. high-intensity backup lights installed in an armor-plated auto used for transporting a person who may be a kidnap or assassination target. Backups are designed to blind a pursuing driver.

bad bag. an oversize shopping bag used by shoplifters. Also called a booster bag.

bad trip. an unpleasant reaction to the use of a drug, especially an hallucinogen.

badger game. a form of blackmail in which the victim is framed by catching him in the act of intercourse with a female posing as the wife of the extortionist.

bag. originally a small glassine envelope containing 50-100 milligrams of diluted heroin. Heroin is now generally sold in smaller amounts in aluminum foil or paper. The term currently applies to plastic and cellophane bags containing marihuana, cocaine, phencyclidine, and other drugs in powder form.

bag cutter. a thief who specializes in stealing purses from lady shoppers in crowded stores by cutting the straps of purses carried from the shoulder.

bag job. a burglary or illegal break-in, sometimes made by law enforcement agencies in need of otherwise unobtainable evidence.

baglady. a woman who collects or pays off bets as part of a numbers racket.

bagman. a person designated to collect bets, bribes or so-called loans or to pay off other racketeers or dishonest politicians; anyone holding or receiving money during the course of an illegal transaction; a peddler of dangerous drugs.

bag thief. a thief who specializes in stealing momentarily unwatched shopping bags or handbags from shoppers.

bail. security given to a court in exchange for the release of a person in custody to assure his presence in court at a later time.

bail bond. the bond taken with securities at the time a defendant is released, conditioned on due appearance of the defendant.

bail bondsman. one who posts bail for others for a fee, generally 10 percent of the value of the bond. The term is applied to those who post such bonds regularly for a livelihood.

bailiff. a court attendant who performs a variety of duties, for example, maintain order in the courtroom, guard prisoners, run errands for the judge, pass papers and exhibits to authorized persons, and guard the jury room.

bailment. the delivery of personal property to another for a special purpose. Such delivery is made under a contract, either expressed or implied, that upon completion of the special purpose, the property shall be redelivered to the bailor or placed at his disposal.

bait-and-switch. a technique of advertising a bargain sale and when a customer shows interest the seller offers a similar product alleged to be superior but which is more expensive. Frequently the seller will claim that the bargain item has been sold out or found to be faulty.

bait money. money in a bank teller's or cashier's drawer set to trigger a robbery alarm if it is removed; money that has been marked or recorded for identification after it has been taken.

balanced detection. the condition in which two or more sensors must activate within a preset time interval for an alarm to be initiated.

balanced door. a door equipped with double-pivoted hardware so designed as to cause a semi-counterbalanced swing action when it is opened.

balanced line. a circuit with two conductors, each of which is equal to the other in voltage and opposite in polarity. Also, a line protected by a sensor input that utilizes a terminating resistance value. If the balance is upset by a change in the circuit, the sensor input goes into alarm.

balanced magnetic contact switch. a sensor that triggers an alarm when the switch is displaced by a change in the magnetic field it creates. A balanced switch is more difficult to defeat than a standard magnetic contact switch.

balanced pressure sensor. an intrusion detection sensor consisting of two liquid-filled hoses buried underground about 12-15 inches deep, 4 feet apart. The weight of an intruder is detected by pressure change.

balanced resistive bridge network. a circuit used in alarm transmission systems to provide line supervision. The network sets up maximum and minimum current limits which, if exceeded, activate an alarm indicating a line fault.

balanced telephone line. a telephone line which is floated with respect to ground so that the impedance measured from either side of the line to ground is equal to that of the other side to ground.

balance sheet. an itemized statement which lists the total assets and the total liabilities of a given business to portray its net worth at a given moment in time.

Balkan route. a route used by heroin and opium smugglers which begins in Afghanistan, Iran and Pakistan and transverses Turkey and the Balkans into Western Europe.

ballistics. as related to firearms, the science of the motion of projectiles.

balloon hazer. a homemade harassment device constructed of a balloon or condom filled with urine, bleach, ink or similar substance and thrown at or dropped upon law enforcement or security officers during disturbances.

balloon room. a place or room where marijuana is smoked; a meeting place for marijuana smokers and drug pushers.

bam. a mixture of barbiturate and amphetamine.

bandpass. a specific range of frequencies that will be passed through a device.

bandpass filter. a filter that will pass only a specific band of frequencies.

bandsplitter. a voice scrambler that inverts the frequency content of speech. The speech band is broken up into a number of smaller frequency bands which are inverted and interchanged during transmission.

bandwidth. the difference between the upper and lower frequency response of a communication channel.

Bangalore torpedo. a dynamite-filled length of pipe detonated by a blasting cap or a fuse.

Bangkok connection. the exportation of narcotics to the United States and Canada from Southeast Asia through the port of Bangkok, Thailand.

banji. a type of hashish plant grown in Arabia, Iran and other Middle Eastern countries.

bank. the degree to which the outside edge of a roadway is higher than the inside edge at a specified point on a curve; the change in elevation per unit distance across a roadway from the inside of its curve to the outside edge.

bank camera. a type of camera so named for its use in banks to obtain photographs during a robbery. It operates photomechanically as opposed to a television process, and is typically activated by a concealed switch or a money clip device.

banker. the person who finances a numbers game or who backs the house in dice, poker and other gambling games.

Bank Robbery Note File. a collection of holdup notes and other writings of known bank robbers maintained by the FBI Laboratory for use in identifying known writers and in determining if questioned notes originated from the same source.

bank routing transit number. a unique identification number that appears on checks issued by a bank. The number identifies the issuing bank.

Barberios test. a micro crystal test in which a solution of picric acid is added to a suspected seminal stain. If spermine is present in the stain, characteristic crystals will form which can then be viewed under a microscope.

barbidex. a mixture of barbiturate and amphetamine.

barbital. a drug classified as a Schedule IV Controlled Substance.

barbiturates. drugs frequently prescribed to induce sedation and sleep. About 2500 derivatives of barbituric acid have been synthesized, but of these only about 15 remain in medical use. Small therapeutic doses tend to calm nervous conditions, and larger doses cause sleep 20 to 60 minutes after oral administration. As in the case of alcohol, some persons may experience a sense of excitement before sedation takes effect. If dosage is increased, however, the effects may progress through successive stages of sedation, sleep, and coma to death from respiratory arrest and cardiovascular complications. Barbiturates appear in the

Controlled Substances Act as Schedule II, III and IV depressants. The trade or other names of barbiturates include Phenobarbital, Tuinal, Amytal, Nembutal and Seconal.

barbituric acid. a depressant classified as a Schedule III Controlled Substance.

bar code. a series of lines forming a code which can be read by a computer.

barium ferrite. a material embedded in plastic and encoded with magnetic spots to produce individual codes, for use in card reader systems.

barometric bomb. a bomb triggered by a change in air (barometric) pressure. Also called an altimeter bomb.

barratry. the act of encouraging lawsuits and inciting quarrels which ultimately end in litigation.

barrel key. a key with a bit projecting from a round, hollow key shank which fits on a post in the lock.

barrel striations. distinctive markings impressed on a projectile as it passes through the barrel in firing. Striations appear as minute lines and scratches, and have importance in firearms identification.

barricade. an obstruction or block to prevent passage or access.

barricade bolt. a massive metal bar that engages large strikes on both sides of a door. Barricade bolts are available with locking devices, and are completely removed from the door when not in use.

barrier guard. a device designed to protect operators and others from hazard points on machinery and equipment.

barrier line. a line, which when placed parallel to a center line or lane line, indicates that all traffic must not cross the line for purposes of overtaking or passing; a double line consisting of two normal solid yellow lines delineating the separation between travel paths in opposite directions where overtaking or passing is prohibited in both directions.

barrister. a lawyer in the United Kingdom and in certain British Commonwealth countries who is authorized to represent a party in court, in contrast to a solicitor, who is primarily an office lawyer.

bar type grating. an open grid assembly of metal bars in which the weight-bearing bars, running in one direction, are spaced by rigid attachment to cross bars running perpendicular to them or by bent connecting bars extending between them.

base wad. the paper filler at the rear of the powder charge inside the head of a shotgun shell.

base man. that person situated at the leading position in an offensive riot control formation, such as the wedge, triangle (diamond),

or echelon (diagonal). Also called the point man.

BASIC. an acronym for Beginners' All-purpose Symbolic Instruction Code, an introductory computer language.

basic component. in nuclear security, a plant structure, system, component or part thereof necessary to assure: the integrity of the reactor coolant pressure boundary; the capability to shut down the reactor and maintain it in a safe shutdown condition; or the capability to prevent or mitigate the consequences of accidents which could result in potential offsite exposures.

basic life support. an emergency procedure consisting of the recognition of respiratory and/or cardiac arrest and the proper application of cardiopulmonary resuscitation (CPR) to maintain life until a victim recovers or advanced life support assistance is available.

batch processing. a mode of computer processing in which all commands to be executed by the operating system are placed in a file or punched onto cards and submitted to the system for execution.

baton. a short, heavy club or stick with an attached strap or handle typically used as a defensive weapon.

battered child syndrome. a general term describing the social phenomenon of child abuse.

battering ram. a tool used in firefighting operations to knock down walls or doors. It is usually pole-shaped with grasping handles that permit it to be swung in a pendulum fashion.

battery. an unlawful beating or wrongful physical violence or constraint inflicted on another without consent. Assault is the actual offer to use force or violence while the using of it is the battery.

battery backup. a standby battery kept fully charged for use during a primary power failure. A battery backup is an essential element of any electrically operated security system.

baud rate. a measurement of data communications speed. A baud is equal to one signal element per second. Baud rate is usually expressed in bits per second, but only when one signal element equals one bit.

bazooka. a hand-held weapon which launches a missile capable of piercing armor. The bazooka is a favorite weapon of the terrorist.

beam break. a method of sensing an intrusion by detecting a break in a laser or photoelectric beam. An intruder passing through a beam (flowing from transmitter to receiver) will cause a momentary decrease in the energy at the receiver. Detection circuitry in the receiver interprets this condition as an intrusion and initiates an alarm signal.

beam divergence. in reference to active sensors, the amount of divergence of the beam from the source, expressed in degrees; the angle between the outer limits of a beam.

beam utilization. the percentage of beam lumens utilized on the area to be lighted.

beard. a person whose job is laying off bets for bookmakers.

beat a mark. successfully pick the pocket of a victim.

beat it. to run, flee; to have successfully avoided arrest or conviction or to win an appeal following conviction.

beat the machine. to lie during a polygraph examination and not be detected.

bee. a cherry bomb with tacks glued to the outside.

beef. a complaint, or to complain.

behaviorism. an approach in psychology, based on the study of observable behavior, which rejects the scientific validity of concepts referring to mental states, such as "value" or "attitude."

behavior modification. a therapeutic intervention in which conforming behavior is rewarded and unacceptable behavior is punished. Typically, it consists of a deliberate effort to change behavior by praising or otherwise rewarding desired behavior and ignoring or otherwise failing to reward undesirable behavior.

bell cutoff. a timer circuit that turns off power to a bell or siren after a pre-set length of time.

belt boosting. a shoplifting technique in which the thief places several garments against the stomach and holds them in place with a belt. A loose fitting topcoat conceals the stolen items from view.

bench trial. a trial without a jury, in which the verdict is handed down by one or more judges.

bench warrant. a document issued by a judicial officer directing that a person who has failed to obey an order or notice to appear be brought before the court.

benny. a benzedrine (amphetamine) pill.

Bent Spear. a Department of Defense term used when identifying or reporting a significant incident involving a nuclear warhead, weapon and/or component.

Benzedrine. the trade name for amphetamine sulfate which is regulated under the Controlled Substances Act as a Schedule II stimulant.

benzethidine. an opiate classified as a Schedule I Controlled Substance.

benzidine test. a screening test used for the detection of blood. It is based on the ability

of a chemical (in blood or other substances) called peroxidase to change a colorless reagent to blue when hydrogen peroxide is added. It is extremely sensitive, making it a very valuable negative test. If used properly in a two stage test, under certain conditions, some experts consider it to be almost specific for blood.

benzodiazepines. a family of depressants that relieve anxiety, tension, and muscle spasms, produce sedation and prevent convulsions. They are marketed as anxiolytics (mild tranquilizers), sedatives, hypnotics or anticonvulsants. The forms of benzodiazepine currently sold in the US are alprazolam (Xanax), chlordiazepoxide (Librium), clanazepam (Clonopin), clorazepate (Tranxene), diazepam (Valium), flurazepam (Dalmane), halazepam (Paxipam), lorazepam (Ativan), oxazepam (Serax), prazepam (Centrax), temasepam (Restoril), and triazolam (Halcion). Benzodiazepines appear in the Controlled Substances Act as Schedule IV depressants. They are widely abused and prolonged use can produce physical and psychological dependence and withdrawal symptoms.

benzphetamine. the generic name of a stimulant sold legally as Didrex. It is a Schedule III drug.

benzylmorphine. an opium derivative classified as a Schedule I Controlled Substance.

bequeath. to give personal property by will to another.

bequest. a gift of personal property by will to another. If the property given is real property, it as known as a devise.

bertillonage. a technique for identifying criminals or others based upon measurements of certain unchanging parts of the skeleton. It is based on the Bertillon system.

Bertillon system. an identification system developed by Alphonse Bertillon using anthropometric measurements, standardized photographs, notation of markings, color, thumb line impressions and other data.

best evidence rule. a rule of law requiring that only the original of a document or an object is admissible evidence. A copy or facsimile is admissible only if the original is not available.

bestiality. a sexual connection between a human being and an animal.

betacetylmethadol. an opiate classified as a Schedule I Controlled Substance.

betameprodine. an opiate classified as a Schedule I Controlled Substance.

betamethadol. an opiate classified as a Schedule I Controlled Substance.

betaprodine. an opiate classified as a Schedule I Controlled Substance.

between lines entry. a technique for deliberate active access to computer-stored information.

beveled dice. dice which have been beveled on their edges to increase the chances of certain point combinations.

beveled wound. a wound in which the skin is penetrated at an angle. One margin of the wound is beveled and the other margin overhangs it.

beyond a reasonable doubt. a term referring to the evidence that must be shown by the state in a criminal case for the accused to be found guilty of the charge.

bezitramide. an opiate classified as a Schedule II Controlled Substance.

B girl. a female employed in a drinking establishment to entice male patrons to purchase expensive drinks. A B girl will frequently engage also in prostitution.

bhang. a powder made from ground hemp leaves, usually ingested.

bicentric pin tumbler cylinder. a cylinder having two cores and two sets of pins, each having different combinations. Two separate keys, used simultaneously, are required to operate it. The cam or tail piece is gear operated.

bifurcated trial. in criminal proceedings, a special two-part proceeding in which the issue of guilt is tried in the first step, and if a conviction results, the appropriate sentence or applicable sentencing statute is determined in the second step.

bifurcation. in fingerprint science, the forking or dividing of one line into two or more branches.

bigamy. the criminal offense of willfully and knowingly contracting a marriage while being married to a third party.

big con. a large scale confidence game.

Big John. a drug abuser's term for the police.

bigot list. a restrictive list of persons who have access to a particular, and highly sensitive, class of information.

bill of attainder. originally, the complete loss of rights and privileges on being condemned of treason or another felony. In recent times, it is a legislative conviction without a criminal trial. The United States Constitution specifically forbids a bill of attainder.

bill of exception. a legal procedure by which a defendant protests a particular ruling of the court or question of law.

bill of exchange. a written order or draft authorizing a designated amount to be deducted from the account of the issuing party payable to another party.

bill of indictment. the written response of a grand jury which accuses a person of a crime. Also called a true bill.

bill of lading. an agreement between a shipper of freight and a common carrier.

bill of particulars. a statement by the prosecution filed by order of the court, at the court's own request or that of the defendant, of such particulars as may be necessary to give the defendant and the court reasonable knowledge of the nature and grounds of the crime charged, such as the time and place, means by which it was alleged to have been committed, or more specific information.

Bill of Rights. the first ten amendments to the US Constitution. Several of them govern criminal trial procedures and rights of the accused, and were applied to state criminal courts in a series of Supreme Court decisions. Some state constitutions contain provisions similar to those in the Bill of Rights.

billy. a small bludgeon that may be carried in the pocket.

bimetallic heat detector. a heat detection device that uses a sensing element comprised of two metal strips having a different coefficient of expansion. The element deflects in opposite directions depending on the temperature to which it is exposed. Element deflection beyond a preset range results in an alarm.

binary machine code. the internal instruction format used by computers. It is called binary because only two characters, 0 and 1, are used.

binary system. a numbering system that uses 2 as a base, as opposed to the decimal system which uses 10. The binary system uses only two symbols, 0 and 1, to represent any number.

bind over. to require by judicial authority that a person promise to appear for trial, appear in court as a witness, or keep the peace.

bindle. a small paper folded to transport heroin or other illegal drugs in powder form.

bingler. a seller of narcotics.

biometric access control. a method of access verification in which the person seeking entry is identified by fingerprints, retinal eye pattern, palm pattern, hand geometry, voice analysis and similar features.

biphase code. a method of data transmission that has a built-in verification technique for ensuring that proper logic values have been transmitted for each bit of information. Each bit in the data word consists of two halves. The value of the first half of the pulse contains the logic value for that bit. A transition then occurs and the opposite value is transmitted during the second half of the pulse.

Biphetamine. the trade name for a stimulant that combines amphetamine and dextroamphetamine which are regulated under the Controlled Substances Act as Schedule II drugs. Street names include speed, upper, black beauty, crank, meth, bam, and pink.

bipolar smoke detector. a type of smoke detector having two individual detection chambers for sensing the presence of smoke.

birdie powder. a mixture of heroin and morphine.

bird dog. that member of a pickpocket team who looks for and distracts the police while the team is operating.

birefringence. in crime laboratory analyses, the difference between two refractive indices. Birefringence is determined by first placing a sample parallel to polarized light and then measuring the refractive index. The sample is then placed perpendicular to polarized light and the refractive index is measured. Birefringence is determined by computing the difference between the indices.

bit. the smallest entity of computer memory in which a value can be stored. Also, a blade projecting from a key shank which engages with and actuates the bolt or level tumblers of a lock.

bite. money paid by a loan shark to a middleman who lines up a borrower.

bit key. a key with a bit projecting from a round shank. It is similar to the barrel key, but has a solid rather than hollow shank.

black. a term used to indicate reliance on illegal concealment of an activity rather than on cover.

black bag job. warrantless surreptitious entry, especially an entry conducted for purposes other than microphone installation, such as physical search and seizure or photographing of documents.

black box. a device for bypassing a telephone company's switching system so that calls can be made without charge by, or knowledge of, the telephone company; any technical device used in gathering intelligence, which may range from a telephone wire tapping apparatus to an aerial satellite.

black gungi. marijuana grown in India.

black intelligence. information obtained through espionage.

black leg. an employee who continues to work for an organization while it is being struck by co-workers.

black light. an ultraviolet light used to detect fluorescent dyes, dust or paints which transfer to the skin or clothing of persons suspected of handling decoy objects such as bait money.

black list. an official counterintelligence agency listing of actual or potential hostile collaborators, sympathizers, or other persons viewed as threatening to friendly military forces; in business, a list of persons to be denied employment or to be punished in some other manner, or a list of vendors or suppliers to be avoided; to put on a blacklist.

blackmail. to obtain something of value from a person by means of threatening to expose them to injury, disgrace, libel, or other harm.

black money. funds not reported to tax collectors, usually because they were gained by gambling or illegal operations.

blackout. an unintentional, complete loss of AC line voltage typically caused by failure of major pieces of generating equipment.

black powder. an explosive frequently used in the construction of homemade bombs.

black propaganda. disinformation consisting of lies combined with some distortions, half-truths and even bits of the whole truth; propaganda which purports to emanate from a source other than the true one.

black Russian. a very dark and very potent variety of hashish.

black tar heroin. a form of heroin having at the street sale level a purity between 60-90 percent, as compared with white (Asian) and brown (Mexican) heroin having a purity between 2-6 percent. Black tar heroin is mostly manufactured at clandestine laboratories in Mexico.

blank check. a check no longer acceptable to most banks due to the Federal Reserve Board regulations that prohibit standard processing without encoded characters. A blank check may be used, but it requires a special collection process on the part of the bank. Also called a universal check.

blank endorsement. the writing of one's name on an instrument without any additional words. Its effect is to make the paper payable to the bearer. Thus, a finder or thief might transfer the note to a third party for a consideration, and the third party might then enforce payment against the maker or the endorser.

blanket bond. a type of fidelity bond which covers losses caused by the dishonesty of all employees as opposed to bonds which specifically identify only certain employees to be covered.

blanket crime policy. an insurance policy which provides coverage for employee dishonesty, loss of money and securities inside and outside the premises, depositor's forgery, loss of money orders, and counterfeit paper currency.

blanket position bond. a type of blanket fidelity bond in which the amount of coverage applies separately to each position covered.

blasphemy. any oral or written reproach maliciously cast upon God, His name, attributes, or religion.

blast tube. a steel tube fitting over and extending beyond the barrel of a gun so as to provide added protection against blast.

blast wave. in bomb incident investigations, a movement of air away from the point of detonation that reaches velocities up to 1100 fps and pressure up to 1.5 million psi. In an explosion, more damage is done by blast than by any other effect.

bleached note. a counterfeit bill created by bleaching a low denomination genuine note and then printing on it, with a counterfeit plate, a high denomination note.

bleeder. in a numbers operation, a bet on any combination of two of the three digits. Also called a bolita, or double action.

blockbusting. the illegal practice of introducing a nonconforming user or undesirable into a neighborhood for the purpose of causing an abnormally high turnover of property ownership in the area.

blocking. the intentional full or partial concealment of an item intended to be shoplifted. A purse in a shopping cart is commonly used to block the targeted item.

block watch. a neighborhood program in which residents actively look for and report criminal activity.

blood alcohol concentration. the relative proportion of ethyl alcohol within the blood, based upon the number of grams per alcohol per millimeter of blood, and often expressed as a percent.

blood alcohol zones. standards which are commonly employed as measures of intoxication. In this measure, the parts of alcohol per thousand parts of blood are expressed as a percentage. Three zones are used: Zone 1 includes blood alcohol values from 0.00 to 0.5 percent and is considered fairly good evidence that the person is sober. Zone 2 ranges from 0.5 to 0.15 percent and is inconclusive as to whether or not the person is under the influence. Zone 3 relates to findings above 0.15 percent. At this level a person is considered to be intoxicated. Its equivalent is to drink 8 ounces of whiskey or eight 12-ounce bottles of beer.

blood feud. a long-running, violent quarrel between clans or families.

blood pressure cuff. in polygraphy, a fabric arm cuff containing an inflatable rubber bladder. It is typically attached to the arm of the examinee during a test for the purpose of detecting blood pressure changes. The cuff is part of the sphygmomanometer component of the polygraph instrument.

blood pressure tracing. in polygraphy, the inked tracing that represents changes in the blood pressure of a person being tested. The tracing appears on a polygram created by the movement of chart paper beneath a stylus. The polygraphist interprets the tracing.

blooming. in a CCTV system, an out-of-focus condition caused by subjecting the camera to a source of extremely bright light.

blotter acid. LSD impregnated in paper.

blow. that step in a confidence game when the victim is permitted to win or gain something in order to build up the victim for the "score."

blowback. an exposure of espionage activity due to an unsuccessful attempt to recruit a secret agent.

blown. destroyed, as when an undercover agent's identity has been discovered.

blown away. a narcotically-induced euphoria.

blown cover. the discovery of an undercover agent's identity.

blow off. that point in time during a confidence game when the victim's money or property is taken.

bludgeon. a short clublike weapon with one end loaded or thicker than the other.

blue acid. pale-blue liquid LSD-25.

blue angels. amytal (barbiturate) tablets.

bluebirds. capsules of sodium amytal.

blue box. an electronic device used illegally to dial toll-free exchanges. Once the original call is completed, the device holds the line open so that additional calls can be placed at no cost to the caller.

blue devils. amobarbital capsules.

blue flu. when police officers informally strike by calling in sick, they are said to be suffering from a disease so unique it affects only the police.

blue laws. rigid laws or religious regulations that prohibit certain activities on Sunday, such as shopping or drinking alcoholic beverages in public places.

blue ribbon jury. a special jury selected from the upper or upper-middle socioeconomic strata, or from persons with some special expertise. Such selection was sometimes used to form grand and petit juries, but is no longer legal in the United States.

blue sky bargaining. unreasonable and unrealistic negotiating demands by either side, made usually at the beginning of the negotiating process.

blue-sky laws. laws that have been enacted by most of the states to protect the public from fraud in the offering of securities. Such laws are an exercise of the police power of the states. They supplement interstate regulation of securities offerings, securities exchanges, and speculative practices, through the Securities and Exchange Commission.

Protection is achieved through specific legislation of blue-sky laws, and through enforcement of the statute of frauds.

blue tip. an incendiary bullet identified by its blue-painted tip.

BNC connector. a standard coaxial cable connector with a bayonet locking mechanism. It is commonly used in CCTV equipment interconnections.

bodily harm. any touching of the person of another against his will with physical force, in an intentional, hostile, and aggressive manner, or a projecting of such force against his person.

body-cavity search. an anal or vaginal search for contraband such as diamonds or narcotics.

body transmitter. a small radio transmitter concealed on a person's body. Generally used to provide instant communication to back-up persons nearby, or for consensual monitoring.

boiler house. a slang term meaning to make up or fake a report.

boilerplate. written materials characterized by excessive verbiage.

bolita. in a numbers operation, a bet on any combination of two of the three digits. Also called parlay, bleeder, or double action.

bolt. that part of a lock which, when actuated, is projected from the lock into a retaining member, such as a strike plate, to prevent a door or window from moving or opening.

bolt attack. a category of burglary attack in which force, with or without the aid of tools, is directed against the bolt in an attempt to disengage it from the strike or to break it.

bolt mechanism. the mechanism in a lock that moves the bolt in and out of the strike.

bolt projection. the distance from the edge of the door, at the bolt centerline, to the furthest point on the bolt in the projected position. Also called bolt throw.

bomb disposal unit. a team of experts trained in the disposal of unexploded bombs.

bombing incident. the detonation or attempted detonation of an explosive or incendiary device for a criminal purpose, or with willful disregard of the risk to the person or property of another.

bomb sniffer. a dog trained to detect the presence of bombs or narcotics; any mechanical, chemical or electronic device used for the detection of bombs.

bona fide. in good faith; without fraud or deceit; genuine.

bond. an agreement by one person to guarantee that another person will appear in court.

bond ratio. a type of capitalization ratio which represents the face value of outstanding bonds divided by the total of bonds, preferred stock, common stock, capital surplus, and accumulated retained earnings.

bondsman. one who gives security to procure the release from legal custody of a person arrested or imprisoned.

booby trap. a disguised explosive device intended to cause human injury.

boodle. the stack of money used by confidence men in the "switch game." On either end of the stack is a high denomination bill, with the middle of the stack being one dollar bills or pieces of paper made to look like currency. The "switch" consists of the boodle being exchanged for a stack of money belonging to the victim.

bookie front. a place of business, frequently a tavern, news stand or barber shop, that serves as a front for a bookie operation.

booking. a police administrative action officially recording an arrest and identifying the person, place, time, the arresting authority, and the reason for the arrest.

bookmaker. a professional betting man who accepts wagers on sporting events, most frequently horse racing.

boost. that member of a confidence game who encourages or builds up the victim prior to the "score." Also called a shill.

booster. a shoplifter; a person who steals from cars, such as hub caps, radios, CB units and tape decks. Also called a car clout.

booster bloomers. pocket-fitted undergarments used by shoplifters to secrete stolen merchandise.

booster box. an innocuous looking box or package carried by a shoplifter and used to conceal stolen items. It is typically fitted with a hinged side or bottom.

booster explosive. an explosive material detonated by the primary explosive and which in turn detonates the main charge. It is the third element in the basic firing chain typical of most explosions. Examples of booster explosives are tetryl, PETN and RDX. A booster explosive is also called a secondary explosive.

booster pants. oversize pants with deep pockets used to hold shoplifted merchandise.

boosting an invoice. increasing the figures on a supplier's invoice, often done by an employee of the purchaser in collusion with the supplier.

boot. in computer usage, a technique or device designed to bring itself into a desired state by means of its own action, such as a routine whose first few instructions are sufficient to bring the rest of itself into memory from an input device.

bored lock (or latch). a lock or latch whose

parts are intended for installation in holes bored in a door.

bottom-up method. a method of organizing and planning in which goals are set by managers for their own departments.

bouncer. a person employed to preserve the peace in night clubs and similar places of evening entertainment.

box. a safe.

box man. a safe burglar.

box strike. a strike plate that has a metal box or housing to fully enclose the projected bolt and/or latch.

brainstorming. a group effort structured to generate suggestions or ideas that can serve as leads to problem solving.

braking distance. the distance through which brakes are applied to slow a vehicle; the shortest distance in which a particular vehicle can be stopped from a specified speed on a particular surface; the distance from application of brakes to collision.

brass knuckles. a weapon worn on the hand over the knuckles and so made that in hitting with the fist considerable damage is inflicted. Originally made of brass, the term is now used without reference to the metal of which the weapon is made.

breach. in computer usage, a break in the system's security.

breach of contract. the failure or refusal by one of the parties to a contract to perform some act the contract calls for without legal excuse. A contract may also be breached by preventing or obstructing performance by the other party, or by "anticipatory" breach, as the unqualified announcement by a seller, before delivery date, that he will not deliver the goods.

breach of peace. a violation of the public order, such as a riot, an unlawful assembly, or an illegal demonstration.

breach of trust. to take for personal use anything of value which is being held in trust for someone else.

breach of warranty. a warranty made by a vendor which proves to be false. For the breach, the buyer has a choice of four remedies: (1) accept or keep the goods and set up the breach to reduce the purchase price; (2) keep the goods and recover damages for the breach of warranty; (3) refuse to accept the goods if title has not passed and bring an action for damages for breach of warranty; and (4) rescind the contract, or if the goods have been delivered, return them, and recover any part of the purchase price that had been paid. The buyer can claim only one of the remedies.

break alarm. an alarm signal produced by opening or breaking an electrical circuit.

break alarm pad. a panel laced with foil or fine wire and placed on the surface of a door or inside a wall. A forced entry through the panel breaks the foil or wire and causes an alarm condition.

break-down revolver. a general class of revolver constructed to allow the breech end of the barrel, along with the cylinder, to be tilted forward and upward from the frame for unloading and loading.

break even analysis. the determination of the amount of income required to recover the amount of the initial investment.

break even point. the amount of income needed to just meet the total amount of expenses for a project.

break-in attempt. in computer usage, an effort made by an unauthorized source to gain access to the system. Break-in attempts primarily refer to attempts to login illegally. These attempts focus on supplying passwords for users known to have accounts on the system, through informed guesses or other trial and error methods.

breaking. as used in criminal law, forcibly separating, parting, disintegrating, or piercing any solid substance.

breaking and entering. illegal and forcible entry of a premises, as by breaking a lock or a window, removing a door, or cutting through a roof or wall. When the entry is for the purpose of committing a theft, it is usually charged as burglary.

Breathalyzer. a breath testing device used by the police to determine alcohol concentrations in the blood of drivers suspected of being under the influence of alcohol.

breechblock marks. unique tooling marks permanently affixed to a weapon during the process of manufacture; the marks placed upon an expended cartridge by the unique breechblock characteristics of a weapon. Also called breechface marks.

bribery. the giving or offering of anything of value with intent to unlawfully influence a person in the discharge of his duties, and the receiving or asking of anything of value with intent to be unlawfully influenced.

brick. a compressed brick-shaped block of hashish, marijuana, morphine or opium. A brick usually weighs one pound or one kilogram.

bridge. a means of isolating one transmitter from another so that a failure of one does not affect the other.

bridging sequential switcher. a sequential video switcher with separate outputs for programmed sequence monitors and extended play monitors. Bridging switchers allow constant viewing of a scene selected from the standard camera sequence.

brisance. the shattering effect of an explosive. The higher the velocity of an explosive, the more brisant it is said to be.

Broken Arrow. a Department of Defense term used when identifying or reporting a significant incident involving a nuclear weapon, warhead and/or component.

brothel. a house kept for the purpose of prostitution.

brownout. a deliberate reduction in AC line voltage by a utility company during periods of unusually high demand or insufficient generating capacity.

brown sugar. Asian heroin, often adulterated with caffeine and strychnine.

Brown v. Mississippi. a case in which the U.S. Supreme Court ruled that the use of physical coercion to obtain a confession was in violation of the 14th Amendment.

browse. to use a computer terminal to look at someone else's computer files.

"B" substance. the substance in body fluids that would be secreted by a person of blood group B or AB.

bucket brigade. a firefighting technique consisting of two lines of persons passing buckets, full toward the fire and empty toward the water source.

bucket shop. an office or place (other than a regularly incorporated or licensed exchange) where persons engage in pretended buying and selling of commodities as part of some fraudulent operation; a place which accepts wagers on market price fluctuations.

bufotenine. an intoxicant snuff obtained from the pods and seeds of a shrub found in parts of South America and the West Indies. It is classified as a Schedule I Controlled Substance.

bug. a clandestine listening device, usually consisting of a hidden microphone and radio transmitter; a computer programming error; an alarm sensor, especially of the type attached to surfaces to detect vibrations.

bugging. the process of monitoring conversations by electronic means.

building security system. an integrated system to protect against a wide variety of events such as intrusion, espionage, vandalism, theft, fire, unsafe conditions and faulty equipment operation. A building security system usually features the control of traffic and operation of entrances and exits from a remote location. Use is made of humans, procedures, physical safeguards, mechanical, electrical and electronic devices, and combinations thereof.

bullet entrance wound. typically a neat, round hole made by a bullet entering the body or head of the victim.

bullet exit wound. typically a ragged or torn hole made by a bullet leaving the body or the head of the victim. It is usually much larger than the size of the bullet.

bulletin board system. a system for computer users to communicate and exchange information over a telephone line connected to a computer and display terminal. Also called BBS.

bullet resistant acrylic products. lightweight, tempered plastics in thicknesses beginning usually at one and one quarter inches.

bullet resistant glass. glass consisting of two or more plates bonded with plastic interlayers, generally resistive to penetration by bullets from medium to high power arms.

bullet resistant glass-clad polycarbonate. a multi-ply laminate consisting of one-ply polycarbonate surrounded by several plies of glass, using elastic interlayers to compensate for expansion/contraction differences. The product combines the impact resistance characteristics of polycarbonate with the fire and chemical-resisting properties of glass.

bullet resistant glazing product, level I. a glazing product, such as glass or polycarbonate, rated to resist penetration of bullets from medium-power small arms, such as the .38 Super.

bullet resistant glazing product, level II. a glazing product rated to resist penetration of bullets from high power small arms, such as the .357 Magnum.

bullet resistant glazing product, level III. a glazing product rated to resist penetration of bullets from super power small arms, such as the .44 Magnum.

bullet resistant glazing product, level IV. a glazing product rated to resist penetration of bullets from high power rifles, such as the 30.06 rifle.

bullet resistant glazing product, level V. a glazing product rated to resist penetration of bullets from super power rifles, such as those which use the 7.62 NATO armor piercing bullet.

bullet resistant laminated polycarbonates. polycarbonate sheets bonded with interlayer film. Depending on the number of layers and thickness, the glazing product will provide super power bullet resistance.

bull jive. adulterated low-grade marijuana.

bump-and-run. a mugging technique in which one mugger knocks the victim down while another mugger snatches the victim's handbag or valuables.

bumper beeper. a radio beacon transmitter hidden in or on a vehicle for use with radio direction finding equipment.

bumping. a method of opening a pin tumbler

lock by means of vibration produced by a wooden or rubber mallet.

bunco artist. a card sharper, confidence man or swindler.

bunco game. any trick, artifice, or cunning calculated to win confidence and to deceive, whether by conversation, conduct, or suggestion.

burden of proof. the duty to prove the facts in a case. The burden of proof is on the government in a criminal case.

burglar-resistant glazing. any glazing which is more difficult to break through than the common window or plate glass, such as glass designed to resist "smash and grab" burglary attacks. This glazing typically consists of two layers of plate bonded with a plastic interlayer.

burglary. unlawful entry of a structure, with or without force, with intent to commit a felony or larceny.

buried-line intrusion detector. a buried seismic-type sensor consisting of a coaxial cable with piezoelectric ceramic disks located between the center conductor and the shield at equal intervals. Pressure from seismic motion on the disks causes them to generate a signal.

burned. exposed as a surveillant or undercover operative; cheated in a drug transaction.

burn-in. an image permanently frozen on the photo-sensitive region of a television camera tube. It is caused by exposing the tube to an extremely bright scene for an extended period.

burning bar. a bar packed with aluminum and magnesium wire or rods, and connected through a regulator to an oxygen container. It burns like a high-powered sparkler and is consumed while being used. A burning bar is capable of defeating most safes currently manufactured. Also called a thermal lance.

burning point. the lowest temperature at which an oil or fuel will burn when an open flame is placed near its surface.

burn job. a safecracking method in which a cutting torch is used to burn a hole into the side of the safe. The cutting tool is usually an oxyacetylene torch, a thermal burning bar or a thermite grenade. Also called a torch job.

burn time estimate. the time a fire started, as estimated by a fire investigator. It is based on an examination of the material burned, depth of char, presence of accelerants, wind, oxygen availability, moisture content and other factors.

business control. the management of a process or application. Business controls are func-

tions and attributes which render the process or application manageable. They enable management to: safeguard assets and prevent their loss or unintended use; detect and understand errors, omissions and aberrations; take corrective actions; verify correctness of results; and recover from disruption.

business entries. records which show the truth of their content and which may be admitted into evidence as an exception to the hearsay rule.

businessman's high. the street name for dimethyltriptamine (DMT), an hallucinogenic drug the effects of which are of short duration.

business opportunity scheme. any one of a number of fraudulent schemes and deceptions concocted within the framework of an allegedly lucrative business venture. It may appear in almost any type financial dealing, e.g., vending machines, product dispensing, distributorships in limited areas, and multilevel sales organizations.

business record or entry. an entry made in the conduct of regular business.

busy air. airwaves cluttered with police or other radio calls.

"but for" rule. a rule of law which holds that a defendant's conduct is not the cause of an event if the event would have occurred without it. Also called the sine qua non rule.

butisol. a commonly abused barbiturate, usually taken orally or injected. Also called barb, downer, blue, yellow jacket and sleeping pill.

buttress lock. a lock which secures a door by wedging a bar between the door and the floor. Some incorporate a moveable steel rod which fits into metal receiving slots on the door and in the floor. Also called a police bolt/brace.

buzzer. a vibrating reed device in which an armature continuously vibrates for as long as operating power is applied.

buzzwords. the technical vocabularies of an occupational specialty.

by color of office. acts committed by a public official acting in an official capacity although the acts are not authorized by the official position.

byproduct material. in nuclear security, any radioactive material except special nuclear material.

by social harm involved. a custom of classifying crimes according to the particular type of social harm resulting from their commission. A classification scheme by social harm involved might list offenses according to the objects of commission such as persons, habitations, property, and government.

bystander. a person, other than the perpetrator, police, or victim, in the vicinity of a crime. The bystander may be a witness, someone who is incidentally injured, or who intervenes as a Good Samaritan.

byte. a character of computer storage made up of a number of bits, typically eight.

C

C. when appearing on a numbers slip, a symbol that indicates a three digit number to be played in any possible transposition.

C-4. a military plastic explosive that usually appears as a white, semi-soft, moldable plastic putty. It is typically used in shape charges.

cable coupler. a device used to join lengths of similar and dissimilar cable having the same electrical characteristics.

cable fault locator. a device that finds electrical faults in concealed or buried cable. A variety of such locators are manufactured and they are frequently described by principal of operation, e.g., tone, pulse, high-voltage surge generator with signal analyzer, and capacitance meter.

cacodyl. a garlic-like odoriferous poison used as an explosive because it ignites spontaneously in dry air.

cadaver. a dead human body; a corpse.

cadaveric spasm. stiffening of the arms or hands at the time of death. A person who dies holding something might clutch it tenaciously.

calculated risk. an action undertaken to achieve a particular purpose after the probable consequences have been estimated. A calculated risk is a risk judged to be acceptable after thorough consideration of the planned operation. Also called residual risk.

calendar. the list of cases established in a court to determine their orderly disposition and trial.

caliber. the nominal bore diameter of a barrel measured in hundredths of an inch (.01) or in millimeters (mm). Firearms are frequently referred to by their caliber designations.

caliber designation. a descriptor denoting a specific cartridge case size and configuration. While some cartridges will interchange, most are specific for particular weapons. Examples of caliber designations are the .38 Special, .44 Magnum and 6 mm Remington.

call outs. notes on an engineering drawing which further explain the details presented.

calumny. defamation; slander; false accusation of a crime or offense.

cam. the part of a lock or cylinder which rotates to actuate the bolt or latch as the key is turned. The key may also act as the bolt.

camera dome. a spherical high-impact plastic dome that covers a camera for purposes of concealment and/or protection from the environment.

Camorra. a group of Italian-dominated organized crime leaders and their followers that originated in Sicily. Also called the Mafia.

camouflet. an underground cavity created when an explosive ordnance penetrates the earth and explodes at a depth not sufficient to rupture the earth's surface.

cam switch. a type of contact switch that closes certain electrical contacts or combinations of contacts at various positions of a cam.

cancel call. a manual abort mode on some dialers that allows a manual override of a call initiation caused by an alarm input.

cancellation ink. a special ink having forgery prevention qualities, typically used on official documents and legal tender.

cancellation for audio detection. a feature of an audio detection system in which a listening device is positioned outside the protected area for the purpose of detecting extraneous noise such as sonic boom and passing trucks. Such activation of the outside detector causes the main system in the protected area to cancel (ignore) the extraneous sound and thus avoid a false alarm.

candela. the unit of luminous intensity in a given direction. One candela is commonly called one candle power.

candidate material. in the DoD Industrial Security Program, material that is referred to collectively as special nuclear materials and nuclear weapons.

cannabinoids. the highly potent, rapid-acting psychoactive ingredients of cannabis products such as marijuana and hashish.

cannabinoid screen. a field test or preliminary test used to detect the presence of cannabinoids in a sample, such as a urine specimen.

cannabis. the generic name for marijuana.

cannabis sativa L. the hemp plant from which cannabis products are obtained. It is a single species that grows wild throughout most of the tropic and temperate regions of the world. Also called the cannabis plant or marihuana plant.

cannelure. small channels or grooves on a cartridge case; indentation rings on a bullet.

cannon. a revolver or pistol. Also, the member of a pickpocketing team who does the actual stealing.

canon law. a body of law governing the organization and administration of the Catholic, and other Christian churches, and the conduct of its communicants in matters of concern to the church.

can opener. a large prying tool used in a safe

ripping job. The tool is used to rip or peel the safe's outer covering.

cap. a capsule of narcotic drug.

capacitance alarm. an alarm system that operates by setting up an electromagnetic field around a protected object. Movement near the object disrupts the field and causes an alarm.

capacitance card. a type of access card containing a series of capacitor plates arranged in a code pattern.

capacitance detection. the generation of an alarm signal by making use of the capacitance effect of the human body or other large mass in a tuned electronic circuit.

capacitance sensor. a large electric condenser that radiates energy and detects changes in the capacitive coupling between an antenna and a ground. When an intruder enters the energy field the balance between the antenna and ground is disrupted, causing an alarm.

capacitive pickup. a transducer that functions by capacitance rather than by direct connection to a circuit.

capacitor. a circuit component that stores electrical energy. Also called a condenser.

capacity to commit. a concept of law which demands that a person should not be held criminally punishable for his conduct unless he is actually responsible for it. Young persons and mentally afflicted persons, for example, may be recognized as not having the capacity to commit crimes.

capax doli. capable of committing crime, or capable of criminal intent; the condition of one who has sufficient intelligence and comprehension to be held criminally responsible for his or her deeds.

capias. an order or writ directing the arrest of a person.

capital. net worth of an organization.

capital crime. any crime for which a convicted person can be sentenced to death.

capital equipment. equipment purchased for the purpose of increasing capital assets; items used in the normal course of business but which are not sold as products of the business.

capital expenditures. money spent to increase or improve capital assets.

capital gain. income that results from the sale of an asset and not from the usual course of business. Capital gains are taxed at a lower rate than ordinary income.

capital intensive. a term relating to the ratio of capital investment to the number of employees. For example, a capital intensive industry is one in which the capital needs are high in relation to the number of persons employed.

capital recapture. the manner in which an investment is to be returned to the investor, normally stated as a rate or dollar amount per unit of time.

capper. an agent of gamblers who seeks new trade. Also, in some swindles based on gambling, the capper will aid in deceiving the victim by appearing to win large sums.

capture. in alarm technology, to defeat a sensor by introducing an effective bypass. An example would be the use of an infrared transmitter, other than the originally installed transmitter, to keep the sensor from activating while the protected zone is being penetrated.

carat. a measure of weight for diamonds and other precious stones, equivalent to 3.5 grains Troy; also a standard of fineness for gold, 24 carats being used to express absolute purity.

carbon microphone. a microphone that depends for its operation upon the variation in resistance of carbon granules.

carbon-zinc battery. the traditional battery type for general purpose security applications.

carborundum pencil. a tool used to inscribe identification marks on metallic evidence items such as firearms and knives.

car clout. a person who steals parts from cars, such as hub caps, radios, CB units and tape decks. Also called a booster.

card access. a general term denoting a type of access control that uses access cards and card readers at entry and exit points.

card cage. an enclosure with restraining brackets mounted inside to hold the printed circuit boards that compose a computer's central processing unit; any enclosure having the purpose of holding printed circuit board assemblies.

card encoder. a device that places a unique access code on or within an access control card.

cardioactivity monitor. in polygraphy, a volumetric plethysmograph that records the radial pulse. It consists of a sensor unit containing a transducer, amplifier, and pen motor. It is commonly called a CAM.

cardiopulmonary resuscitation (CPR). a life saving technique which combines the application of artificial respiration (rescue breathing) and artificial circulation (external cardiac compression).

cardiosphygmograph. that component of the polygraph instrument which mechanically records in ink, on paper, a subject's blood pressure and pulse rate variations.

cardiosphygmomanometer. a subcomponent of the polygraph instrument. It is an in-line pressure dial in a closed air circuit capable of representing the circuit's pressure in units of millimeters of mercury.

card key. a plastic card containing encoded information to open a locked door. The card reading device may be an integral part of the lock, or it can be located in the immediate vicinity of the door. Also called an access card.

card mastering. coding of access control cards to allow universal access to specified groups of locks. Also called master coding.

card reader. a device that reads the magnetic bits or particles arranged in a magnetic key card. Card readers fall into one of two categories: intelligent and on-line. The intelligent reader compares data on a card against preprogrammed parameters. Entry or exit is granted or denied by the card reader at the reader location. The on-line reader does not have the capability of making the entry/exit decision. It communicates with a central processor which performs the decision function. An intelligent reader is also called a stand-alone or off-line reader.

card stimulation test. a test which uses ordinary playing cards to stimulate a polygraph examinee and to demonstrate to the examinee the accuracy of the polygraph instrument. Typically, the examinee chooses a card from among several and is told to deny the selection when asked during a polygraph test. This technique tends to reduce the emotional tension of the innocent, and increase the tension of the guilty subject. A card stimulation test is a type of controlled peak of tension test.

career criminal. a person whose principal activity or occupation is criminal; a person who makes his living through profits generated by crime.

career criminal program. a prosecution program designed to identify repeat offenders and to flag such cases for expeditious processing by specialized units or with intensive procedures.

carnal. pertaining to the body, its passions and its appetites; sensual; sexual.

carnal abuse of a minor. intercourse, sodomy, or other sexual relationship with a child under the legally stated age, with or without the consent of the child-victim.

carnal knowledge. sexual intercourse.

carotid choke hold. a type of choke used by the police to subdue violent subjects. Pressure is applied to the carotid artery, which is the main blood supply to the brain. Because the hold is lethal, it is banned by policy or law in many jurisdictions.

car pocketing. stealing the contents of a car, usually from the glove compartment.

carriage trade. a prostitute's clientele.

carrier. high frequency energy that can be modulated by voice or signaling impulses.

carrier current. a method of alarm signal transmission using high-frequency alternating current on a standard voice-grade telephone line.

carrier on microwave. a means of transmitting many voice messages on one microwave channel. Transmission is point-to-point by microwave antennas.

carrier on wire. a means of transmitting many voice messages on a single pair of wires. Widely used by telephone companies.

carrier system. a means of conveying a number of channels over a single path by modulating each channel on a different carrier frequency and demodulating at the receiving point.

carry away job. a criminal method in which a safe or similar container is carried from the scene to a remote, concealed location where it is forced open.

carrying. in shoplifting, the practice of carrying, usually in the hand, a concealable item just prior to concealment.

cartel. an unlawful association of companies within the same industry which exists to control prices and minimize competition.

cartwheel. an amphetamine sulfate tablet.

Carve-Out. a classified contract issued in connection with an approved Special Access Program in which the Defense Investigative Service has been relieved of inspection responsibility in whole or part under the Defense Industrial Security Program.

case. the housing in which a lock mechanism is mounted and enclosed.

case-hardened lock. a lock having a strengthened metal casing to protect it from physical tampering.

caseload. the total number of cases assigned to one court, judge or other agency or person; for example, the number of active cases under investigation by a police detective.

casement window. a type of window which is hinged on the vertical edge.

case officer. an intelligence agency staff officer who is responsible for handling agents.

cash flow. receipt or payment of a stream of money; the amount of money generated from the operation of a business. It is determined from the net income, less depreciation and non-cash expenses.

cash position. a term used to describe the solvency of a business and which has special reference to the degree of readiness in which assets can be converted into cash without a loss. If a firm's current assets cannot be converted into cash to meet current liabilities, the firm is said to be in a poor cash position. Also called liquidity.

cast. in criminal investigations, a positive impression made from a mold.

casual criminal. a generally law-abiding citizen who commits a crime out of some pressing need not necessarily related to greed.

casual supplier. a person who furnishes an illegal drug to another for the convenience of the user rather than for gain.

catalyst. a substance that alters, accelerates or instigates chemical reactions without itself being affected.

catatonia. a state of muscular rigidity, sometimes observed in schizophrenics.

catch a hydrant. to drop a firefighter off at a hydrant or to lay out line from a hydrant.

cathode. the negative element of any electrical device as opposed to the anode. Electricity enters a circuit at the cathode.

cathode ray tube display. the viewing screen of a computer terminal or television receiver. It is typically used to display operating instructions, alarm information, live video surveillance, and graphic maps.

cattle prod. an electric device sometimes used to control violent people in mobs and riots.

CATV security system. a central station alarm system using existing cable television coaxial links to subscribers as the alarm signal transmission media. The alarm signal receiver is located at the head end of the CATV system.

causa mortis. a legal term meaning imminent death; the prospect of imminent death, as relates to a dying declaration.

causation. the relationship that must be established to hold a person responsible for a consequence of his action.

cause and origin expert. a qualified expert witness in arson cases, usually a fire investigator, who testifies as to a fire's cause and point of origin.

cause of action. the legal basis on which the plaintiff relies for recovery against the defendant.

cause in fact. the causal connection between an act or omission of the tortfeasor and plaintiff's injury. It is a basic element in a tort cause of action.

caveat emptor. a legal term meaning "let the buyer beware."

cavity resonator. a type of microwave transducer that modulates a microwave beam in the presence of audio frequencies.

cease and desist order. a ruling, frequently issued in unfair labor practice cases, which requires the charged party to stop conduct held to be illegal and take specific action to remedy the practice.

ceiling hook. in firefighting operations, a pole with a pointed end and a hook. It is used to pull down ceilings or partitions and to create holes for ventilating purposes.

celerity. speed or swiftness in the apprehension, trial, and punishment of an offender. Believers in the concept of deterrence regard it as a major factor in the effectiveness of punishment.

center-hung door. a door hung on center pivots.

center of mass. in police combat shooting, a term referring to the upper torso where the heart, lungs and major arteries are located.

center of the field. the point at which an object being examined by a magnifying glass or microscope is centered so as to attain the best image.

center rail. the horizontal rail in a door, usually located at lock height to separate the upper and lower panels of a recessed panel type door.

central computer facility. a protected area containing one or more ADP systems and associated communications equipment. This term does not include remote facilities, terminals or peripheral devices located outside the protected area.

centrally planned economy. an economic system that includes public ownership of or control over all productive resources and whose activity is planned by the government.

central pocket loop. in fingerprint science, a pattern which has two deltas and at least one ridge making a complete circuit. An imaginary line drawn between the two deltas will touch or cross at least one of the recurving ridges. This pattern is only slightly differentiated from a plain whorl.

central processing unit. in computer usage, the hardware that handles all calculating and routing of input and output as well as executing programs. The CPU is the part of the computer that actually computes.

central station. the control center of a system in which the alarm signal is relayed to a remote panel located at the facilities of a privately owned protection service company manned by persons employed by the protection company.

central station grading. the use of Underwriters' Laboratories (UL) designations for different classes of central stations, based on degree of protection afforded and specific standards for equipment, personnel, procedures, records and maintenance. Grading designations include Grade AA central station, Grade A central station, and Grade B central station.

central tendency. a characteristic of frequency distributions indicated by statistics such as the mean, mode, and median.

certificate of deposit. a written receipt by a

bank which indicates that there is a certain sum of money on deposit in the name of the designated person.

certified copy. a copy of a written instrument, document or writing which contains the identical information, record or transcript as the original, with an attached attestation by a certifying official (usually a notary public).

Certified Protection Professional program. a program managed by the Professional Certification Board in which certificates are awarded to applicants who meet prescribed educational, experiential and competency standards.

certiorari. an order or writ from a higher court ordering that a lower court send up the record of a case for review.

chain and Ts. a steel chain fitted with steel Ts at either end, used to restrain unruly prisoners. As the Ts are twisted, the chain applies increasing pressure on the prisoner's wrists.

chain bolt. a vertical spring-loaded bolt mounted at the top of a door. It is manually actuated by a chain.

chain door interviewer. an auxiliary locking device which allows a door to be open slightly, but restrains it from being fully opened. It consists of a chain with one end attached to a keyed metal piece which slides in a slotted metal plate attached to the door. Some chain door interviewers incorporate a keyed lock operated from inside.

chain link fence fabric. a fencing material made from wire helically wound and interwoven so as to provide continuous mesh.

chain referral scheme. a scheme that typically involves sales of grossly overpriced products through false representation that the cost will be recovered by commissions the promoter will pay on sales to the purchaser's friends, if only the purchaser will permit them to be contacted with the same proposition.

challenge. an objection, usually regarding a specific prospective juror, made to the judge by a party to a case, requesting that the person in question not be allowed to serve on the jury. A challenge may be for cause or peremptory. The defendant in a court-martial may challenge a member of the court for cause.

Chalnicon. trade name for a television image pickup tube of the direct readout type. Designed for low light applications, it is characterized by high sensitivity, good resolution, and decreased susceptibility to burn-in.

changeable characteristics. in observation and description, the alterable characteristics of a person, e.g., hair color and style, clothing and cosmetic changes.

change key. a key that will operate only one lock or a group of keyed-alike locks, as distinguished from a master key.

change of venue. the removal of a case by the court in a criminal action to a court in another location at the request of the defendant if, in the opinion of the court, an impartial trial cannot be had in the court where the case is pending.

channel. a path for electrical transmission between two or more stations or channel terminations.

Chaos. a CIA nickname for domestic security files and operations.

Chapter X. a term understood to mean corporate reorganization under bankruptcy court.

Chapter XI. a term understood to mean corporate reorganization under bankruptcy court, but still in debtors' control and subject to a compromise arrangement on debts owed.

Chapter XII. a term understood to mean bankrupt and in the process of being liquidated.

character evidence. objects and/or testimony demonstrating a defendant's character. It can be used to evaluate the credibility of a defendant, but not to show that he/she is the type of person likely to commit a crime.

character witness. a person called to testify that the defendant does or does not possess an upright character.

charge. a formal allegation that a specific person has committed a specific crime.

charge to jury. statements or comments given by a judge to the jury on a particular point of law so they might appreciate the matter in its proper perspective.

charged line. a line of hose or pipes filled with water and under pressure and ready for operation in case of fire.

charlatan. one who pretends to more knowledge or skill than he has.

chart identification. an administrative procedure incident to a polygraph examination. The examinee's name, signature, date and time of test, name and signature of examiner, and other identifying details are placed on the examinee's polygraph chart. The purpose of the procedure is to create a record that links the chart with the examinee and the examiner.

chart markings. markings placed on a polygraph chart by the examiner during the course of a test to (1) show mechanical adjustment of instrument components, (2) identify artifacts introduced into the polygrams by the examinee, and/or (3) show the mechanical or electrical settings of components.

chart minutes concept. a concept which holds that the various components of the polygraph are differentially effective depending on how much chart time has elapsed during a test. Overall, the polygraph technique is considered most effective between the 4th to 12th minute of chart time.

chase the dragon. to use a mixture of heroin and barbiturates.

chaste. never voluntarily having had unlawful sexual intercourse; an unmarried woman who has had no carnal knowledge of men.

chattel. any item of personal property as distinguished from land, which is real property.

C-head. a cocaine addict or user of LSD.

checkering. a pattern inlaid or cut on the foreends and grips of rifles, shotguns and handguns for ornamentation or to facilitate gripping.

check fraud. the issuance or passing of a check, draft or money order that is legal as a formal document, signed by the legal account holder but with the foreknowledge that the bank or depository will refuse to honor it because of insufficient funds or closed account.

checkpoint. a pre-designated location on a convoy route used to coordinate travel time and ascertain the security of the convoy or its cargo.

cheese box. an electronic device connected between two telephone lines for the purpose of preventing call tracing.

chemical breath testing device. an instrument which uses photoelectric or other sophisticated techniques to quantitatively determine blood-alcohol concentrations. Examples of such devices are the Alco-analyzer Gas Chromatograph, Alco-tector, Breathalyzer, Gas Chromatograph Intoximeter, and the Photo Electric Intoximeter.

chemical explosion. an explosion that results from an extremely rapid conversion into gases of a solid or liquid explosive compound, characterized by an instantaneous change normally called a detonation or deflagration.

chemical fuse. a bomb fuse which depends upon a reaction between a chemical and some other substance to initiate the firing action such as induced flame or induced metal fatigue. A chemical fuse depends upon the calculated reaction of various chemicals to produce electrical, mechanical, or chemical energy to function.

chemical initiator. a strong corrosive acid used to eat away in a predetermined time an item or material that restrains detonation.

chemical sensor. a device that evaluates air in

a protected area. If suspicious effluvia are detected, the sensor can read and record the change, and signal as programmed.

chemical stability. in bomb investigations, the potential of an explosive to react with its container.

Chicago school. a major school of sociological thought in the United States between the two world wars. It had a strong impact on criminological theory and research, stressing particularly the need to study criminals, delinquents, vagrants, prostitutes and other social outcasts in their natural environments and to perceive the world from their vantage points.

chief executive officer. the individual who is personally accountable to the board of directors or the electorate for the activities of the organization or the jurisdiction.

child abuse. physical assault inflicted on a young child, often by parents, endangering the child's life, health, and welfare. Excessive psychological mistreatment can also be considered child abuse.

child molestation. any sexual solicitation, contact, or intercourse of an adult with a child. The term usually refers to children below the age of puberty. Child abuse can be heterosexual or homosexual.

chillum. an Indian-style cylindrical pipe held vertically while smoking hashish.

chime. a short, single-stroke audible signal commonly used as a pre-signal to advise response persons that a fire condition is about to be announced.

Chimel vs California. a 1969 case in which the U.S. Supreme Court ruled that a search made incident to arrest must be confined to the person of the arrestee and the area within his immediate control.

China White. high quality heroin, so named for its whiteness and for its origin in the Far East.

Chinese connection. Chinese controlled and operated narcotic smuggling, extending from the Golden Triangle and Hong Kong to Amsterdam and to U.S., Canadian, Central American and Mexican airports and seaports.

chip. a microminiature circuit on a tiny silicon wafer or other conductive material.

chip-in card. a plastic identification card embedded with an integrated circuit chip. The card has both a coded memory and microprocessor intelligence. It can record card transactions and store data. Also called a smart card.

chipping. using drugs occasionally.

chippy. a part-time drug user.

chi-square. a statistical procedure that estimates whether the observed values in a distribution differ from the expected distribution and thus may be attributable to the operation of factors other than chance.

chloracetophenone. tear gas.

chloral betaine. a drug classified as a Schedule IV Controlled Substance.

chloral hydrate. the oldest of the hypnotic, or sleep-inducing drugs. Its popularity declined after introduction of the barbiturates. Chloral hydrate is a liquid, marketed in the form of syrups and soft gelatin capsules. It is not a street drug of choice, and its main misuse is by older adults. Chloral hydrate appears in the Controlled Substances Act as a Schedule IV depressant. Chloral hydrate is an hypnotic or sedative technically known as trichloroacetaldehyde, but more popularly called joy juice, knockout drops or mickey finn.

chlordiazepoxide. the generic name for a barbiturate regulated under the Controlled Substances Act as a Schedule IV depressant. It is legally sold as Librium.

chlorhexadol. a depressant classified as a Schedule III Controlled Substance.

choke hold. a self-defense technique used by the police to overcome or control violent persons.

choline. a chemical found in seminal fluid which is tested for by means of a crystal test called the Florence test. Because it is also found in other body fluids, this chemical alone is not specific for seminal fluid. However, if it is found in a stain which also contains acid phosphatase and spermine, the stain is or contains seminal fluid.

chop job. a safecracking method in which a chopping tool, such as an axe or chisel, is used to penetrate a safe, usually through the bottom.

chop shop. a criminal operation in which stolen autos are dismantled and the parts sold.

Christmas ball hazer. a homemade device in the shape of a hand-size ball and made of styrofoam or similar material. The sharp points of needles and nails protrude from the ball. It is sometimes soaked with urine or other irritant and thrown at law enforcement and security officers during disturbances.

chromatic aberration. a condition that occurs when the characteristics of a lens are such that different wavelengths of light are focused at varying distances from the lens. The result is color-fringing or halos around objects in the image.

chrysoidine. a tracing powder used to mark objects likely to be touched by a culprit. The powder is converted to an orange-colored dye by the skin's natural moisture.

ciphertext. data that are unintelligible until transformed by secret keys into intelligible data (plaintext).

circles of protection. a physical security design in which a criminal target is placed within two or more protective rings such as a perimeter fence, a building, a room and a vault.

circuit. a complete path in which electrons can flow. In alarm systems, a circuit begins with the negative terminal of a voltage source, continues through wire and the contacts of protective devices, and terminates at the positive terminal of the same source.

circulating main. a water main designed to supply water for firefighting purposes in such a way that water can be supplied from more than one direction and with greater force and volume.

circumstantial evidence. evidence which tends to prove a fact, but does so indirectly.

circumvent. to bypass alarm sensors by physically avoiding them.

citation. a written notice which orders a person to be in court at a stated time and place to answer for a crime.

citizen's arrest. the arrest, without a warrant, of an alleged offender by a person who is not a law enforcement officer, for a felony or a breach of the peace committed in the citizen's presence.

citizen's complaint. a complaint of a citizen against a government official, usually a law enforcement officer.

Citizens Crime Watch. a neighborhood nonprofit effort in which citizens cooperate with local police by reporting crimes in progress and suspicious activities.

civil action. a proceeding for the redress of a private grievance or the enforcement of a private right.

civil commitment. the action of a judicial officer or administrative body ordering a person to be placed in an institution or program for custody, treatment or protection.

civil death. the loss of numerous rights and privileges as a result of a sentence of death or life imprisonment. Such losses may include nullification of a marriage, distribution of an estate, or denial of the right to sue or be sued.

civil disabilities. rights or privileges denied a person as result of a conviction or a guilty plea, in addition to or other than the imposed legal penalty.

civil disobedience. deliberate, overt, and nonviolent lawbreaking in which the perpetrator justifies his action on the ground that a particular law is immoral; for example, activities conducted in violation of the segregation laws. Those engaged in civil disobedience seek to change an immoral law by focusing attention on it.

civil disturbance system file. a file maintained by the Department of Justice as an intelligence aid. A subject index lists persons involved in civil disturbances, and the incident index contains records of civil disorder events. The indexes are cross-referenced.

civil law. the body of law relating to the rights of citizens.

civil liberty. freedom from restraint of or interference with the affairs, opinions, or property of a person except in the interest of the public good.

civilly dead. a principle of law which holds that an individual who is not legally dead can forfeit his/her civil rights upon conviction of treason or imprisonment for life.

civil rights. the rights of every citizen which are guaranteed under the Constitution.

Civil Rights Acts of 1866, 1870 and 1971. laws intended to insure equality before the law in a variety of functional areas (ability to enter into contracts, sue, give evidence, and secure equal protection of persons and property) and establish that individuals or governments denying any rights or privileges shall be liable for legal action. These acts are often used in conjunction with, but are not replaced by, other civil rights acts as the basis for suits.

Civil Rights Act of 1957. a law generally considered to be the beginning of contemporary civil rights legislation. It established the US Commission on Civil Rights and strengthened the judiciary's ability to protect civil rights.

Civil Rights Act of 1960. a law intended mainly to plug legal loopholes in the Civil Rights Act of 1957.

civil wrongs. wrongs that infringe on private rights and duties. Remedy against them is sought by private action. Tort and breach of contract are among the more common civil wrongs.

clandestine operations. intelligence, counter-intelligence, and other information collection activities and covert political, economic, propaganda and paramilitary activities, conducted so as to assure secrecy.

Class A Alarm System. a fire protection specification that requires alarm operation even in the event of a single break or ground fault in the signal line.

Class A Circuit. a type of four-wire alarm circuit used to detect an alarm or line fault. The circuit allows reporting of an alarm condition even when a trouble condition has occurred. Two conductors run from the alarm panel to the sensor, and two return. A single break does not prevent the reception of an alarm signal, but does initiate a trouble condition.

class action. a search for judicial remedy that one or more individuals may undertake on behalf of themselves and all others in similar situations.

Class A Document. an identification document regarded as generally reliable. Examples include passports and armed forces identification cards.

Class A Vault. a vault approved by the Department of Defense. It features 8 inch-thick reinforced concrete walls that extend to the underside of the roof slab; a monolithic reinforced-concrete roof slab of a thickness not less than the walls and floors; and where the underside of the roof slab or roof construction exceeds twelve feet in height, a normal reinforced-concrete slab is in place over the vault area at a height not to exceed nine feet. The vault lock conforms to UL Standard 768 Group L-R and is equipped with a top-reading, spy-proof type dial.

Class B Alarm System. a fire protection specification that requires the detection of an alarm, a single break, or a ground fault in a signal line. A break or ground fault causes further alarms to go undetected.

Class B Circuit. a four-wire system in which two conductors travel from an alarm panel, connect with one or more alarm sensors, and return to the panel. One broken conductor prevents reception of an alarm signal from any point beyond the break, causing a trouble condition. A Class B Circuit can also consist of a two-wire system in which only one conductor travels from the panel to sensors and back again. A single break prevents all alarm transmissions and initiates a trouble condition at the panel.

Class B Document. an identification document regarded as often reliable. Examples include photo-bearing driver licenses and photo-bearing employee cards issued by national firms.

Class B Vault. a vault approved by the Department of Defense. It features a monolithic concrete floor of the thickness of adjacent concrete floor construction but not less than four inches thick; brick, concrete block or masonry walls not less than 8 inches thick, except that monolithic steel-reinforced concrete walls at least four inches may also be used, and are used in seismic areas; a monolithic reinforced-concrete roof slab of a thickness determined by structural requirements; and where the underside of the roof slab exceeds twelve feet in height, a normal reinforced-concrete slab is placed over the vault at a height not to exceed nine feet. The lock specifications are the same as for a Class A Vault.

Class C Document. an identification document

regarded as doubtfully reliable. A document of this type will usually not contain a photo, serial number, or a means by which it can be verified.

class characteristics. marks made on an object as a result of the manufacturing process. Such marks have significance to the analysis of foot and tire prints, tool marks and similar forms of physical evidence.

class conflict. the struggle between competing classes, specifically between the class that owns the means of production and the class or classes that do not.

Class C Vault. a vault approved by the Department of Defense. It features walls of not less than 8 inch-thick hollow clay tile (vertical cell double shell) or concrete block (thick shell), except that monolithic steel-reinforced concrete walls at least four inches thick may also be used, and are used in seismic areas; and walls back of the exterior wall-faction of the building are concrete, solid masonry, or hollow masonry units filled with concrete and steel reinforcement bars. The floor, roof, ceilings, and lock specifications are the same as for a Class A Vault.

Class I Data. computer data that require off-site storage of backup copies under secure vault conditions with timely restoration in case of operational information loss.

Class II Data. computer data that require off-site storage of backup copies under conditions that resist accidental damage with timely restoration in case of operational information loss.

Class III Data. computer data that require no off-site storage of backup copies because the data can be regenerated if needed at a cost that is less than the cost of off-site storage, or loss of the data would result in a cost that is less than the cost of off-site storage.

Class D Document. an identification document regarded as unreliable. This type of document can be obtained without proving identity, as in the case of a social security card.

classical conditioning. a process whereby a neutral stimulus when paired with a reward to evoke a reflexive response comes to elicit that response when presented by itself.

classical school of criminology. a dominant trend in the history of political and philosophical thought on crime that flourished for about a century beginning in the 1760s. The classical school assumed the existence of free will, imputed responsibility and accountability to all perpetrators, and stressed the necessity of meting out punishment sufficiently severe to deter would-be criminals, but not so severe as to be cruel, unjust or unnecessary.

classification. procedures during which a new

inmate of a penal institution is assigned a security status, an educational, work or therapeutic program, and appropriate institutional housing; a method of categorizing fingerprints for easier storage, retrieval and comparison.

classification authority. the authority vested in an official of the originating or user agency to make a determination that certain information requires protection against unauthorized disclosure.

Classification Guide. in the DoD Industrial Security Program, a document issued by an authorized original classifier that prescribes the level of classification and appropriate declassification instructions for specified information to be classified derivatively.

classified. subject to prescribed asset protection controls, including controls associated with classifications and control statements.

classified contract. a contract that requires access to classified information by the contractor or contractor employees.

classified destruction. the process of destroying or rendering unintelligible materials that are classified or contain classified information.

Classified Information. in the DoD Industrial Security Program, information or material owned by, produced by or for, or under the control of the US Government which has been determined to require protection against unauthorized disclosure and is so designated.

Class 1 Safe. a General Services Administration-approved insulated security filing cabinet affording protection for 30 man-minutes against surreptitious entry, 10 man-minutes against forced entry, 1 hour protection against fire damage to contents, 20 man-hours against manipulation of the lock, and 20 man-hours against radiological attack.

Class 2 Safe. a General Services Administration-approved insulated security filing cabinet affording protection for 20 man-minutes against surreptitious entry, 1 hour protection against fire damage to contents, 5 man-minutes against forced entry, 20 man-hours against manipulation of the lock, and 20 man-hours against radiological attack.

Class 3 Safe. a General Services Administration-approved non-insulated security filing cabinet affording protection for 20 man-minutes against surreptitious entry, 20 man-hours against manipulation of the lock, 20 man-hours against radiological attack, and zero man-minutes against forced entry.

Class 4 Safe. a General Services Administration-approved non-insulated security filing cabinet affording protection for 20 man-minutes against surreptitious entry, 5 man-minutes against forced entry, 20 man-hours against manipulation of the lock, and 20 man-hours against radiological attack.

Class 5 Safe. a General Services Administration-approved non-insulated security filing cabinet affording protection for 30 man-minutes against surreptitious entry, 10 man-minutes against forced entry, 20 man-minutes against manipulation of the lock, and 20 man-hours against radiological attack.

Class 6 Safe. a General Services Administration-approved non-insulated security filing cabinet affording protection for 30 man-minutes against surreptitious attack, 20 man-hours against manipulation of the lock, and 20 man-hours against radiological attack. It has no forced entry requirement.

Class I Vault Door. a vault door that meets the UL standard for 30 minute resistance to expert burglary attack utilizing common mechanical tools, electric tools and cutting torches, and any combination thereof. The door lock also meets UL Standard 768 or 887.

Class II Vault Door. a vault door that meets the UL standard for one hour resistance to expert burglary attack utilizing common mechanical tools, electric tools and cutting torches, and any combination thereof. The door lock also meets UL standard 768 or 887.

Class III Vault Door. a vault door that meets the UL standard for two hour resistance to expert burglary attack utilizing common mechanical tools, electric tools and cutting torches, and any combination thereof. The door lock also meets UL standard 768 or 887.

Class V Vault Door. a Department of Defense-approved door designed to afford protection for 30 man-minutes against surreptitious entry, 10 man-minutes against forced entry, 20 man-hours against manipulation of the lock, and 20 man-hours against radiological attack.

Class VI Vault Door. a Department of Defense-approved vault door designed to afford protection for 30 man-minutes against surreptitious entry, 30 man-minutes against lock manipulation, and 20 man-hours against radiology techniques.

clean change room. a room where workers put on clean clothing and/or protective equipment in an environment that is free of toxic and/or hazardous substances.

clear. to reset, as in restoring an alarm to normal condition.

clearance. in Uniform Crime Reports terminology, the event where a known occurrence of a Part I offense is followed by an arrest or other decision which indicates a solved crime at the police level of reporting.

clearance rate. in Uniform Crime Reports terminology, the number of offenses cleared divided by the number of offenses known to police, expressed as a percent.

clear and present danger. a concept that gives to the government a right and a duty to curtail otherwise constitutionally protected speech when utterance of the words in a specific context threaten imminent and grave harm.

cleartext. data that are intelligible until transformed by secret keys into unintelligible data. Also called plaintext.

clear zone. an area on either or both sides of a perimeter barrier that has been cleared of any materials that offer concealment to an intruder.

cleavage line wound. a gaping wound produced by cutting or stabbing perpendicularly to a cleavage line. The wound will appear to have been caused by a large blade or a deep cutting action. The gaping aspect, however, results from a distortion of the muscle fibers that provide a normal tension to the skin.

clevis. a metal link used to attach a chain to a padlock.

clicker. a marijuana cigarette soaked in formaldehyde (embalming fluid).

climb detector. a type of intrusion sensor typically consisting of three low voltage wires strung across the top of a wall, fence or building.

clock disk. the recording part of a watchman's clock. It makes a record of each time a key check was made during a patrol round.

clonitazine. an opiate classified as a Schedule I Controlled Substance.

Clonopin. the trade name for clonazepam, a depressant in the family of benzodiazepines. It is a commonly abused drug and is regulated under the Controlled Substances Act as a Schedule IV depressant.

clorazepate. a controlled ingredient sold legally as Tranxene, a barbiturate. It is a Schedule IV drug.

closed area. a controlled area established to store classified material which because of its size or nature cannot be placed in storage containers or kept under constant surveillance.

closed bomb. a bomb in which none of the component parts are visible to the naked eye.

closed case. an investigation that has been closed because it is completed or because there are no further investigative leads to follow.

closed circuit. a protective circuit consisting

of all normally closed devices connected in a series. A break in the circuit or activation of one or more sensors triggers an alarm.

close-range gunshot wound. a wound caused when the muzzle at time of discharge is 2-24 inches from the victim.

closing arguments. arguments by the prosecutor and defense counsel in which each side attempts to persuade the jury to reach a favorable verdict.

closing signal. a signal, transmitted from a protected premises to a central station or other monitoring location, which informs that the alarm system has been disarmed by an authorized person.

cloudy hairline. a tell-tale sign of a counterfeit bill as evidenced by an indistinct hairline on the head of the person depicted on the bill.

clutch-head screw. a mounting screw used to apply devices to openings that require protection. The screw has a uniquely designed head for which a screwdriver is not commonly available. It can be tightened but once in place it cannot be removed.

C-mount. the threaded mounting portion on the rear of a lens. It has a pitch of 32 threads per inch, and is an industry standard applicable to film and video cameras and lenses.

coaxial cable. a type of cable capable of passing a wide range of frequencies with very low signal loss. In its simplest form, it consists of a hollow metallic shield with a single wire placed along the center of the shield and isolated from it.

COBOL. an acronym for Common Business Oriented Language, a procedure-oriented computer language that resembles standard business English.

cocaine. the most potent stimulant of natural origin. It is extracted from the leaves of the coca plant. Many of cocaine's therapeutic applications are obsolete as the result of the development of safer anesthetics. Illicit cocaine is distributed as a white crystalline powder, often diluted by a variety of other ingredients, the most common of which are sugars such as lactose, inositil, mannitol, and local anesthetics such as lidocaine. The drug is most commonly administered by being "snorted" through the nasal passages. Less commonly, for heightened effect, the drug is injected directly into the bloodstream. It is also smoked by a method called "freebasing" in which cocaine hydrochloride (the usual form in which it is sold) is converted to cocaine base. Inhalation of the fumes produces a rapid and intense effect. Cocaine has a potential for extraordinary psychic dependence. Although technically a stimulant, cocaine appears in the Controlled Substances Act as a Schedule II narcotic. The

street names for cocaine include coke, flake, and snow.

cocaine base. a form of cocaine converted from its normal form, usually for the purpose of smoking it (free basing).

cocaine paste. a white, semi-solid or solid preparation containing cocaine sulphate and other coca alkaloids. It can be mixed with tobacco or marihuana and smoked. Also called coca paste, cocaine sulphate and cocaine basic paste.

cocked striker. in bomb construction, a firing pin held under tension. Upon release of the tension, the pin initiates the bomb's firing train.

coded cable. an electrical cable that has distinctly colored wire coverings and shields so that individual leads are readily distinguishable from each other at any point along the cable's length.

coded system. a feature of a fire alarm system in which not less than three rounds of coded alarm signals are transmitted, after which the signals may be manually or automatically silenced.

codefendant. one of the accused in a trial in which two or more persons are charged with the same criminal act or acts and are tried at the same time. A defendant in such an instance may request a separate trial, or severance.

codeine. an alkaloid found in raw opium. Although it occurs naturally, most codeine is produced from morphine. As compared with morphine, codeine produces less analgesia, sedation, and respiratory depression. It is widely distributed in products of two general types. Codeine for the relief of moderate pain may consist of codeine tablets or be combined with other products such as aspirin or acetaminophen (Tylenol). Some examples of liquid codeine preparations for the relief of coughs (antitussives) are Robitussin AC, Cheracol, and elixir of terprin hydrate with codeine. It is also manufactured to a lesser extent in injectable form for the relief of pain, and is by far the most widely used naturally occurring narcotic in medical treatment. Codeine products appear in the Controlled Substances Act as Schedule II, III and V drugs.

codeine methylbromide. an opium derivative classified as a Schedule I Controlled Substance.

codeine-N-oxide. an opium derivative classified as a Schedule I Controlled Substance.

code of ethics. a statement of professional standards of conduct to which the practitioners of a profession say they subscribe.

Code of Federal Regulations. executive agency

regulations published in the Federal Register.

Code of Hammurabi. Babylonian laws of the twenty-second century BC, generally regarded by historians as a moderate and humanitarian code for its period. It is one of the oldest codes of law.

Code of Justinian. the codification of Roman law by Justinian I in the sixth century AD in the form of a body of law.

code wheel. the component that actuates a relay to produce coded signals on a McCulloh circuit transmitter. The code is created by removing actuator teeth on the wheel.

codicil. an addition to a will.

coding siren. a siren with the capability of emitting controlled bursts of sound.

coerced confession. an admission of guilt obtained by threat or the use of force.

coercion. compelling a person to do that which he does not have to do, or to omit what he may legally do, by some illegal means such as by threat or force.

cognizant security office. in the DoD Industrial Security Program, the office of the Defense Investigative Service Director of Industrial Security who has industrial security jurisdiction over the geographical area in which a particular facility is located.

cohabit. to live together.

coherent. as used in security communications, a condition in which individual waves of one frequency are locked in phase, as opposed to random, incoherent waves.

Cointelpro. a now defunct FBI counterintelligence program that monitored the activities of suspected subversives.

coitus. sexual intercourse.

coke-head. cocaine addict.

cold hardware. an unregistered or untraceable firearm.

cold site. a computer backup site that has all necessary hookups to accommodate rapid installation of a data processing operation. Also called an empty shell.

cold surveillance. secretive tailing or bugging of a target.

cold water ground. a connection to a cold water pipe, which may run long distances underground, helping to insure an effective electrical ground.

cold weather pack. a heating unit that keeps card readers and similar electronic devices within proper operating temperatures in a cold environment.

collateral consequence. any harm that may result from a guilty plea or a conviction, in addition to the preordered punishment. Examples include deportation, disenfranchisement, disbarment, or loss of license to practice certain professions.

collateral fact. a fact not directly related to an issue; extraneous information.

collected standards. handwriting specimens collected for comparison purposes. Typically, they are not in direct connection to the crime and are obtained from various public and private files.

collection. the acquisition of information by any means and its delivery to an intelligence processing unit for use in the production of intelligence.

collision diagram. a schematic drawing of a street intersection or other roadway location showing, by symbols, the traffic unit movements and conflicts that have occurred in a given time period. The symbols represent vehicle types, travel directions, pedestrians, bicycles, manner of collision, and indicate where the collisions were fatal or caused injury or property damage.

collusion. an agreement between two or more persons to proceed fraudulently to the detriment and prejudice of an innocent and ignorant third party.

color of authority. authority based on a prima facie right; that which is presumed because of apparent legal authority. For example, the police act under color of authority.

combination smoke detector. a smoke detector that contains both ionization and photoelectric sensing elements. One type of combination smoke detector goes into alarm if either one of the sensing elements is activated. In another type, both sensing elements must activate before the detector goes into an alarm mode.

combination tool mark. a tool mark consisting of an abrasion and a negative impression. The abrasion is caused by the movement of the tool against a surface. The impression is formed when the tool is applied as a lever. Combination tool marks are frequently made by crowbars and jimmies.

combustible. capable of undergoing combustion; apt to catch fire; inflammable.

come-along. a type of hold or a device used by a police officer when taking a resisting person into custody.

come home. an undercover agent's withdrawal from active operations.

comer. a younger person who seems to have the potential for moving into a top management position.

comet tailing. a condition appearing on a video display screen that is caused by partial burn-in combined with image movement.

command. in computer usage, an instruction, generally an English word, typed by the user or included in a command procedure that requests the software to perform some well-defined activity such as copy, delete, transfer or print.

commercial bribery. conferring or offering or agreeing to confer benefit upon an employee, without consent of the employer, with intent to influence the employee's conduct in relation to his employer's affairs. The crime is also committed when the employee solicits, agrees or accepts such benefit. It is a crime separate from traditional bribery and usually applicable to conduct involving non-public, business persons.

commission. doing or perpetration; the performance of an act.

commit. to order into custody, either to a correctional facility or a mental institution.

commitment. the written order by which a court or magistrate directs an officer to take a person to prison; authority for holding in jail one accused of crime.

common carrier. a person or company who carries or holds itself out as carrying persons and/or goods for hire to all who apply.

common entry door. any door in a multiple dwelling which provides access between the semi-public, interior areas of the building and the out-of-doors areas surrounding the building.

common knowledge. matters which the court may declare applicable to action without necessity of proof. It is knowledge that every intelligent person has.

common law. a system of law, or body of legal rules, derived from decisions of judges based upon accepted customs and traditions. It was developed in England. It is known as the common law because it is believed that these rules were generally recognized and were in full force throughout England. Common law is now the basis of the laws in every state of the United States, except Louisiana, which bases its laws upon the early laws of France. Statutes have been enacted to supplement and supersede the common law in many fields. The common law, however, still governs where there is no statute dealing with a specific subject. Although the common law is written, it is called the unwritten law in contradistinction to statutory law enacted by the legislatures.

common-law marriage. a union not solemnized in the ordinary way, but created by an agreement to marry, followed by cohabitation.

common mode noise. a form of electrical noise interference that typically results from lightning, grounding faults, radio and television transmitters and poor motor brush contacts.

common nuisance. a danger or damage threatening the public.

communications intelligence. technical and intelligence information derived from foreign communications by other than the intended recipient.

communications security. the protective measures taken to deny unauthorized persons information derived from telecommunications and to ensure the authenticity of such communications.

communicator. a device that electronically dials one or more prerecorded telephone numbers using digital codes and reports alarm or supervisory information to a receiver.

community control. a method of policing in which the community determines patrol priorities. It is intended to relieve police-community tensions.

community corrections. any type of supervision over a person convicted of delinquent or criminal activity in which the supervision takes place outside an institution of confinement. Examples include probation and parole.

community restitution. public work done for the community, in lieu of or in addition to other criminal sanctions, as punishment for a crime. Vandalism is an offense for which community restitution is sometimes ordered.

commutation of sentence. an act of clemency in which a sentence of death is changed to a term in prison, or in which a prison sentence is lessened, sometimes to time already served, in order to permit the convict's release without delay.

companionate crime. crime committed by two or more persons against another, as in a holdup or a mugging.

company doctor. a slang term for an expert brought in to save a company from severe difficulties.

company spy. someone hired by an employer to report on what is happening in the company, usually at the operating level and frequently within a union.

comparative negligence. a principle of law which takes into account the negligence of both sides in an accident.

comparison microscope. a microscope having an optical bridge that permits an examiner to view and thereby compare two samples at the same time. It is often used to identify bullets. If the ends of two bullets are brought together in a single fused image and their separate striations match, the ballistics examiner would conclude that both bullets were fired from the same weapon.

comparison spectrum. a spectrum which contains a number of sharply defined, well identified lines of standard wavelength, which is used as a standard of comparison in studying other spectra, usually photographed on the same plate above and below of the spectrum studied.

compartmentation. the use of barriers to surround an asset.

compelling impulse. an accused's claim (but not a legal defense) that the crime committed was done because of an irresistible urge.

compensation. a human condition characterized by actions that serve to conceal personal weaknesses by emphasizing desirable traits. A person who compensates is likely to make up for frustration in one area by over-gratification in another area.

compensatory damages. a sum of money awarded to a plaintiff by a court or jury as a fair and just recompense for injury sustained to a person, property or reputation.

competency. as used in the law of evidence, the presence of those characteristics, or the absence of those disabilities, which render a witness legally fit and qualified to give testimony in a court of justice. The term is applied in the same sense to documents or other written evidence.

competency to stand trial. the concept that a defendant should be tried only if he has sufficient ability at the time of trial to understand the proceedings against him, to consult with his lawyer with a reasonable degree of understanding, and to assist in his own defense.

competent. legally fit for acceptance in a court.

competent court. a court having lawful jurisdiction.

compiler. in computer usage, a system component that translates a program written in a high-level language into a binary machine code.

complainant. the person who, as a victim of a crime, brings the facts to the attention of the police.

complaint. a formal written accusation made by any person, often a prosecutor, and filed in a court, alleging that a specified person has committed a specific offense.

complementary metal-oxide semiconductor. a solid-state switching device used in alarm products and computerized alarm systems. A CMOS circuit consumes relatively little power, but is susceptible to transients.

component failure. a cause for failure or improper operation of an element in a system.

composite. a forged document made from piecing or recombining other documents.

composite door. a door constructed of a solid core material with facing and edges of different materials.

composite drawing. a drawing of a suspect made by a police artist from information provided by witnesses.

Composition C. a powerful plastic explosive used for military and demolition purposes.

compounded larceny. a larceny accompanied by another offense such as battery.

compounding a crime. the taking, or agreeing to take, money, property, gratuity or reward upon an understanding to conceal a crime, or violation of statute, or to abstain from, discontinue or delay prosecution, or to withhold any evidence thereof, except in a case where a compromise is allowed by law; the offense of receiving or offering to give a monetary or other consideration in return for a promise not to prosecute or aid in the prosecution of a criminal offender. Also known as misprision of a felony.

compound microscope. a normal-light microscope used for making crime laboratory examinations. It has two lenses or sets of lenses, the first being the eyepiece or eyepiece assembly, and the other the objective or objective assembly.

Comprehensive Drug Abuse Prevention and Control Act. a 1970 law that superseded all other federal narcotics laws. The act has four titles. Title II, which is concerned with control and enforcement, is called the Controlled Substances Act.

compromise. the disclosure of classified information to persons not authorized access thereto.

compulsion. forcible inducement to the commission of an act; an impulse or feeling of being irresistibly driven toward the performance of some act.

compulsory. involuntary; forced; coerced by legal process or by force of law.

compurgation. a process, used at the time of the origin of the jury system, in which a defendant attempted to prove his innocence by calling witnesses who testified as to their belief in his innocence.

computer. a machine that processes information or provides data by automatically following preprogrammed directions. It is variously called a central processor, distributed processor, shared logic processor, word processor, office system processor, digital transmission controller, and other names.

computer crime. a popular term for crimes committed by use of a computer or crimes involving misuse or destruction of computer equipment or computerized information, sometimes specifically theft committed by means of manipulation of a computerized financial transaction system, or the use of computer services with intent to avoid payment.

computerese. jargon used by computer specialists.

computer program. a set of data fed into a

computer to be evaluated or to be used to process other data or solve a problem.

computer network. the interconnection of communications lines (including microwave or other means of electronic communication) with a computer through remote terminals, or a complex consisting of two or more interconnected computers.

computer program. a series of instructions or statements, in a form acceptable to a computer, that permits the functioning of a computer in a manner designed to provide appropriate products from the computer system.

computer-related crime. any illegal act for which knowledge of computer technology is essential for performance of the act.

computer security. a collection of measures designed to minimize the cost of security plus the cost of security losses at a computer facility.

computer systems. a machine or collection of machines, one or more of which contain computer programs and data, that performs functions including, but not limited to, logic, arithmetic, data storage and retrieval, communication, and control.

concentrated explosion. an explosion characterized by an extremely rapid combustion, known as detonation reaction, which occurs through the action of explosives such as dynamite, TNT, nitroglycerin, pentaerythritol-tetranitrate, and various "plastic" explosives.

concentric-zone theory. a theory of urban development which holds that cities grow around a central business district in concentric zones, with each zone devoted to a different land use.

concertina. a coil of barbed wire typically used as a temporary fence.

concession. in the oil and gas industry, a tract of land granted by a government to an individual or company for exploration and exploitation to recover minerals.

conclusion of fact. a determination by a jury based on facts produced in evidence.

conclusion of law. a determination arrived at by applying to the facts pleaded certain artificial rules of law.

conclusive. shutting up a matter; shutting out all further evidence; not admitting of explanation or contradiction; beyond question or beyond dispute.

conclusive evidence. that which is incontrovertible, either because the law does not permit it to be contradicted, or because it is so strong and convincing as to overbear all proof to the contrary and establish the proposition in question beyond any reasonable doubt.

conclusive presumption. a presumption which cannot be challenged no matter how strong the evidence to the contrary may be.

concubinage. the act or practice of cohabiting, without the authority of law or a legal marriage.

concurrent jurisdiction. a jurisdiction that applies when the Federal Government and a state have all the rights accorded them under the Constitution with the broad qualification such rights run concurrently. Exact equivalence of rights is not present, however. At all times the Federal Government has the superior right to carry out federal functions unimpeded by state interference. State criminal laws are, of course, applicable in the area of enforcement of the state. The same laws are enforceable by the Federal Government under the Assimilative Crimes Act, which is applicable to areas under concurrent and exclusive jurisdiction of the United States. Other federal criminal laws also apply. Most crimes fall under both federal and state sanction and either the federal or state government, or both, may take jurisdiction over a given offense.

concurrent sentences. two or more sentences to be served simultaneously. Concurrent sentencing effectively reduces the severity of a sentence, while also ensuring the state the right to continue confinement if a court of appeals should overturn the guilty verdict on one of the charges.

concurrent validity study. in employee screening, a study in which the ratings assigned to employees on the basis of objective criteria are compared against integrity test scores. If the integrity test is valid, there will be a correlation between the test scores and the objective criteria.

condemnation. the legal machinery by which an authorized governmental agency takes private property for public use.

condenser. a form of heat exchanger in which the heat in vapors is transferred to a flow of cooling water or air, causing the vapors to form a liquid. In electricity, a condenser is also called a capacitor.

condenser microphone. a microphone in which a sound-activated diaphragm is one side of a single capacitor. A condenser microphone is quite sensitive, but has a very low-level output.

conditional endorsement. a special endorsement with words added that create a condition which must happen before the special endorsee is entitled to the payment. The endorser is liable only if the condition is fulfilled. Example: "Pay to Middleburg Corn Growers Association upon delivery of warehouse receipt for twenty-five standard bushels of corn, high grade. John Jones."

conditional plea. a plea of guilty or nolo contendere which is entered on the understanding that the defendant will still be allowed to appeal a prior adverse ruling which otherwise would be forfeited by entry of the plea.

conditional privilege. a defense in criminal libel which contends that the defendant has made the allegedly libelous statement in order to fulfill a public or private duty to speak.

conditional release. the release by executive decision from a correctional facility of a prisoner who has not served his or her full sentence and whose freedom is contingent upon obeying specified rules of behavior.

condition diagram. a map drawn to scale of a street intersection or other roadway location that shows pavement widths, curbs or shoulders, sidewalks, view obstructions, grades, traffic controls, lighting, access driveways and other important features that can affect traffic movements.

conditioning. political agitation caused by the successful use of disinformation.

conductance. the ability of an electrical conductor to pass current. Conductance is the reciprocal of resistance.

conduct unbecoming an officer. in police and military disciplinary proceedings, a charge involving violation of the rules and regulations or professional and ethical standards of the department or service.

conduit. solid or flexible tubing for protecting wires.

cone pattern. a cone shaped pattern that appears in glass plate fractured by a penetrating force. In a cross sectional view, the tip of the cone is on the entering side of the glass with the large end of the cone on the exiting side. Also called saucer pattern.

confabulation. the filling in of memory gaps with false and often irrelevant details.

confess. to admit as true; to admit the truth of a charge or accusation.

Confessing Sam. a person who regularly confesses to sensational crimes he/she has not committed.

confession. a voluntary statement of guilt; a complete acknowledgement of guilt.

confession distance. the distance between the interrogator and the person being interrogated within which the interrogator establishes feelings of friendship, acceptance, intimacy and reassurance.

confidence game. a popular term for false representation to obtain money or any other thing of value, where deception is accomplished through the trust placed by the victim in the character of the offender.

Confidential. as used in the DoD Industrial Security Program, a designation applied to information or material the unauthorized disclosure of which could be reasonably expected to cause damage to national security. Examples of damage include the compromise of information that indicates strength of ground, air and naval forces in the US and overseas areas; disclosure of technical information used for training, maintenance and inspection of classified munitions of war; and revelation of performance characteristics, test data, design and production data on munitions of war.

confidential communication. an oral or written communication between two persons which because of their relationship may not be divulged unless waived. The relationship may be that between a lawyer and client, doctor and patient or investigator and informant.

confidential information. information protected by statute or by rules of an organization. Examples of confidential information might be military secrets, or a company's trade secrets.

confidential source. as used in the DoD Industrial Security Program, any individual or organization that has provided, or that may reasonably be expected to provide, information to the United States on matters pertaining to the national security with the expectation, expressed or implied, that the information or relationship, or both, be held in confidence.

confinement. the restraint or restriction of a person's freedom of movement.

confirmation. in drug investigations, the reanalysis of a sample found to be "positive" in a preliminary test or field test.

confiscation. the act of taking private property as a penalty and a forfeit for public use. Also the act of taking contraband.

conflict of interest. a situation where a decision that may be made (or influenced) by an office holder may (or may appear to) be to that office holder's personal benefit.

conformal projection. a mapping method that does not preserve size, distance or area or scale of lengths, but preserves the shapes of the objects depicted.

confrontation. the right of a person to face the witnesses who charge him with a crime.

confusion agent. an individual dispatched by his sponsor to confound the intelligence or counterintelligence apparatus of the opposition, as opposed to the direct task of collecting and transmitting information.

Congressional Assassination Act. a law which makes killing or plotting to kill a member of Congress a federal crime.

conjugal visit. a visit of a spouse with a prisoner in privacy to allow a conjugal (marital) relationship.

connecting bar. a flat metal bar attached to the core of a cylinder lock to operate the bolt mechanism.

consanguinity. blood relationship; the relationship of persons descended from a common ancestor.

consecutive sentence. a sentence that is imposed separately and which must be served one after the other. Also called cumulative sentence.

consensual crime. a violation of law committed by or between two or more adults with the voluntary consent of each participant, as in the crimes of adultery, sodomy and gambling.

consensual monitoring. the monitoring of conversations between two individuals with the consent and knowledge of one of the individuals.

consent. a concurrence of wills; agreement; voluntarily yielding the will to the proposition of another; a voluntary accord between two people in their contractual relationship.

consequent cost. the cost to an organization that results from disruptions caused by a loss event. Consequent cost may result from lost man hours, underutilized equipment or missed business opportunities, but does not reflect the direct cost of the loss itself. For example, a consequent cost might be the loss of revenue resulting from the theft of a van used in a delivery service, but does not include the replacement cost of the van.

consignee. a person, firm or activity designated as the receiver of a shipment; one to whom a shipment is consigned.

consignor. a person, firm or activity from whom materials are sent. The consignor is also usually the shipper.

consignment. the delivery of goods by the owner or the consignor to the consignee.

conspiracy. a joining together of people to commit an unlawful act; a section of the US Code that makes it a violation of Federal law when two or more persons conspire to commit any Federal offense, provided that at least one of the conspirators takes some action to effect the object of the conspiracy. The law is found in 18 USC, Section 371.

conspiracy of concealment. efforts to conceal or cover up any evidence of crime or wrongdoing.

constant-ringing drop. a latching relay that continuously activates an alarm annunciator until reset.

constant voltage transformer. a device that provides regulation for AC line loads ranging from 15 VA to 15,000 VA. It compensates continuously for incoming voltage fluctuations by raising and lowering output voltage. Also called a ferroresonant regulator.

Constitutional right. a right guaranteed to the citizens by the Constitution and so guaranteed as to prevent legislative interference therewith.

Constitution of the United States. the basic law of the United States, with which all other federal and state laws must not conflict, lest they be declared null and void on the ground of being unconstitutional.

construction master keying. a keying system used to allow the use of a single key for all locks during the construction of large housing projects. In one such system, the cylinder cores of all locks contain an insert that permits the use of a special master key. When the dwelling unit is completed, the insert is removed and the lock then accepts its own change key and no longer accepts the construction master key.

constructively present. a legal term describing the presence at a location other than the crime scene of an aider or abettor. A lookout who functions at a considerable distance from the scene of a burglary may be said to be constructively present.

constructive possession. a condition in which a person, who is not actually in possession of property, is, because of the circumstances of the case, treated as if he or she were in actual possession.

constructive sentence. a sentence designed to make the punishment fit the crime.

consumer. a person or agency that uses information or intelligence produced either in-house or obtained from other agencies.

Consumer Credit Protection Act of 1970. an act that limits the amount of an employee's disposable income which may be garnisheed and protects employees from discharge because of one garnishment.

consumer fraud. deception of the public with respect to the cost, quality, purity, safety, durability, performance, effectiveness, dependability, availability and adequacy of choice relating to goods or services offered or furnished, and with respect to credit or other matters relating to terms of sales.

consumer report. a written, oral or other communication of any information by a consumer reporting company, bearing on a consumer's credit worthiness, credit standing, credit capacity, character, general reputation, personal characteristics, or mode of living used in whole or in part as a factor in establishing a consumer's eligibility for credit, employment, insurance or other benefits.

contact. an electrically conductive point or set of points that opens/closes a circuit; any device that when actuated opens or closes a set of electrical contacts, such as a switch or relay.

contact block. that portion of a magnetic contact containing the switching element. The magnet is housed in the actuating block.

contact gunshot wound. a wound produced when the muzzle is in contact or very close to the victim's body. The edge of the entry hole and the bullet track are burned, and particles of powder and clothing debris can be found inside the wound.

contact microphone. a microphone designed to be attached directly to a surface, such as a wall. Also called a spike microphone.

contact writing. impressions or minute tracings of ink from one piece of paper to another directly below it.

containment. restricting the spreading of fire. Also applied to the escape of radioactive gases, waters and other materials associated with nuclear power plants. In nuclear security, the application of any devices designed to limit the mobility of nuclear material, the access of personnel, or the unauthorized operation of equipment such as transfer valves and sampler lines, and structural elements, including the design of buildings and layout of equipment, which minimize and control access to nuclear material.

containment system. in nuclear security, the components of the packaging intended to retain radioactive material during transport.

containment theory. a theory of criminality, and particularly of juvenile delinquency, which postulates that delinquency and crime occur to the extent that there is a breakdown in "inner" and "outer" containing or restraining forces of society. The inner restraints consist of moral, religious, and superego forces. The outer restraints derive from family, educators, and other potentially disapproving forces.

contaminated print. an impression of a skin surface coated with a foreign substance such as blood or grease. A contaminated print is also known as a patent print.

contamination control station. a place specifically designated for controlling movement of persons and equipment into and from an area contaminated by radiation.

contempt of court. any act which is calculated to embarrass, hinder, obstruct a court, or which is calculated to lessen its authority or dignity.

contiguous. in close proximity; near, though not in contact; neighboring, adjoining.

continental system. the system of criminal prosecution prevailing in most of continental Europe, Japan and other countries, in contrast to the English and American adversary system. In the continental system, a judicial officer has the responsibility to investigate and examine, and adjudication is not limited to the facts adduced by the parties. Also called the inquisitorial system.

contingency management. a management style that recognizes that the application of theory to practice must necessarily take into consideration, and be contingent upon, the given situation.

contingency plan. a document that sets forth an organized, planned, and coordinated course of action to be followed in case of an emergency event such as fire, explosion, or release of hazardous waste.

contingency planning. problem solving before the fact; planning to counter emergencies or unexpected occurrences.

continuance. the adjournment or carry-over of a legal proceeding to another scheduled date.

continuous hinge. a hinge designed to be the same length as the edge of the moving part to which it is applied. Also called a piano hinge.

continuous visual surveillance. in nuclear security, unobstructed view at all times of a shipment of special nuclear material, and of all access to a temporary storage area or cargo compartment containing the shipment.

contraband. any article which has been declared illegal to possess.

contra bonos mores. against good morals.

contracting officer. an official with authority to enter into and administer contracts, and make determinations and findings with respect to contracts.

contract security. protective services provided by one company, specializing in such services, to another company on a paid, contractual basis.

contraexpenses. operational revenues obtained through cost reduction, cost avoidance and similar savings.

contra pacem. against the peace.

contributing to the delinquency of a minor. any act or behavior by one or more adults involving a minor, or committed in the presence of a minor, that might reasonably result in delinquent conduct. Examples include encouraging a minor to steal or commit vandalism.

contributory negligence. an act or omission amounting to want of ordinary care on the part of a complaining party, which, concurring with the defendant's negligence, is the proximate cause of injury. Contributory negligence generally applies to a condition of employment, either express or implied, with which an employee agrees that the dangers of injury ordinarily or obviously incident to the discharge of required duties shall be at the employee's own risk.

control elements. software and data performing or supporting control functions such as access control, logging, and violation detection. Examples are password data sets, files of cipher-keys, and log files.

control group. a group which is not exposed to the independent variable of interest to a researcher, but whose members' background and experience are otherwise like those of the experimental group which is exposed to the independent variable.

controlled access area. in nuclear security, any temporarily or permanently established area which is clearly demarcated, access to which is controlled and which affords isolation of the material or persons within it.

controlled burning. the use of fire to destroy marihuana, opium and cocaine yielding crops. Also the destruction by fire of confiscated drugs.

controlled lighting. a technique of exterior lighting that directs illumination on a particular area, such as the illumination of a wide strip inside a fence or the floodlighting of a wall or roof.

controller. an agent's direct supervisor or case officer; the chief accounting officer of an organization.

control man. in a numbers operation, a person using two or more writers who are submitting their work products to him. A control man usually has an agreement with the backer regarding his personal financial remuneration. He may work on a percentage of play turned in, plus a percentage of the house win.

control panel. a centrally located assembly containing power supplies, relays, amplifiers and other equipment needed to receive, interpret and supervise alarm signals from a protected area; a device that arms, disarms and supervises an alarm system at the subscriber's premises. Control panels may also serve as an interface between the subscriber's security system and the alarm company's central station.

control point. an entry or exit point where access is monitored and subject to restriction.

control question. in polygraphy, a question related to a similar but unconnected issue. It is asked in a general question test in such a manner that the examinee will lie in responding to it. The examiner compares the chart tracings for the control question against tracings related to questions directly relevant to the issue under investigation.

control theory. an explanation of delinquency and crime which postulates that criminal and delinquent acts occur when the bonds that tie people to the law-abiding society are weakened. These bonds include attachment to others, commitment to conventional lines of action, involvement in conventional activity, and belief in the laws governing forbidden behavior.

control unit. the main controlling device in an alarm system. The control unit processes alarm signals for annunciation. The control unit may have the ability to supervise signal lines and change zones to various modes.

contusion. a bruise; an injury to any external part of the body by the impact of a fall or the blow of a blunt instrument, without laceration of the flesh and without tearing the skin.

convective column. in firefighting operations, a column of warm air rising above the fire source.

conversion. an ego defense process which converts emotional conflicts into physical illness symptoms.

conveyance. a document by which ownership in real estate is transferred.

convict. to find a person guilty of a criminal charge.

conviction. a verdict of guilty; the opposite of an acquittal.

conviction rate. the number of convictions, including guilty pleas, as a percentage of the total number of prosecutions in a given area for a given crime.

convict lease system. the nineteenth-century practice of selling the labor of prisoners to private employers who paid the state a fee for each of the prisoners and then took on the responsibility of guarding and feeding them. In exchange, the employer received the profits of the convicts' labor.

cooker. a small receptacle, such as a spoon or bottle cap, in which heroin is dissolved.

cooptation. a social process by which people who might otherwise threaten the stability or existence of an organization are brought into the leadership or policy-making structure of that organization.

copyrighted software. any software that is purchased, rented or borrowed and which remains the property of the manufacturer by the terms of agreement. Acquisition of copyrighted software buys the right to use it, not own it.

copyright infringement. a law which makes it a federal crime for anyone who willfully for purposes of commercial advantages and private gain infringes on another's copyright.

coram nobis. a writ issued by a court for the purpose of correcting a judgment entered in the same court, on the ground of error of fact.

cord trap. a simple intrusion detector consisting of a length of cord extended in a concealed manner at the perimeter of a protected area. One or both ends of the cord can be attached to a switch that activates an alarm when the cord is displaced.

cordite. an explosive powder made of nitroglycerin and formed into the shape of string or cord.

core. the approximate center of a fingerprint impression.

core key. a special key that removes the entire core from a removable core lock and replaces it with another core.

core body temperature. the predictable rate of loss of body temperature following death.

coroner. a medical examiner charged with determining the cause of any death where there is reason to believe the death was not natural.

corporal punishment. physical punishment as distinguished from pecuniary punishment or a fine; punishment inflicted on the body.

corporate crime. an illegal act or acts committed by a corporate body or by executives or managers acting on behalf of the corporation. Such acts include consumer fraud, price-fixing, and restraint of trade.

corporate fraud. the intentional misstatement of financially material facts for the purpose of deceiving the hearers or readers to their detriment, coupled with or independent of the misapplication of organizational assets by the employees, officers or executives of a publicly held company.

corporation. an artificial legal entity created by government grant and endowed with certain powers; a voluntary organization of persons either actual individuals or legal entities, legally bound to form a business enterprise.

corporeal. a term descriptive of things that have an objective, material existence and are therefore perceptible by the senses of sight and touch.

corpus delicti. the legal term for the actual tangible evidence that proves a crime was committed.

corpus juris. a body of law.

correctional day program. a publicly financed and operated nonresidential educational or treatment program.

correctional officer. a government employee having supervision over alleged or adjudicated offenders in custody. The term is usually not applied to persons supervising juveniles in detention.

correctional reform. a movement to bring about changes in the correctional system, usually involving less punitive and more humane treatment of prisoners, shorter sentences, and the introduction of rehabilitative programs.

correlation. in statistics, an observed association between a change in the value of one variable or set of data and a change in the value of another variable or set of data.

corroborate. to strengthen; to add weight or credibility to a thing by additional and confirming facts or evidence.

corrosive poison. a poison that produces vomiting and severe pain in the gastrointestinal tract. The presence of a corrosive poison is revealed by the strong odor of the victim's breath and any regurgitated material. Corrosive poisons are found in such household items as bleach, solvents, disinfectants, fertilizer and many types of industrial chemicals. Corrosive poisoning can produce shock and coma as well as death.

corruption. the act of an official who unlawfully and wrongfully uses his position to procure some benefit for himself or another person, contrary to duty and the rights of others.

Cosa Nostra. a group of Italian-dominated organized crime leaders and their followers that originated in Sicily.

Cosmic Top Secret. a classification of information or property of the North Atlantic Treaty Organization (NATO) and subject to special security controls.

cost abatement. the reduction of loss-related costs through the purchase of insurance coverage.

cost avoidance approach. a method for establishing economic justification of a security program by showing that anticipated losses did not occur as the result of security. When the costs of security are less than the avoided losses, there is economic justification for the program.

cost-benefit analysis. any process by which an organization seeks to determine the effectiveness of spending, in relation to costs, in meeting policy objectives.

cost-benefit ratio. the ratio of project input cost to an impact measure when the latter is assigned a dollar value. For example, dollars spent compared to dollars saved by preventing theft.

cost center. an organizational unit to which specific costs are charged. A cost center can be a distinct office or department, or it can be an accounting point in a particular ledger where costs are calculated.

cost-effectiveness evaluation. a form of evaluation in which input is measured in terms of dollars and output is measured in terms of the achievement of some desired objectives; a management guide for the balancing of costs and results; performing a job at the lowest cost consistent with output at a given level of quality; deriving the greatest possible return for an expenditure.

costing-out. determining the actual cost of a contract proposal that includes wages, fringe benefits and similar costs.

cost, insurance and freight. the terms in a contract for the sale of merchandise which requires the seller to pay the insurance, cost and freight of the goods to the point of destination. Commonly called CIF.

cost of security loss. a measure in dollars of the direct cost of a lost asset or the indirect cost of lost income.

cotton shot. an injection by a drug addict of water that has been strained through cotton previously used to administer heroin.

count. an allegation in an indictment; a charge.

counter check. a check used by some banks. It is issued to depositors when they are withdrawing funds from their accounts, and is not good anywhere else. Sometimes a store will have its own counter checks for the convenience of customers. A counter check is not negotiable and is so marked.

counterespionage. those aspects of counterintelligence concerned with aggressive operations against another intelligence service to reduce its effectiveness, or to detect and neutralize espionage.

counterfeit. to manufacture or attempt to manufacture a copy or imitation of a negotiable instrument with a value set by law or convention, or to possess such a copy without authorization, with the intent to defraud by claiming the genuineness of the copy. Counterfeit items include bonds, coins, currency, food stamps, postage stamps and similar negotiables. Because mere possession without knowledge or criminal intent is no crime, extreme caution is required with respect to a customer or other person who has transferred or attempted to transfer counterfeit currency. The prudent practice, therefore, is for a merchant to retain the currency, request the name, address, and telephone number of the passer, and then notify the local police or federal authorities.

counterforce car. a heavily-armored, specially equipped, highpower automobile used by persons who have reason to fear capture or assassination.

counterinsurgency. military action planned to oppose guerrilla underground efforts.

counterintelligence. activities conducted to destroy the effectiveness of intelligence operations and to protect information against espionage, subversion and sabotage.

countermeasure. a specific activity intended to improve one or more aspects of the se-

curity system or contribute to the solution of a specific security-related problem.

countermeasures. as used in security communications, defensive techniques designed to detect, prevent or expose the use of electronic audio or visual surveillance devices.

courier. a messenger responsible for the secure physical delivery of something of value.

courtesy supervision. supervision by the correctional agency of one jurisdiction, of a person placed on probation by a court or on parole by a paroling authority in another jurisdiction, by informal agreement between agencies.

court jurisdiction. the legal right or authority of a court to hear a case or controversy.

court-martial. a military court for the trial of members of the armed forces and certain civilians said to be "accompanying the armies in the field."

court of appeals. a court that reviews a trial court's actions, or the decisions of another (but lower-level) appellate court, to determine whether errors have been made and to decide whether to uphold or overturn a verdict.

court of general jurisdiction. a court which has jurisdiction to try all criminal offenses, including all felonies, and which may or may not hear appeals.

court of limited jurisdiction. a court of which the trial jurisdiction either includes no felonies or is limited to less than all felonies, and which may or may not hear appeals.

cover. a protective guise used by a person, organization, or installation to prevent identification with clandestine activities and to conceal the true affiliation of personnel and the true sponsorship of activities.

cover sheet. a piece of paper, usually color coded and imprinted with a warning or notice, placed in front of a classified document.

covert action. clandestine activity designed to influence the opposition.

crash. a computer system's response to an unstable condition. Rather than continuing to operate and possibly damaging itself, the system stops functioning.

crash bar. the cross bar or level of a panic exit device which serves as a push bar to actuate the lock.

crash cushion. a traffic barrier designed to prevent errant vehicles from striking a rigid object located on the roadside, either by smoothly decelerating such vehicles to a stop or by redirecting them away from the rigid object as well as from the opposite flow of traffic. Crash cushions are typically made of plastic or light metal barrels filled with sand or water.

crashing. a period of unpleasantness and

depression that follows the sudden sensation (known as a "flash" or "rush") obtained by the administration of a drug, usually intravenously.

crazed glass. in arson investigations, glass that has been cracked in a particular pattern by fire. The pattern can be interpreted as to the fire's point of origin. Crazed glass also suggests that a fire accelerant was used.

created error. an error purposely inserted into the ongoing operations of a security system to determine if the error is discovered, responded to, and reported in the manner required by the system's procedures.

credibility. the believability of a witness at a trial as to his testimony.

credit card fraud. the use of a credit card in order to obtain goods or services with the intent to avoid payment.

credit card palming. deliberate retention by an employee of a customer's credit card so that the card can be used for some fraudulent purpose.

credit card swindle. mail-fraud swindle in which people are urged to charge some attractive product to their credit cards. The charge is billed but the product is not delivered.

credit risk. the danger that a borrower will not repay a loan; a person judged to be unlikely to repay a loan.

creeper. a pickpocket working in collusion with prostitutes.

crime. an act or omission which is in violation of the law.

crime against nature. an unnatural sexual act, such as sodomy or bestiality.

crime family. an association of people, related to each other by blood or marriage or having common ties of cultural-ethnic heritage, close bonds, and networks, engaged in ongoing criminal activities.

crime index. an indicator of fluctuations in criminality. In the United States it is based on the number of certain serious crimes known to the police and reported by the FBI in its Uniform Crime Reports. The eight offenses used to construct the crime index are known as the index crimes.

crime index. in Uniform Crime Reports terminology, a set of numbers indicating the volume, fluctuation and distribution of crimes reported to local law enforcement agencies, for the United States as a whole and for its geographical subdivisions, based on counts of reported occurrences of UCR Index Crimes.

crime in the suites. a play on words to "crime in the streets." It refers to corporate embezzlement, fraud and thefts by business executives.

crime of commission. any criminal act involving a specific violation of law, such as burglary or theft.

crime of omission. a failure to fulfill a requirement imposed by law, such as failure to pay a tax.

crime of passion. assault or murder incited by the infidelity of a lover or a mate or a murder committed in the heat of anger or other passionate outburst.

crime of violence. a criminal act involving injury or threat of injury to the victim. Examples include murder, rape, assault and armed robbery.

crime prevention through environmental design. a field of study and experimentation which seeks to develop comprehensive crime risk management systems involving both physical design and social action strategies on a community-wide scale.

crime rate. the number of reported crimes per a specified number (usually 100,000) of inhabitants.

crime rate by opportunity. a comparison of the number of crimes of a particular type with the number of potential targets of that particular crime over a defined period of time.

crimes against habitations. a general descriptor for referring to offenses affecting homes. Arson and burglary are offenses that fall into this category.

crimes against persons. a general descriptor for referring to offenses that victimize individuals. It is a category of crime in which force or the threat of force is used by the offender. Of the index crimes, those against persons include murder and non-negligent manslaughter, forcible rape, aggravated assault, and robbery. Arson is classified as a crime against property, although it may result in death or injury to persons.

crimes against property. a category of crime in which force or violence is neither used nor threatened, and where the offender seeks to make unlawful gain from, or do damage to, the property of another. Of the index crimes, those against property include burglary, larceny-theft, automobile theft, and arson.

crimes cleared by arrest. a category in the Uniform Crime Reports that discloses the number and percentage of crimes of a distinct type or in a given area for which an arrest is made and for which the police are satisfied that the crime has been solved.

crimes known to police. all illegal acts that have been observed by or reported to police, or about which the police otherwise become aware.

crimes mala in se. acts immoral or wrong in themselves, such as burglary, larceny, arson, rape, murder; those acts which are wrong by their very nature.

crimes mala prohibita. acts prohibited by statute as infringing on others' rights, though no moral turpitude may be attached, and are crimes only because they are so prohibited.

crime score. a number assigned from an established scale, signifying the seriousness of a given offense with respect to personal injury or damage to property.

crime statistics. tabulations of crimes by time period, geography, characteristics of offenders and victims, modus operandi, effectiveness of police response, arrests, convictions, sentences and other data.

crime tax. a phrase referring to the increased price paid by customers of gambling, drug and prostitution operations as a result of higher operating costs caused by vigorous law enforcement efforts.

crime wave. an unusual perceived increase in the total amount of crime committed, or in any single offense or type of crime. It may be caused by increased news media attention, by changes in enforcement or reporting procedures, or by an actual increase in crime.

criminal. one who has committed a crime; one who has been legally convicted of a crime. Also, that which pertains to or is connected with the law of crimes, or the administration of penal justice, or which relates to or has the character of crime.

criminal action. the proceedings by which a person charged with a crime is accused and brought to trial and punishment.

criminal anthropology. a school of thought which postulates that criminal types are discernible and identifiable on the basis of human body characteristics.

criminal assault. physical attack against another person, typically involving actual or attempted sexual contact. Rape is a criminal assault.

criminal biopsychology. a science which investigates the psychosomatic personalities of criminals.

criminal contempt. any act deemed disrespectful of the authority and dignity of the court.

criminal conversion. the conversion or misappropriation for personal gain of another's property or rights.

criminal court. a court having the authority to try persons accused of criminal law violations and to sentence them if they are found guilty.

criminal fence. a receiver of stolen goods or a place where stolen goods are exchanged for money or other considerations.

criminal hacker. a person who seeks to obtain access to a computer system for the purpose of illegal gain.

criminal history information. any information about a person's arrest record, conviction/non-conviction or correctional and release history.

criminal homicide. the causing of the death of another person without justification or excuse.

criminal informant. an individual who provides information to law enforcement authorities and whose relationships with criminals requires that his or her identity be kept confidential.

criminal information process. a continuous cycle of interrelated activities directed toward converting raw information into material useful for law enforcement purposes. The process has six steps: collection of information, evaluation, analysis, collation, reporting, and dissemination.

criminal intelligence. the surreptitious investigation of crime and the gathering of information concerning plans and activities in a criminal subculture or underworld, generally obtained through informants, infiltration and electronic eavesdropping. The term also applies to crimes committed within a state, or internationally, by organized criminal groups or individuals.

criminal intent. an intent to do an act which the law denounces, without regard to the motive that prompts the act, whether or not the offender knows that what he or she is doing is in violation of the law.

criminalistics. a fact-finding process for detecting crime; police science; scientific detection and investigation of crimes. Criminalistics includes ballistics, blood-stain analyses, and other tests of a scientific nature.

criminalization. the passing of legislation imposing criminal sanctions for commission or omission of an act that had formerly been legal or had been an infraction rather than a crime; a process or influence that affects the development of a criminal.

criminal justice. the entire system of crime prevention and detection, apprehension of suspects, arrest, trial, adjudication of guilt or innocence, and handling of the guilty by correctional agencies, together with the executive, legislative, and judicial rules governing these procedures and processes.

criminal law. that body of legislation and judicial interpretations which define criminal acts (substantive criminal law), in contrast to laws specifying procedures for determination of guilt or innocence (procedural criminal law); the statutes and general dicta that forbid certain actions or conduct as detrimental to the welfare of the state and that provide punishment therefor. Criminal acts are prosecuted by the state, as opposed to civil wrongs, which are prosecuted by an individual. A wrong may be both a criminal wrong and a civil wrong; for example, assault and battery.

criminal mischief. intentionally destroying or damaging, or attempting to destroy or damage, the property of another without his consent, usually by means other than burning.

criminal negligence. wanton and willful disregard of the probable harmful consequences of an act.

criminal opportunity reduction. the anticipation, recognition and appraisal of a crime risk and the initiation of some action to remove or reduce it.

criminal possession. having on one's person or under one's effective control objects or substances illegally possessed, as guns or drugs. Criminal possession applies also to objects legally possessed when there is the intention of using them to commit a crime, as a crowbar used in a burglary.

criminal sociopath. a person who has failed to develop a conscience or understand the difference between right and wrong.

criminal syndicalism. advocacy of force, terror and violence to bring about economic or political changes.

criminal target. the place, person or thing that a criminal seeks to take or destroy.

criminogenic factor. a factor that is crime-producing. Examples might include the break-up of the family, excessive emphasis on materialism, a lack of ethical standards, lawless abuse of alcohol and other drugs, slum environments, and social disintegration.

criminology. the study of crime causes, prevention, detection and correction; the study of crimes, criminals and victims.

criminosis. psychoneurotic behavior marked by criminal acts or a tendency to engage in criminal activity.

criminotechnol. a descriptor of criminological technology, such as the use of electronic and photographic devices and techniques to apprehend criminals and secure evidence needed for their conviction.

crisis intervention. a formal effort to help an individual experiencing a crisis to re-establish equilibrium.

crisis management team. a contingency planning group charged by a senior authority (e.g., a Board of Directors) to assess significant overall organizational vulnerabilities that would result in major crisis situations. The disciplines typically represented on the CMT of a corporate organization are secu-

rity, legal, finance, personnel, public relations, communications and facilities management. The types of contingencies addressed by the CMT include terroristic acts, kidnapping, labor violence, civil disorders, industrial disasters, and natural catastrophes.

criteria for inferring causality. evidence that two variables are correlated, that the hypothesized cause preceded the hypothesized effect in time, and evidence eliminating rival hypotheses.

critical DP system. a data processing system which if interrupted would cause substantial loss.

critical function. an operation or activity which is essential to the continuing survival of a system.

critical incident review technique. a technique for identifying in a work process any minor tasks which if not performed correctly could have a serious effect on the total process.

critical intelligence. information or intelligence of such urgent importance that it is transmitted at the highest priority before passing through regular evaluative channels.

criticality assessment. a methodology for measuring the impact upon an organization that the loss of an asset would impose.

criticality rating. an arbitrary designation, applied to a particular loss event, which expresses the impact of the loss upon the organization. Examples of ratings might be: fatal to the business, very serious impact on the business, moderately serious, less than serious, and not serious.

critical nuclear weapons design information. as used in the DoD Industrial Security Program, highly classified information that reveals the theory of operation or design of the components of a thermonuclear or implosion-type fission bomb, warhead, demolition munition or test device. Specifically excluded is information concerning arming, fusing, and firing systems; limited life components; and total contained quantities of fissionable, fusionable, and high explosive materials by type. Among these excluded items are the components which DoD personnel set, maintain, operate, test or replace.

critical path method. a network-analysis technique for planning and scheduling. The critical path is a sequence of activities that connect the beginning and end of events or program accomplishments.

cross alarm. an alarm signal generated by crossing or shorting an electric circuit.

cross cut shredding. a feature of some paper shredders in which documents are cut into small shreds by the slicing action of blades moving in a cross cut pattern.

cross examination. questions which are asked of a witness by the opposing side in a legal case.

crossover. an insulated pad that is used to prevent grounding, and to carry foil across windows and dividers such as those found on two or four pane windows.

crosstalk. an undesired signal from a different channel which interferes with the desired signal.

cross zoning. the practice of suppressing an alarm signal until two or more detectors in separate zones register alarm conditions. The practice is frequently used in computer rooms where detectors are placed in ceiling and floor zones.

crown fire. an intense fire that spreads through the tops of trees.

CRT terminal. a data entry terminal consisting of a keyboard for data entry and a cathode ray tube display screen.

cruel and unusual punishment. punishment which exceeds that normally given for a specific offense; punishment that is inhumane, such as torture or enslavement. It is a phrase used in the Eighth Amendment to the United States Constitution but not defined with specificity by the Supreme Court.

cruncher. a machine that destroys tape ribbon cassettes and similar information-containing items too large for destruction by a shredder.

Crypto. a marking or designator that identifies communications security keying material used to protect or authenticate telecommunications carrying national security-related information.

cryptoanalysis. the breaking of codes and ciphers into plaintext without initial knowledge of the key employed in the encryption.

cryptography. the enciphering of plain text so that it will be unintelligible to an unauthorized recipient.

crypto key. a code key that encrypts or decrypts data in a cryptographic operation.

cryptology. the science that embraces cryptoanalysis, cryptography, communications intelligence and communications security.

cryptomaterial. the various documents, devices, equipment and apparatus used in the encryption, decryption or authentication of telecommunications.

cryptonym. a name assigned to cover a secret operation or a secret operative; secret name.

cryptosystem. the hardware, firmware, software, documents and/or associated procedures used to effect the encryption and decryption of data.

crystal microphone. a microphone that depends for its operation on the generation of an electric charge by the deformation of a crystal.

crystal violet. a tracing powder used to mark objects likely to be touched by a culprit. The powder is converted to a violet colored dye by the skin's natural moisture.

cuff-and-lead chain. a single handcuff attached to a length of chain ending in a ring. It is used for leading prisoners or holding them to some stationary object.

culpability. a state of mind on the part of one who has committed an act which makes him liable to prosecution for that act.

culpable. blamable; censurable; involving the breach of a legal duty or the commission of a fault.

culpable negligence. conscious disregard of the rights of another in the commission of an act.

cultural determinism. the view that the nature of a society is shaped primarily by the ideas and values of the people living in it.

cultural relativism. the view that the customs and ideas of a society must be viewed within the context of that society.

cumulative dose. the total dose of radiation resulting from repeated exposure of the whole body or part of the body.

cumulative evidence. additional or corroborative evidence to the same point; that which goes to prove what has already been established by other evidence.

cumulative sentence. a sentence imposed separately and which must be served one after the other.

cumulative voting. a system of voting for directors of a corporation under which each stockholder is entitled to a number of votes equal to the number of shares he owns multiplied by the number of directors to be elected. He may cast all the votes for one candidate, cumulate them or he may distribute his votes among the candidates in any way he sees fit. This system enables the minority stockholders to elect one or more of the directors. The right to cumulative voting cannot be claimed unless provided for by statute, by the corporation's charter or bylaws, or by contract among all the stockholders, provided the agreement is not otherwise illegal.

cunnilingus. a sexual act committed with the mouth and the female sexual organ.

current assets. assets that can be turned into cash within a specified period of time, usually 90 days; assets that will be consumed in the operations of a business.

current intelligence. summaries and analyses of recent events.

current liabilities. debts that must be paid within a specified period of time, usually 90 days. Examples are accounts payable, wages payable, taxes payable, the current portion of long-term debt, and interest and dividends payable.

current loop. a circuit that is sensitive to current variations but not voltage changes. It is used in communications and alarm circuits.

current market value. the current new price of something, usually a piece of equipment; the cost required to buy new equipment of a similar type at today's prices.

current ratio. a ratio of a firm's current assets to its current liabilities. The current ratio includes the value of inventories which have not yet been sold, making it not the best evaluation of the current status of the firm. The acid test ratio, covering the most liquid of current assets, provides a better evaluation.

curriculum vitae. a resume or biographical description.

curtilage. the inclosed space of ground and buildings immediately surrounding a dwelling house.

custodial interview. an interview of a suspect that is conducted while the suspect is in custody of the police, or is otherwise deprived of his freedom in any significant way.

custodian. an individual who has possession of or is charged with the responsibility for safeguarding something, such as custodians of records, evidence or classified information.

custody. legal control over a person or property. Custody of a child consists of legal guardianship and the right of physical control of the child's whereabouts. Custody of a juvenile or adult consists of such restraint and/or physical control as is needed to ensure his presence at any legal proceedings, or of responsibility for his detention or imprisonment resulting from a criminal charge or conviction. Custody of property consists of immediate personal care of property not owned by the custodian, who is responsible for guarding and preserving it.

customer code. a code, usually in the form of an account number, used in the commercial alarm business to identify a customer or location of equipment.

Customs Automatic Data Processing Intelligence Network. a computerized data-bank system concerning known or suspected smugglers wanted by the US Bureau of Customs.

cut card. in a numbers operation, a card that lists the numbers which are currently being accepted by the operation on a cut odds basis. The card will sometimes contain other rules that are laid down by the backer for the information of the writers.

cutis anserina. a goose flesh appearance on the skin of a cadaver.

cut-out. a person who is used to conceal contact between members of a clandestine activity or organization.

cutter. that person in a chopshop/car theft operation who removes the saleable parts of a stolen automobile, usually by cutting, and destroys the remainder.

cut the odds. in a numbers operation, a procedure in which the odds of winning are cut to a lower level in order to protect the backer financially.

Cylert. the trade name of a stimulant regulated under the Controlled Substances Act.

CYMBALS. an acronym that facilitates remembering the basic description factors relating to motor vehicles. The factors are: color, year, make, body style, and license serial number.

cypher lock. a digital, push-button type combination lock typically used as a means for controlling personnel access to a sensitive area.

cyprenorphine. an opium derivative classified as a Schedule I Controlled Substance.

D

dactylography. the science of the study of fingerprints as a means of identification.

dactyloscopy. the technique of identifying people by their fingerprints.

Dalmane. the trade name for flurazepam, a depressant in the family of benzodiazepines. It is a commonly abused drug and is regulated by the Controlled Substances Act as a Schedule IV substance.

damage. loss, injury, or deterioration, caused by the negligence, design, or accident of one person to another, in respect of the latter's person or property.

damages. money awarded to compensate for financial loss to the injured party in a lawsuit.

damped sensor. an inertia or vibration sensor having low sensitivity. Damped sensors are used in locations where heavy ambient movements or vibrations would cause a standard sensor to activate.

dangerous weapon. an instrument dangerous to life; an instrument the use of which a fatal wound may probably or possibly be given. Because the manner of use enters into the consideration, the question as to a dangerous weapon is often one of fact for the jury, but not infrequently one of law for the court.

dark figure of crime. a term related to criminal acts that are not observed, reported or recorded in crime statistics, either because they are unknown except to the offenders or because of reluctance by victims or witnesses to make complaints.

Darvon. the trade name for propoxyphene hydrochloride, a Schedule IV narcotic drug.

das. dextroamphetamine sulfate, a central nervous system stimulant.

data above voice. a term referring to special telephone-line channels that provide the equivalent of a direct data wire link using existing voice-grade lines. Alarm signals may be transmitted over the voice lines at any time, even while voice communications are in progress. The alarm signals are communicated at a much higher frequency than voice. In this way, polling alarm signal transmissions may occur simultaneously with voice communications. The technique is also called piggybacking.

data base management system. a system with management and administrative capabilities for control of record selection, updating and reporting from a data base.

data card. a card sometimes included in close-up pictures of evidence photographed on-scene or in a crime laboratory. The card contains certain identifying data such as case number, date, and name of photographer/investigator. Data cards are also used to record details pertaining to the camera, lens, film, filter, and shutter setting.

data communications. the transmission, reception and validation of data.

Data Encryption Standard. a standard for data encryption adopted by the US National Bureau of Standards. DES is a complex non-linear ciphering algorithm capable of high-speed operation in hardware applications. It is used for sensitive, but unclassified data transmission, mostly within the federal government.

data I/O. the input/output port for transfer of data.

data leakage. loss of data from a computer system through covert means.

data link. a point-to-point radio communication channel designed primarily for transmission of data rather than audio signals.

data processing facility. the personnel, hardware, software, data files and floor space organized and managed as a single element to perform data processing.

DAWN. Drug Abuse Warning Network, a program of the Drug Enforcement Administration.

day/night switch. a device for switching a detection system on and off, usually with a key or key pad.

day zone. in security alarms terminology, a feature of an intrusion detection system that uninterruptedly monitors a highly sensitive area even when the system is disarmed.

deadbolt. a type of bolt that is moved in and out of the strike mechanically, as by a thumb latch knob.

dead drop. a hiding place where an agent deposits or collects messages and materials.

dead end. a water main supplied from only one direction, or a fire hydrant served by such a main.

dead latch. a spring-actuated latch bolt having a bevelled end and incorporating a feature that automatically locks the projected latch bolt against return by end pressure.

dead lock. a lock equipped with a dead bolt. Also, a key-equipped standard ignition cylinder used by a car thief to replace the original cylinder pulled from its housing by a slapper or slam hammer.

deadly force. any force involving a deadly weapon or a physical attack likely to inflict death or grievous bodily harm.

deadly weapon. any object, instrument or weapon capable of producing death or great bodily injury.

dead man control. a device which automatically shuts off power to equipment when the equipment operator releases the control.

dead time delay. the interval between a stimulus and a response. For example, the delay experienced between an alarm activation and an alarm response.

dead work. in a numbers operation, slips that are not turned in at the office by an established deadline, or as is the common practice, slips in the possession of trusted pickup men.

dead zone. an area within a protection pattern in which the sensor is not effective. A dead zone may result from improper adjustment of the sensor or interference from surrounding objects or structural members.

deal. to sell drugs.

death. the cessation of life; the ceasing to exist; defined by physicians as a total stoppage of the circulation of the blood, and a cessation of the animal and vital functions consequent thereto, such as respiration and pulsation.

death ship. a vessel deliberately destroyed, scuttled or wrecked by its owner in order to collect insurance.

debauchery. excessive indulgence in sensual pleasures; sexual immorality or excesses, or the unlawful indulgence of lust.

debt capital. money borrowed for a particular business purpose.

debt service. the annual amount to be paid by a debtor to retire an obligation to repay borrowed money.

debt service coverage. a requirement that earnings be a percentage or dollar sum higher than debt service.

debug. a defensive technique designed to detect, prevent or expose the use of electronic audio or visual surveillance devices; to correct the syntax and logic of a computer system.

deception indicated. a term used by polygraph examiners when giving an opinion that a tested subject was untruthful. Also called DI.

deception response. a deviation from the norm in the chart tracings of a polygraph instrument. It results from emotions produced in the examinee as a consequence of a question.

Deceptograph. the commercial name of a type of polygraph instrument.

decision tree. a graphic method of presenting various decisional alternatives so that the various risks, information needs and courses of action are visually available to the decision-maker.

deck. a small glassine envelope or folded paper packet containing heroin, morphine or cocaine; a small bindle of drugs.

declassification. a determination that classified information no longer requires protection against unauthorized disclosure, together with a removal or cancellation of the classification designation.

declassification event. an event that eliminates the need for continued classification of information.

decode. to convert from a code into characters that can be interpreted.

decontrol. to remove access controls.

decorative mesh. a type of fencing material made from expanded metal.

decoy object. an object marked with a fluorescent substance or dyestuff and placed where it would be touched by a person engaged in a criminal act.

decree. a formal determination of a court, usually made in writing.

decriminalization. the removing of criminal sanctions from formerly criminal behavior. Decriminalization may reduce the behavior to an infraction or a violation of a local ordinance, as some states have done with respect to the possession of marihuana, or it may consist of outright legalization of the behavior, as was the case in the repeal of Prohibition.

decryption. the process of transforming encrypted data (ciphertext) to intelligible data (plaintext); the process that restores encoded information to its original unencoded form.

dedicated line. a telephone line connecting two points, such as a protected premises and a central station, for alarm signaling. Also called leased line, direct wire, and direct connect.

dedicated security mode. a mode of operation in which an automated data processing system, its peripherals, and remotes are exclusively used and controlled by specific users or groups of users to process a particular type and category of sensitive material. Users of the system must have a need-to-know for all material in the system.

dedicated vehicle. a patrol vehicle equipped with two-way radio communication that is used exclusively to provide quick responses to intrusions or alarms.

deductive reasoning. a logical analysis based on facts from which a conclusion may be made; the deriving of a conclusion from reasoning; a process in which a deduction follows from the premises; the reasoning which starts out from an assumption or premise and proceeds by logical steps to deduce a solution to the problem or question.

deep six. to conceal or permanently remove something by dumping it at sea.

de facto. arising out of or founded upon fact, but not necessarily upon legal authority. For example, a de facto officer may be someone who assumes to be an officer under some color or right, acts as an officer, but in point of law is not a real officer.

defalcation. misappropriation of funds held in a fiduciary capacity.

defamation. a statement made orally or in writing which injures a person's reputation in the community; that which tends to injure the reputation of a living person or the memory of a deceased person and to expose him to public hatred, disgrace, ridicule, or contempt, or to exclude him from society.

default. the failure to appear and defend a lawsuit.

defeat. render an alarm system ineffective.

defective delinquent. a juvenile with retarded mental development who commits an act that would constitute juvenile delinquency or criminality if committed by a normal juvenile.

defendant. a person against whom a criminal proceeding is pending.

Defendant Statistical Program File. records maintained by the Drug Enforcement Agency which provide statistical data concerning drug abuse patterns and offender characteristics.

defenestration. suicide by throwing oneself out of a window; tossing a person or a thing out of a window.

defense. the justification put forward by the defendant of a lawsuit which is intended to relieve him of blame and of financial obligation.

defense against sound equipment. electronic and physical means taken to prevent surreptitious monitoring, wiretapping or eavesdropping.

defense attorney. an attorney who represents the defendant in a legal proceeding.

Defense Central Index of Investigations. a locator file maintained by the Department of Defense. It identifies the location of files concerning past and present military members, DOD civilian employees, and contractors.

Defense Supply Agency File. an index of personnel cards maintained by the Defense Supply Agency. It details security clearance information on persons employed by contractors engaged in classified work for the Department of Defense and certain other federal agencies.

defense wounds. in homicides and assaults by cutting and stabbing, wounds that are found on the victim's hands and arms. The wounds

evidence the manner in which the victim maneuvered to fend off the attacker.

defensible space. a theory which holds that proper physical design of housing encourages residents to extend their social control from their homes and apartments out into the surrounding common areas. In this way, residents change to private territory what had been perceived as semi-public or public territory. Collective care and attention to the common areas results in a form of social control that discourages crime.

deferred sentence. a penalty whose imposition is not disclosed or imposed until a later time. For example, a sentence may be deferred pending preparation of a presentence investigation report.

definite sentence. a sentence to a fixed time of incarceration.

deflagration. an exothermic (heat, burning) reaction which expands rapidly from burning gases to unreacted material by conduction, convection and radiation.

defraud. to cheat another person out of what is justly his.

degauss. to erase or rearrange the recorded bits on a magnetic tape so as to render the information unintelligible.

degradation of energy. any process as a result of which available energy becomes unavailable.

degradation of radiation. the transformation of a radiation into one lower in frequency and in quantum energy.

degraded mode. a feature of an access control system which allows a card reader to operate independently of the system's central control unit. A system in a degraded mode typically grants access by code only and does not verify time zone or area authorization.

degree. the seriousness of a crime.

degree of care. a duty owed to others which depends on circumstances. For example, persons who invite others on their premises, those who invite children on their premises, and those who sell what might be considered inherently dangerous products are all required to take different degrees of care to prevent harm to others.

delay circuit. a timed circuit allowing an alarm user a preset number of minutes/seconds to enter or exit the protected premises.

delay impact fuse. a bomb fuse designed to function at a predetermined time after impact. The delay allows the explosive ordnance to penetrate the target before detonation. A delay fuse is normally employed when the intended target is constructed of, or protected by, heavy armor plate or reinforced concrete.

delayed dismissal. a dismissal of a criminal

charge obtained by the defense but which the prosecution withholds for several weeks or months, as a means of warning the defendant, placating the victim, or allowing public and news media interest to subside.

Delcobese. the trade name of a commonly abused amphetamine which is regulated under the Controlled Substances Act.

delegation of authority. the formal assignment of authority to a subordinate to perform specific acts.

delict. a crime, offense, wrong, or injury.

delinquency. failure, omission, violation of duty. A state or condition of one who fails to perform his duty. Synonymous with misconduct and offense.

delirium. in medical jurisprudence, that state of the mind in which it acts without being directed by the power of volition, which is wholly or partially suspended. A person in delirium is wholly unconscious of surrounding objects, or conceives them to be different from what they really are.

delirium tremens. a disorder of the nervous system, involving the brain and setting up an attack of temporary delusional insanity, sometimes attended with violent excitement or mania, caused by excessive and long continued indulgence in alcoholic liquors, or by the abrupt cessation of such use after a protracted debauch.

Delphi Technique. any methodology that pieces together various opinions in order to arrive at a consensus on the probability of a future event.

delta. in fingerprint science, that point on a ridge at or in front of and nearest the center of the divergence of the type lines.

delta-9-tetrahydrocannabinol. the full chemical term for tetrahydrocannabinol or THC. It is one of 61 chemicals found only in cannabis.

deluge system. a fire extinguishment system in which the water supply to all open sprinklers in a given zone is controlled by an automatic valve. When fire is detected, the valve allows heavy concentrations of water to deluge the protected zone.

delusion. an erroneous belief or fancy which cannot be corrected by reason.

demand mask. a self-contained breathing apparatus that supplies air to the wearer on a demand basis, i.e., in relation to the wearer's breathing rate.

dementia. the loss of rational thought due to functional or organic disorder; mental impairment due to brain damage or degeneration.

dementia praecox. a physiologically induced mental disorder that begins at or immediately following puberty. It is characterized by incoherency, lack of judgment, and disassociation with surroundings.

Demerol. the trade name of meperidine (pethidine), a commonly abused synthetic narcotic. It resembles morphine in its analgesic effect, and is probably the most widely prescribed drug for the relief of moderate to severe pain. Tolerance and dependence develop with chronic use, and large doses can result in convulsions or death. Demerol is a Schedule II narcotic.

democratic-collective organization. an organization in which authority is placed in the group as a whole, rules are minimized, members have considerable control over their work, and job differentiation is minimized.

demodulator. a device that separates the information from the carrier frequency in a modulated signal.

demography. the scientific study of population size, composition, distribution and patterns of change in those features.

demonstrative evidence. an exhibit offered at a trial as a means of explaining or illustrating. Examples are diagrams, maps, plaster casts, models and charts.

demurrage. a sum, provided for in a contract of shipment, to be paid for the delay or detention of vessels or railroad cars beyond the time agreed upon for loading or unloading.

demurrer. the answer of a defendant to a charge made against him which denies legal responsibility though it may concede the plaintiff's contention; a written objection to being tried on an indictment because of defects in the indictment.

denial of reality. an ego defense process in which an unpleasant reality is avoided through escapist activities such as becoming sick or being preoccupied with other things.

de novo. anew, afresh, as if there had been no earlier decision.

dependent variable. the variable that occurs or changes in a patterned way due to the presence of, or changes in, another variable or variables.

deponent. one who deposes to the truth of certain facts; one who gives under oath testimony which is reduced to writing.

deportation. the act of sending an alien out of the country and usually banning him from re-entry. Deportation of a criminal alien can take place before a trial, after conviction, or after a sentence has been served.

deposition. the testimony of a witness responding to oral or written questions, made under oath but not in open court, after notice to the adverse party for the purpose of enabling him to attend and cross examine the witness. It is reduced to writing and duly authenticated.

depositor's forgery insurance. a type of protection against the forgery or alteration of instruments such as checks, drafts, and promissory notes purported to have been written by the insured.

depreciation. decrease in value of property due to normal wear or the passing of time.

depreciation rate. the periodic amount or percentage at which the usefulness of an asset is used up, especially the percentage at which amounts are computed to be set aside as an accrual for future depreciation.

depressant. a drug that acts on the central nervous system producing effects that range from sedation to anesthesia. A depressant acts to depress or decrease respiration, blood pressure and heart rate.

depth of field. in photography, the distance between the nearest and farthest objects which gives satisfactory definition in the image plane. The smaller the aperture of a lens, the greater the depth of field. Also, lenses with shorter focal lengths have a greater depth of field than lenses of a longer length when at the same f-stop.

depth of focus. a value that defines the area between the lens and image plane where the image can be sharply focused.

derivative classification. a determination that information is in substance the same information already classified and which therefore requires application of the same classification markings.

desecrate. to violate sanctity of, to profane, or put to unworthy use.

desiccation problem. a fingerprinting problem caused by wrinkled and dried skin, as in the case of deceased persons.

designer drugs. synthetic drugs, chemically related to legitimate drugs, which are produced inexpensively and sold (sometimes legally) as substitutes for the legitimate products they imitate.

desomorphine. an opium derivative classified as a Schedule I Controlled Substance.

Desoxyn. the trade name for methamphetamine hydrochloride which is regulated under the Controlled Substances Act as a Schedule II stimulant.

destruct line. a line shown in a geographical map to represent the perimeter of destruction caused by an explosive device.

destructive readout. a computer process in which data are erased in the source as it is read.

DET. a laboratory-synthesized hallucinogen regulated under the Controlled Substances Act as a Schedule I drug.

detached workers. people assigned to youth gangs in major cities. They seek to transform gang values and organization through individual counseling, influencing interaction within the gang, and developing alternative activities for gang members.

Detacord. a plastic commercial explosive that usually appears in a clothesline form.

detainee. a person held in local, very short confinement while awaiting consideration for pretrial release or first appearance for arraignment.

detainer. an official notice from a government agency to a correctional agency requesting that an identified person wanted by the first agency, but subject to the correctional agency's jurisdiction, not be released or discharged without notification to the first agency with opportunity to respond.

detasheet. a plastic commercial explosive that appears as a flat sheet about one-eighth inch thick.

detection pattern. the arrangement of space protection devices within a particular area of coverage. Also called a detection field.

detection powder. any of several powders (or pastes and similar substances) used to mark decoy objects or objects susceptible to theft. The powder, which is usually fluorescent, will transfer to the skin or clothing of persons who handle the marked objects.

detection range. the maximum effective distance a sensor can detect an intruder. A specified figure for detection range is determined by repeatedly introducing fault conditions at varying distances.

detector. any device that detects intrusion, equipment failure, hazards, smoke, fire or other conditions requiring immediate response.

detention. the legally authorized holding in confinement of a person subject to criminal or juvenile court proceedings, until commitment to a correctional facility or release.

detention center. a government facility that holds a person in confinement pending court disposition.

detention hearing. a proceeding presided over by a judicial officer of a juvenile court to determine whether or not a juvenile is to be detained pending adjudication of his case.

determinate sentence. a prison term for a fixed time, with eligibility for parole before the fixed time has expired.

Detex. the commercial name of a watchman's clock.

detoxification. supervised withdrawal from drug or alcohol dependence, either with or without medication, usually in a hospital or as an outpatient. Frequently, patients in detoxification programs will live in a highly structured drug or alcohol-free environment.

developed latent impression. a latent finger-print impression made visible by powders or chemicals so that it may be preserved and compared. A latent impression is photo-graphed before it is developed.

deviance. conduct, activity, or condition that is disapproved of, stigmatized, and subject to formal and informal punishment.

Dexedrine. the trade name for dextroamphet-amine sulfate which is regulated under the Controlled Substances Act as a Schedule II stimulant. It is commonly abused, and known on the street as speed, upper, black beauty, crank, meth, bam, and pink.

dexies. dexedrine capsules or tablets; dextro-amphetamines.

dextromoramide. an opiate classified as a Schedule I Controlled Substance.

dextromorphan. an opiate classified as a Schedule I Controlled Substance.

diacetylmorphine. heroin.

diagnostic program. in computer usage, a pro-gram that tests hardware, firmware, periph-eral operation, logic or memory, and reports any faults it detects.

diagnostic center. a unit within a correctional institution, or a separate facility for persons held in custody, in which an entering convict will be assigned to a specific correctional facility or program; a special place of deten-tion for sex offenders or seriously mentally disturbed convicts.

diagnostic commitment. the action of a court ordering a person subject to criminal or ju-venile proceedings to be temporarily placed in a confinement facility, for study and eval-uation of personal history and characteris-tics, usually as a preliminary to a sentencing disposition.

dialer. a device that electronically dials one or more prerecorded telephone numbers us-ing digital codes and reports alarm or su-pervisory information to a receiver.

dial up/call back. a technique for restricting access to a computer's dial-up ports. A per-son wishing access to a computer by phone dials a designated number and gives an iden-tification code. If the code is correctly given, the call is transferred to a line that provides access. Also known as handshake or return call verification.

diamond point pencil. a tool used to inscribe identifying marks on metallic evidence items such as firearms and knives.

diampromide. an opiate classified as a Sched-ule I Controlled Substance.

diazepam. a depressant in the family of ben-zodiazepines which is regulated under the Controlled Substances Act as a Schedule IV drug. Valium is the trade name for diaze-pam.

dicrotic notch. in polygraphy, a characteristic formation in the descending leg of the car-diosphygmograph tracing. It results from a slight change of blood pressure caused by the closing of the semilunar valves in the left ventricle of the heart.

Didrex. the trade name for benzphetamine which is regulated under the Controlled Sub-stances Act as a Schedule III stimulant.

diethylpropion. the generic name of a stimu-lant sold legally as Tenuate Dospan. It is a Schedule IV drug.

diethylthiambutene. an opiate classified as a Schedule I Controlled Substance.

diethyltryptamine. an hallucinogen classified as a Schedule I Controlled Substance.

differential association theory. a major theory in American criminology which postulates that criminal behavior, like normative be-havior, is learned, that this learning takes place in association with others already com-mitted to criminality, and that one learns in such association both criminal values and the mechanisms for committing crimes.

differential pressure sensor. a buried sensor that detects perimeter intrusion. The sensor is activated when hydraulic pressure in a tube buried near the surface changes as a result of an individual or vehicle passing over the protected area.

differential sentencing. unequal penalties im-posed on different persons for the same or similar crimes. The inequalities may reflect such legally irrelevant reasons as race or sex, or different sentencing policies among judges or jurisdictions.

diffused explosion. an explosion characterized by a slow expansion over a relatively wide area into a combustion known as deflagra-tion. Most explosives causing this type of explosion have a pushing rather than a shat-tering effect, and a twisting and tearing type of deformation results.

diffusing luminaire. a luminaire that scatters light substantially in all directions as con-trasted with a directional luminaire which confines its light principally in an angle of less than 180 degrees.

digital communication. the transmission of in-formation by the use of encoded numbers, usually based on the binary number system.

digital communicator. a device that electron-ically dials a telephone number and trans-mits a digital tone code to a receiver. It is normally used with central station alarm sys-tems. A digital communicator transmits to a receiver at a central station. When initially tripped by an alarm, the digital communi-cator seizes the telephone line from all in-ternal telephone instruments, hangs up if necessary, and then dials the central station.

Once the central station is engaged, the digital dialer transmits a code that contains subscriber identity and information regarding the nature of the alarm. The receiver transmits an acknowledgment signal and the communicator shuts off. Failure to reach the central station results in several repeated attempts. Complete failure may activate a local alarm backup. Also called a digital dialer.

digital keypad. a pushbutton panel used for arming and disarming an alarm system by inputting numbers.

digital lock. a type of mechanical lock that is opened by pressing the proper sequence of numbered or lettered push buttons. Also called a cypher lock.

digitizing table. a device used with a signature verification system. It typically utilizes a ballpoint stylus with a small sparkgap at the tip which generates sonic shockwaves. The time required for the waves to reach linear transducers on the X and Y axes of the table is translated into electrical pulses. The pattern of pulses can be matched against the pattern of the genuine signature filed within the system.

dihydrocodeine. an opiate classified as a Schedule II Controlled Substance.

dihydromorphine. an opium derivative classified as a Schedule I Controlled Substance.

Dilaudid. the trade name for hydromorphone, a semi-synthetic narcotic analgesic. Because it is two to eight times more potent than morphine, it is highly sought by addicts. Dilaudid is a Schedule II substance. It is also called K-4 on the street.

dime bag. a quantity of illegal drugs worth ten dollars.

dimenoxadol. an opiate classified as a Schedule I Controlled Substance.

dimepheptanol. an opiate classified as a Schedule I Controlled Substance.

dimethylthiambutene. an opiate classified as a Schedule I Controlled Substance.

dimethyltryptamine. an hallucinogen classified as a Schedule I Controlled Substance.

diminished capacity. decreased or less-than-normal ability, temporary or permanent, to distinguish right from wrong or to fully appreciate the consequences of one's act. It is a plea used by the defendant for conviction of a lesser degree of a crime, for a lenient sentence, or for mercy or clemency.

dinoly. a type of primary explosive.

dip. a pickpocket.

diphenoxylate. an opiate classified as a Schedule II Controlled Substance.

dipping the till. stealing money from a cash register or cash drawer, usually by an employee.

diprenorphine. a semi-synthetic narcotic made from thebaine, a minor constituent of opium and the principal alkaloid present in another species of poppy called papaver bracteatum. Diprenorphine is regulated under the Controlled Substances Act.

dipsomania. in medical jurisprudence, a mental disease characterized by an uncontrollable desire for intoxicating drinks; an irresistible impulse to indulge in intoxication, either by alcohol or other drugs.

DIP switch. a device consisting of miniature toggle switches arranged in rows and numbered. It is intended to allow electronic equipment users to change circuit functions without return of the equipment to the manufacturer. The device is so-called because it is designed to fit into a dual in-line package (DIP) socket.

direct action. a catch phrase used by protesters. It can mean illegal activity ranging from minor civil disobedience to bombings.

direct approach. an interrogational approach in which the interrogator assumes an air of confidence with regard to the suspect's guilt and stresses the evidence indicative of guilt. The approach is accusatory in nature and seeks to discover why the suspect committed the act as opposed to learning if the suspect committed the act.

direct burial cable. cable that can be installed underground without the need for protective conduit.

direct connect. a supervised alarm system wired directly to a municipal police or fire department.

direct current. electrical current that travels in one direction and has negative and positive polarity. Batteries are direct current (DC) power sources for supplying secondary or standby power to alarm systems.

directed interview. an interview in which the questioner is in full control of the interview content, typically soliciting answers to a variety of specific questions. It is usually employed with a reluctant or uncommunicative witness.

directed verdict. a jury decision rendered by an order of a trial judge. In modern criminal procedure the directed verdict is always to acquit, although it may be limited to specific counts or specific defendants.

direct evidence. that means of proof which tends to show the existence of a fact in question, without the intervention of the proof of any other fact, and is distinguished from circumstantial evidence, which is often called indirect; information which a witness gained through one of the five senses.

direct examination. interrogation of a witness

by counsel of the party on whose behalf the witness was called.

directional microphone. a microphone extremely sensitive to audio frequencies arriving from one particular direction, while rejecting those that arrive from other directions.

direct loss. a measure in dollars of costs associated with loss of money, negotiable instruments, property, information and personnel; a loss which is a direct consequence of a particular peril.

direct tap. a common form of wiretapping in which a set of wires is attached to a specific phone pair in the phone company's bridge box, usually mounted in the basement or a secluded area of the building where the target telephone is located.

direct wire. a wire connecting a protected premises directly to a monitoring station.

dirty games. insidious work, such as blackmailing a government employee or business executive to force him into espionage.

disability glare. a form of glare lighting produced when peripheral light is much brighter than that on which the eye is focused. An intruder's vision is veiled or masked by the effect.

disable. to place an alarm sensor or system out of service, usually temporarily.

disabling injury frequency rate. the number of disabling injuries per million hours of exposure.

disaffirm. a legal term meaning to renege or refuse to go through with an agreed transaction.

disarm. to de-activate or turn off an alarm system.

disaster control. advanced planning and established procedures for handling emergencies. Major considerations include provisions for protecting personnel, evacuating both the injured and uninjured, and care of the incapacitated. Disaster control frequently focuses on threats posed by fire, civil strife, earthquake, explosion, flood, tornado, hurricane and nuclear accident.

disaster preparedness. any series of actions intended to control and manage major accidents (including nuclear incidents) and bring them to the most satisfactory conclusion possible.

disbar. the act of a court in rescinding an attorney's license to practice at its bar.

discharge gate. a type of valve that controls water flow from a high pressure fire hydrant.

disclosure. the act of making known to the adversary in a criminal case (usually the prosecution) information that might assist in clearing the party making the disclosure (usually the defendant) of alleged guilt.

discounting. the practice of converting cash flow into present value at a selected rate of return, based upon the premise that one would pay less than $1 today for the right to receive $1 at a future date.

discount rate. the correlation between dollars transmitted from a lender to a borrower and dollars that must be repaid by the borrower. For example, if a lender advances $960 and the borrower must repay $1000, the discount rate is 40 divided by 1000, or 4%.

discovery. a motion, usually made by the defense, calling for disclosure to the counsel for the accused all information about a case known to the police and prosecution, or of certain specified information; the disclosure by one party of facts, titles, documents, and other things which are in his knowledge and possession and which are necessary to the party seeking the discovery as a part of a cause of action pending.

discovery sampling. a technique in which a specified level of confidence or precision is stated and one or a few samples are drawn from the population being examined. The objective is to discover a single deviation from the specified level. If a deviation is found, the entire population is examined. This technique is used by auditors looking for fraud.

discretion. the power given to or assumed by officers of the criminal justice system to make decisions, such as whether or not to arrest, negotiate a plea, grant immunity or probation, prosecute, or impose a severe sentence.

discretionary controls. in computer usage, security controls that are applied at the user's option, that is, they are available but not required. Access control lists are typical of such optional security features.

discretionary sentencing. the power of the sentencing judge to decide upon the nature and severity of a sentence to be imposed after a plea or a finding of guilt.

disc tumbler. a spring-loaded flat plate that slides in a slot which runs through the diameter of the cylinder. Inserting the proper key lines up the disc tumblers with the lock's shear line and enables the core to be turned.

disinformation. the spreading of false propaganda and the use of forged documents to create political unrest or scandals.

disinterested witness. a qualified witness who is unbiased regarding the case in question.

disk crash. the destruction of data on a disk due to a physical failure.

disk scavenging. in computer usage, a method of obtaining information from a disk that the owner intended to discard. The information, although no longer accessible to the original owner by normal means, retains a sufficient amount of its original magnetic encoding so that it can be retrieved and used.

dismissal. a decision by a judicial officer to terminate a case without a determination of guilt or innocence.

dismissal without prejudice. the effect of the words "without prejudice" is to prevent the decree of dismissal from operating as a bar to a subsequent suit.

disorderly. contrary to the rules of good order and behavior; violative of the public peace and good order; turbulent, riotous, or indecent.

disorderly conduct. a term of loose and indefinite meaning except as occasionally defined in statutes, but signifying generally any behavior that is contrary to law, and more particularly such as tends to disturb the public peace or decorum, scandalize the community, or shock the public sense of morality.

disorderly house. a place where illegal or immoral activities occur, such as prostitution, gambling or the showing of pornographic materials.

displacement. a phenomenon in which criminals will move their activities to another location or switch to a different type of crime in response to increased prevention efforts.

displacement reaction. the discharge of pent-up feelings, usually hostile in nature, directed at an object less dangerous than that which initially aroused the emotion.

display clock timer. a device that generates and displays the time of day and issues a signal.

disposable alcohol screening device. a device used to conduct a one-time qualitative test of blood-alcohol concentration. It typically consists of a small glass tube containing either a column or multiple bands of an alcohol-sensitive reagent and a breath-volume measuring device such as a balloon or plastic bag.

disposition. the final decision of a trial court in the processing of a case, such as a decision to accept a guilty plea, to render a verdict of guilt or innocence, or not to prosecute.

disprove. to refute; to prove to be false or erroneous, not necessarily by mere denial, but by affirmative evidence to the contrary.

disrepute. loss or want of reputation; ill character; discredit.

dissemination. the distribution of information or intelligence products to legitimate intelligence consumers.

dissociative reaction. a neurotic reaction in which some aspects of behavior and memory are compartmentalized, giving the appearance of multiple personalities.

dissolute. loosed from restraint; unashamed; lawless; loose in morals and conduct; recklessly abandoned to sensual pleasures; lewd.

distinguished visitor. a person who, because of rank or position, may be afforded special protection services to ensure personal safety.

distortion. in polygraphy, a change in chart tracings caused by an unintended outside stimulus; a disturbance of normal polygraph tracings not attributable to a planned stimulus within a test structure. Distortion is usually caused by noises external to the test environment.

distributed card access system. a system in which each card reader has all the intelligence and data required to make access control decisions.

disturbing the peace. unlawful interruption of the peace, quiet or order of a community, including offenses generally called disorderly conduct, vagrancy, loitering, unlawful assembly and riot.

divergence. the spreading apart of two lines which have been running parallel or nearly parallel in a fingerprint pattern.

diversion. the official suspension of criminal or juvenile proceedings against an alleged offender at any point after a recorded justice system intake but before the entering of a judgment, and referral of that person to a treatment or care program administered by a non-justice or private agency, or no referral.

division of labor. the specialization of economic activities, and the tendency for people to become more specialized in what they do; an organization of work in which tasks/functions are grouped or separated so as to achieve efficiency of operation.

DMT. a laboratory-synthesized hallucinogen regulated under the Controlled Substances Act as a Schedule I drug.

do a bong. to smoke marihuana or hashish from a modified water pipe called a bong.

docket. a book containing any entry in brief of all the important acts done in court in the conduct of each case, from its inception to conclusion.

documentary evidence. a writing or recording that is significant because of its content. Examples are letters, photographs and tapes.

document examination. a side-by-side comparison of handwriting, typewriting and other written and printed matter for the purpose of determining authorship; a crime laboratory function based on the improbability of any two writings being exactly alike in all characteristics such as style, speed, slant and spacing. Writing involves a mental process, regardless of the skill and habitual performance, as well as muscular coordination.

DOD Weapons Registry. a Department of Defense central registry which lists the serial numbers of small arms in the DOD inventory. It can be used by any police agency seeking information on particular weapons.

dog chain. an iron chain with a ring at one end and a spike at the other end. It is used in firefighting operations to secure a ladder to a window sill.

dogging device. a mechanism which fastens the cross bar of a panic exit device in the fully depressed position, and retains the latch bolt or bolts in the retracted position to permit free operation of the door from either side.

dogging key. a key-type wrench used to lock down, in the open position, the cross bar of a panic exit device.

Dolophine. the trade name for methadone, a synthetic narcotic used in the treatment of addicts. The effects of Dolophine differ from morphine-based drugs in that its duration will last up to 24 hours, thereby permitting once-a-day administration in detoxification and maintenance programs. Dolophine is a Schedule II narcotic.

DOM. a controlled ingredient technically known as 4-methyl-2,5-dimethoxyamphetamine. It is a chemical variation of amphetamine. When first introduced into the drug culture, it was called STP, after a motor oil additive. DOM, along with DOB, MDA, and MDMA, is one of many chemically-synthesized hallucinogens. These drugs differ from one another in their speed of onset, duration of action, potency, and capacity to modify mood with or without producing hallucinations. They are usually taken orally, sometimes "snorted," and rarely taken intravenously. Because they are produced in clandestine laboratories, they are seldom pure, and the dose in a tablet, in a capsule, or on a piece of impregnated paper may be expected to vary considerably.

domicile. that place where a person maintains a permanent home.

Donnegan Workers. pickpockets and sneak thieves who ply their trade in public restrooms. The typical method of operation is for one of the "workers" to distract a victim in a toilet stall while the accomplice steals the victim's billfold, purse, luggage or other valuables.

door bolt. a rod or bar manually operated without a key, attached to a door to provide a means of securing it.

door check/closer. a device used to control the closing of a door by means of a spring and either hydraulic or air pressure, or by electrical means.

door cord. a short insulated cable connecting a protective device to an alarm system's protective circuit. Typically used as the connector for foil tape.

door clearance. the space between a door and either its frame or the finished floor or threshold, or between the two doors of a double door.

door jambs. the two vertical components of a door frame called the hinge jamb and the lock jamb.

door link. flexible electrical cable which runs from a fixed terminal to a sensor on the moving portion of a protected door.

Doppler Shift. a principle used in alarm operations. In an area to be protected, sound or radio waves are transmitted outward. Upon contact with an intruder, the waves are reflected to the receiver at a different frequency. The frequency differentiation (Doppler Shift) triggers an alarm.

Doriden. the trade name for glutethimide, a depressant regulated under the Controlled Substances Act as a Schedule III drug. Doriden is a barbiturate substitute not having a dependence potential. It is exceptionally difficult to reverse overdoses, which frequently result in death.

dose commitment. in nuclear security, the total radiation dose to a part of the body that will result from retention in the body of radioactive material. For purposes of estimating the dose commitment, it is assumed that from the time of intake of exposure to retained material will not exceed 50 years.

dose rate contour line. a line on a map, diagram or overlay joining all points at which the radiation dose rate at a given time is the same.

dosimetry. the measurement of radiation doses. It applies to the measurement techniques and to the devices used (dosimeters).

dossier. a record, case file, or personnel file containing background information as well as materials relating to a crime or a criminal career. The term is applied to espionage and counterespionage.

double. an agent working for two sides at the same time.

double-acting door. a swinging door equipped with hardware which permits it to open in either direction.

double-action. in a numbers operation, a bet on any combination of two of the three digits. Also called a bolita or bleeder.

double-base powder. a rapid burning propellant containing two explosive ingredients, usually nitroglycerine and gunpowder.

double-bitted key. a key having cuts on both sides.

double celling. the placement of two inmates

in a jail or prison cell originally constructed for the custody of only one.

double-circuiting. using redundant wires to connect all sensors in an alarm system.

double-dipper. a person drawing two government incomes, typically a retired military officer who enters a second career in the federal service.

double drop. a method used in central station systems whereby a reporting line is first opened to create a break alarm and then shorted to create a cross alarm.

double egress frame. a door frame prepared to receive two single-acting doors swinging in opposite directions, both doors being of the same hand.

double female. in firefighting operations, a hose coupling device having two female swivel couplings that permit hose lines to be attached and laid in opposite or reverse directions.

double glazing. two thicknesses of glass, separated by an air space and framed in an opening, designed to reduce heat transfer or sound transmission.

double-hung window. a type of window, composed of upper and lower sashes which slide vertically.

double indemnity. a separate agreement in an insurance policy which obligates the company to pay twice the face amount of the policy if the insured dies as the result of violent and accidental means.

double-jacketed hose. fire hose having two protective jackets outside the rubber lining or tubing.

double jeopardy. to put a person on trial twice for the same offense.

double-keying. a requirement that two persons, each with a separate and different key, must open locks that grant access to a sensitive item or location.

double loop. a fingerprint pattern having two separate loop formations, with two separate and distinct sets of shoulders, and two deltas.

double-pole, double-throw (DPDT) switch. a switch that connects one pair of wires to another pair or to two other pairs of wires.

double strip search. a type of search conducted at an outdoor crime scene. The area to be searched is delineated by marking into one or more large rectangles. Two or three searchers proceed at the same pace within fingertip distance along paths parallel to the base of the rectangle. When a piece of evidence is found, all searchers halt until it is processed. The search resumes at a given signal. When the searchers reach the end of the rectangle, they turn and proceed back along adjacent lanes, and continue the process until the entire rectangle has been covered. At this point the searchers repeat the process except that the direction of travel is parallel to the side of the rectangle.

double supervision. a feature of an alarm system in which the source of power for the trouble signal is supervised by a second trouble signal.

double-throw bolt. a bolt that can be projected beyond its first position, into a second, or fully extended one.

Dover's Powder. a substance containing opium. It is used medically as an analgesic and antidiarrheal. Produces high physical and psychological dependence, and has a potential for abuse.

downgrade. a determination that classified information requires a lower degree of protection against unauthorized disclosure, together with a change of the classification designation to reflect the lower degree of protection.

DP asset protection. selective application, in data processing environments, of protective measures supplemental to normal business controls, safety practices and general provisions for physical security. The focus is on protection from intentional acts and their consequences.

DP assets. computers, computing installations, terminals, supporting facilities, data processing services, software and data.

DP contingency plan. a plan for alternate means of providing data processing services to a user in the event that the normal DP function is interrupted. This may include transfer of DP to another facility, deferral of DP until the interrupted facility is restored to normal, and/or substitution of manual processing.

DP control elements. software and data performing or supporting control functions such as access control, logging, and violation detection. Examples are password data sets, files of cipher-keys and log files.

DP restricted utilities. software that can be used to alter or avoid such control functions as access control, logging, and violation detection.

dragon's blood powder. a fingerprint powder made from the resin of the rattan palm. It provides contrast for latent prints found in light, dark and multi-colored surfaces.

dram shop law. a liquor liability law which provides that a person serving someone who is intoxicated or someone contributing to the intoxication of another may be liable for injury or damage caused by the intoxicated person.

D ratio. a factor used in workers' compensation experience rating plans. It is the ratio of smaller losses plus the discounted value of larger losses, as compared to the total losses which might be expected of an insured party in a particular type of business.

drill job. a safecracking technique in which a high torque or core drill is used. The high torque drill is typically used to create a pattern of drill holes that permits access to and manipulation of the locking mechanism. The core drill has a hollow cylindrical bit that cuts out a solid core. The diameter of the hole is large enough to remove the safe's contents by hand.

Driodine. the commercial name of a product used in developing latent prints by iodine dusting. Driodine consists of porous glass saturated with iodine. It is poured onto a surface and where latents are present the characteristic iodine-colored prints will form.

drip loop. a length of electrical cable arranged in a looped configuration so that moisture collecting on the cable will run to the bottom of the loop and drip off. It is typically used in electrical installations where a cable enters a dry area from a wet area.

drive off. the act of driving off from a service station without paying.

drive-proof spindle. a cone-shaped or shouldered spindle used on a safe's combination lock. The shape of the spindle prevents it from being driven into the safe by striking blows or a penetrating force.

driver pin. one of the pin tumblers in a pin tumbler lock, usually flat on both ends, which are in line with and push against the flat ends of the bottom pins. They are projected by individual coil springs into the cylinder bore until they are forced from the core by the bottom pins when the proper key is inserted into the keyway.

driving tumbler. the tumbler in a safe or vault lock which is connected to the spindle and actuates the other tumblers by picking them up with pegs, studs or mounted pins.

drop. the annunciation of an alarm by some type of mechanical or illuminated signal; a place where numbers writers turn in their slips.

drop annunciator. an annunciator which drops a metal flag into view behind a small window to indicate an alarm condition.

drop-in mouthpiece. a telephone tap transmitter that has the appearance of a telephone carbon microphone.

dropout. as used in security communications, a momentary loss of a signal.

dropping the leather. a scam played on the street by two con artists, A and B. A walks past the victim, V, and appears to accidentally drop a wallet. Before V can react, B comes from behind and grabs the wallet. B

offers to split the wallet's contents with V. The wallet contains a few small bills and a counterfeit high-denomination bill. B sells to V his share of the high-denomination bill for change or other valuables in V's possession.

drop ring. a ring handle attached to the spindle which operates a lock or latch. The ring is pivoted to remain in a dropped position when not in use.

drug. a substance which alters the structure or functions of a living organism.

drug abuse. the use of drugs to one's physical, emotional and/or social detriment without being clinically addicted.

drug addiction. any habitual use of a substance which leads to psychological and/or physiological dependence. As defined by the World Health Organization, it is "a state of periodic or chronic intoxication produced by the repeated consumption of a drug (natural or synthetic), which produces the following characteristics: (1) an overpowering desire or compulsion to continue taking the drug and to obtain it by any means; (2) a tendency to increase the dosage, showing body tolerance; (3) a psychic and generally a physical dependence on the effects of the drug; and (4) the creation of an individual and social problem."

drug dependence. a state arising from repeated administration of a drug on a periodic or continuous basis. It will vary with the agent involved, and types of dependence are frequently designated; for example, morphine dependence or cannabis dependence. Dependence can be said to exist when an individual must continue to take a drug to avoid withdrawal symptoms and/or to gratify some strong emotional need.

drug experimenter. one who has illegally, wrongfully or improperly used a drug for the purpose of experiencing its effect. The exact number of usages is not necessarily as important in determining the category of user as is the intent of the user, the circumstances of use, and the psychological makeup of the user.

dry-chemical extinguisher. a fire extinguisher containing a chemical agent which extinguishes fire by interrupting the chain reaction wherein the chemicals used prevent the union of free radical particles in the combustion process so that combustion does not continue when the flame front is completely covered with the agent. Three types of base chemical agents are used: sodium bicarbonate, potassium bicarbonate and ammonium phosphate. These are used primarily on Class B and C fires; however, multipurpose dry chemicals are also effective on Class A fires.

dry contact. metallic points making (shorting) or breaking (opening) a circuit.

dry glazing. a method of securing glass in a frame by use of a preformed resilient gasket.

drying agent. a material, usually calcium chloride, used to remove moisture from air passing through an iodine fuming gun or tube during the development of latent fingerprints.

dry-powder extinguisher. a fire extinguisher designed for use on combustible metals fires. The principle of extinguishment involves the combination effect of dry-chemical powder.

dual alarm system. a system that sounds a coded alarm signal for a fixed number of rounds at selected locations, and at the same time a constant and continuous alarm signal at all other locations until the system is restored to normal. The coded signal identifies the particular alarm initiating device in operation. A dual alarm system facilitates evacuation of a building by announcing a fire alarm generally in all parts of the building and by simultaneously notifying response personnel so that evacuation and fire fighting can be started without delay at the fire-affected area.

dual rate fire alarm signal. an audible signal that begins with a slowly pulsed annunciation. When a pre-determined length of time has been reached or when a manually operated switch has been activated, the audible signal changes to a rapidly pulsed annunciation. The slow-pulse signal alerts emergency response personnel. The fast-pulse signal informs occupants to evacuate.

dual twisted-pair. a pair of twisted-pair wires, usually enclosed within a single cable.

duces tecum. A Latin term meaning "bring with you." It is applied to a writ commanding the person to whom it is served to bring certain evidence to court. Thus, we speak of a subpoena duces tecum.

due care. that degree of care or action required to be exercised by a person in relation to a given situation in order to avoid negligence or liability.

due process. a Constitutional guarantee that no person shall be deprived of his life, liberty or property without due process of law.

due process of law. law in its regular course of administration through courts of justice.

dummy camera. a genuine-appearing but non-functional camera used as a crime deterrent. It is typically mounted out of reach in a conspicuous spot at a place having a history of employee pilferage, shoplifting, misconduct, robbery, etc. Some models are stationary, some scan, and most are equipped with a red pilot lamp. Also called a simulated camera.

dummy charge. a false or fraudulent claim for payment, typically a bogus or altered invoice.

dummy cylinder. a mock cylinder without an operating mechanism, used for appearance only.

Dun and Bradstreet. a company that provides credit ratings and other business information.

Dunaway vs. New York. a case in which the Supreme Court rejected as evidence a voluntary confession from an illegally arrested person.

Duquenois Analysis. a technique of testing for the presence of cannabis. A sample of the suspect material is added to the Duquenois reagent. A violet or deep blue color reaction indicates the presence of cannabis.

duress. to force a person to do something he doesn't want to do.

duress alarm. a device which enables a person placed under duress to call for help without arousing suspicion.

Durham Rule. a rule enunciated in 1954 by the Federal Court of Appeals for the District of Columbia which holds that an accused is not criminally responsible if his unlawful act was the product of mental disease or mental defect.

dustproof strike. a strike which is placed in the threshold or sill of an opening, or in the floor, to receive a flush bolt, and is equipped with a spring-loaded follower to cover the recess and keep out dirt.

dutch door. a door consisting of two separate leaves, one above the other, which may be operated independently or together. The lower leaf usually has a service shelf.

dutchman. a short fold of hose in a fire truck body arranged in such a way to prevent snags when the hose is played out.

dwelling house. any building used as a dwelling, such as an apartment house, tenement house, hotel, boarding room, dormitory, institution, sanitarium, house or structure used or intended for use as a place of habitation by human beings.

dwell time. in CCTV, the length of time a particular image is programmed to remain displayed on a monitor that is connected to a sequential switcher.

dying declaration. as relates to a prosecution for homicide committed against the declarant, the declarant's statement as to the manner in which he or she met death. It is admissible into evidence provided the declarant acknowledged a sense of impending death and provided the declarant actually died shortly after making the declaration.

dynamic microphone. a microphone containing a pressure-sensitive diaphragm that moves an electrical coil in a magnetic field. The coil induces voltages proportional to the magnitude of audio vibrations sensed by the diaphragm.

dynamic range. that range lying between maximum and minimum acceptable signal levels; the productive or active range within which signals can be processed.

dynamic risk. a situation which carries the potential for both benefit and cost or loss.

dynamite. an explosive compound usually produced in stick form. The explosive charge is surrounded by sawdust entirely wrapped in wax-coated paper. As some dynamite ages it exudes nitroglycerin beads or crystals and in this condition is highly dangerous to handle.

dyspnea. in polygraphy, labored breathing or shortness of breath. It appears on the polygram as suppression or serration of the pneumograph tracing.

earth ground. the portion of a circuit connected to a buried metallic object.

earth shock. in bomb incident investigations, a detonation wave transmitted through the ground.

easy mark. an unwary or unprotected criminal target.

eavesdropping. interception of oral communications in a surreptitious effort to hear what is being said, without knowledge of at least one of the persons speaking. When hidden electronic equipment is used, the process is called bugging, the equipment is a bug, and the premises are said to be bugged.

eccentricity. as used in criminal law and medical jurisprudence, personal or individual peculiarities of mind and disposition which markedly distinguish a person from the ordinary person, but which do not amount to mental unsoundness or insanity.

echolalia. as used in medical jurisprudence, the constant and senseless repetition of particular words or phrases, recognized as a sign of insanity or of aphasia.

echo suppressor. a device that prevents energy from being reflected back to a transmitter; a device that attenuates a transmission path in one direction while signals move in the other direction.

ecstasy. a derivative of mescaline and amphetamine.

EDP auditor. a person who performs operational, computer, computer program, and data file reviews to determine integrity, adequacy, performance, security, and compliance with organization and generally accepted policies, procedures, and standards. This person also may participate in design specification of applications to ensure adequacy of controls, and perform data processing services for auditors.

effective representation. an expansion of the right to counsel requiring that counsel provide a competent defense.

efficacy of light source. a measure of the efficiency of the light source. It describes how much visible energy is and is not produced per watt of power input, measured in lumens per watt. Also called luminous efficiency.

ejector marks. the imprints made on a cartridge case by contact with the ejector of a firearm. These imprints help the firearms examiner to match a cartridge case with a particular firearm.

electret cable. weather-resistant cable having microphonic properties. It is used as a component of sound discriminating sensor systems, such as those installed on boundary fences and gates.

electric circuit card. a type of access card having printed circuits arranged in a coded pattern. This type of card is rarely used.

electric dice. dice that can be influenced by an electromagnetic control concealed in a gaming table.

electric door strike. an electrically activated door-locking mechanism consisting of a solenoid and a mechanical latching device. Application of electrical power causes the solenoid to withdraw the latching pin so that the door is free to open. The electric door strike is widely used in access control systems.

electric eye. the popular name for a photoelectric cell.

electric field. the area of space surrounding an electrically charged body in which the forces due to the charge are detectable; the electric component of the electromagnetic field associated with electrons in motion and with radio waves.

electric field sensor. a perimeter sensor that responds to a disturbance of the electrical field surrounding it.

electric knob. a door knob with an internal solenoid. When the solenoid is powered, the knob may be turned. A device of this type requires a power lead from the knob set to the adjoining door frame.

electric Kool-Aid. a soft drink laced with LSD.

electric microscope. a microscope using electrons instead of light rays and electromagnetic fields instead of glass lenses. It sends a beam of electrons through a thin sample of the material examined, magnifies the resulting shadow by denser portions of the sample, and makes this shadow visible on a fluorescent screen or records it on photographic film. Magnifications up to 100,000 diameters are obtainable, which makes the electron microscope from 50 to 100 times more powerful than the strongest optical microscope. It has important applications in the forensic sciences.

electric resistance. resistance to the flow of electricity. It is the value of the ratio of potential difference at the two ends of a conductor to the current which flows through it.

electric strike. an electrically operated device that replaces a conventional strike plate and allows a door to be opened by using electric switches located away from the door.

electric teeth. police-controlled traffic radar used to detect speeders.

electrode jelly. in polygraphy, a gelatinous substance used to enhance electrical contact between the galvanic skin response attachments and the examinee's fingers or hands.

electromagnetic interference. interference caused by disturbances in the atmosphere, such as lightning, or in the immediate vicinity, such as power lines or electric motors. Also called EMI.

electromagnetic lock. a door lock that uses magnetic attraction to secure the door.

electromagnetic pickup. interception of radiation generated by a computer's control processor, telephone and teleprinter lines or its microwave communications. The intercepted radiation can be revealing as to information communicated through such equipment.

electromagnetic pulses. pulses of gamma and X-rays that would damage electronic equipment, such as computers and communications networks, as a consequence of a nuclear detonation.

electromechanical detection device. any sensor that uses a combination of electrical and moving mechanical components to accomplish its function; generally, any detection device that requires direct physical contact with the intruder to initiate an alarm.

electromechanical lock. a lock that combines electrical energy with mechanical operations.

electromotive force. the force required to make a current flow between two points. It is abbreviated as emf.

electron capture detector. a device that captures and analyzes vapors associated with suspected explosives.

electronic countermeasures. defensive techniques designed to detect, prevent or expose the use of electronic audio or visual surveillance devices.

Electronic Funds Transfer Act. an act that defines the rights, liabilities and responsibilities of the various participants in electronic funds transfer systems. The act also provides for penalties for anyone who uses any counterfeit, altered, forged, fictitious, lost, stolen or fraudulently obtained debit instrument.

electronic lock. a type of electromechanical lock that features various logic operations and high speed computation.

electronic-magnetic regulator. a device that provides immediate correction of sudden voltage changes in a large power line system carrying a high-power load.

electronic stethoscope. a contact (spike) microphone or physician's stethoscope equipped with an electronic amplifier.

electronic surveillance. eavesdropping or wire-tapping by means of electronic listening and recording devices.

electronic tap changer. a device that provides voltage regulation by selective switching among taps in response to input voltage. An electronic tap changer will shield the AC line load from electric noise and rapid voltage fluctuations. Also called a step regulator.

electronic theft detection system. any of several types of electronic article surveillance systems used in retail stores, libraries and other places vulnerable to theft. Also called electronic article surveillance (EAS) system.

electronic vibration detector. a detection device that employs a sensitive contact microphone. It is used to protect safes, art objects and to monitor entry attempts through walls, floors and ceilings.

electrophoresis. a method used to separate certain proteins or enzymes in blood by passing an electrical charge through the blood. For example, it can be used in a crime laboratory to determine whether Sickle cell hemoglobin is present in certain evidence.

electrostatic field sensor. a passive type of perimeter sensor that detects an intruder by a disturbance of the ambient electrical field surrounding the sensor. It is similar in operation to an electric field sensor.

elements of the crime. the conduct defined in law to constitute a crime.

elint. electronic intelligence; the use of electronics technology to intercept messages.

embezzlement. the misappropriation, misapplication or illegal disposal of entrusted property with intent to defraud the owner or beneficiary.

embossed card. a type of card used in card access control that is encoded by raising or embossing a pattern on the surface of the card. The card reader decodes the embossed information.

embracery. as used in criminal law, an attempt to influence a jury corruptly to one side or the other by promises, persuasions, entreaties, entertainments and similar inducements.

embroidery. the pattern of hypodermic-needle abscesses and puncture points commonly found on the arms and legs of drug addicts.

emergency call station. a panel with push buttons that is designed for installation in the home, hospital, or in any location where there is a requirement for rapid communication of an emergency. A push of a button makes a direct connect to a central station or a response person/agency.

emergency descent chair. a conveyance designed to carry a disabled person through a stairwell when elevators are shut down, such as during a fire in a high rise building.

emergency response. the response made by firefighters, police, health care personnel and/ or other emergency service upon notification of an incident in which human life and/or property may be in jeopardy.

emergency stop. a switch installed in an elevator, or other similar piece of equipment, by means of which the power to the operating motor can be turned off in case of an emergency.

eminent domain. the power of the government to acquire land or property of a private individual for a necessary public purpose.

emission. as used in medical jurisprudence, the ejection of any secretion or other matter from the body such as the expulsion of urine, feces or semen.

emotion-evoking question. in polygraphy, a question inserted as the last question in a test. It is designed to elicit a response that will assist the examiner in determining the subject's reaction capacity.

employee assistance program. a company sponsored program intended to make early identification of employees who are problem drinkers and/or drug users so that treatment can be instituted. EAPs are also used with employees who have marital, legal, mental, health, financial and family problems.

employee stock-ownership plan. an employee benefit plan that uses company stock to provide deferred compensation.

empty shell. a computer backup site that has all necessary hookups to accommodate rapid installation of a data processing operation. Also called a cold site.

encipherment. the process of transforming intelligible data (plaintext) into unintelligible data (ciphertext). Also called encryption or privacy transformation.

encoder. a device that provides coding of a signal in response to some input. The principle of operation may be mechanical, electrical, electromechanical, or magnetic.

encrypting transformations. coded data so designed that plaintext is uniquely recoverable from ciphertext. Encrypting transformations preserve the data that has been operated on so as to allow a reversal of the process. Also called reversible transformations.

encryption. a process of encoding information so that its content is no longer immediately obvious to anyone who obtains a copy of it.

encumbrance. an impediment or legal claim to real estate.

end-of-line resistor. a resistor used to terminate an electrically supervised line. It can make a line electrically continuous and also provide a fixed reference for measuring changes that produce an alarm signal.

end-of-line supervision. the use of a resistor or diode within a sensor circuit to limit the amount of, or control the direction of, the supervisory current. End-of-line supervision causes an alarm if there is an attempt to jump the circuit. It sets up a specific impedance or polarity which when changed causes an alarm.

end-of-the-line question. a question asked by an interviewer at the end of a line of questions or at the end of an interview. For instance, "Is that all of what you saw?" or "Is there something you wish to add, change or delete?"

endorsement. writing one's name, either with or without additional words, on a negotiable instrument or on a paper (called an allonge) attached to it. By an endorsement, the endorser becomes liable to all subsequent holders in due course for payment of the instrument if it is not paid by the maker when properly presented and if he is given notice of dishonor.

energizing technique. that element of an intrusion detection system's control function which provides the means for testing and programming the system to report any activation of a sensor as an unauthorized intrusion.

energy management system. a system that combines monitor and control functions for the provision of optimum efficiency of energy consumption within the environment managed by the system. A system of this type performs such functions as automatically turning off lights and lowering the temperature during nondemand times.

energy signature. a unique pattern of electromagnetic emissions (signals, pulses and radio waves) that can be picked up and associated with a specific computer or its peripherals.

enjoin. require or command, as in the injunction of a court directing a person or persons to do or not do certain acts.

entrance delay circuit. a circuit that permits an authorized person entering or leaving protected premises a reasonable amount of time to disarm or arm the system before causing an alarm.

Entrance National Agency Check. a Department of Defense personnel security investigation scoped and conducted in the same manner as a National Agency Check except that a technical fingerprint search of the FBI files is not conducted.

entrapment. the act of an agent of the government to induce a person to commit a crime which was not contemplated by such person, for the purpose of instituting criminal prosecution. The mere act of furnishing the opportunity to commit a crime where the accused is predisposed to commit the crime is not entrapment.

entrepreneur. an innovator of a business enterprise who recognizes opportunities to introduce a new product, a new process or an improved organization, and who raises the necessary money, assembles the factors of production, and organizes an operation to exploit the opportunities.

entry/exit delay. a feature of an intrusion detection system that suspends triggering of an alarm for a pre-set number of seconds after an access door has been opened.

enveloping question. in polygraphy, a question inserted at the beginning and end of a probing peak of tension test. An enveloping question is beyond the realm of possibility concerning the issue being evaluated, i.e., it is neutral or irrelevant. Also called a padding question.

environmental impact statement. a report required of all agencies of the federal government to accompany proposals for legislation or other major federal actions significantly affecting the quality of the human environment.

EOD incident. the suspected or actual presence of explosive ordnance which constitutes a hazard.

epidemiological concept of cause. a descriptive model for use in defining causal relationships. Causation is interpreted as a combination of forces from at least three sources: the host, the agent, and the environment in which both the host and agent exist.

episodic excessive drinker. a classification of alcohol user who becomes intoxicated at a rate of four times per year.

equity. the monetary value of a property or business that exceeds the claims and/or liens against it by others.

equity theory. a management theory which holds that a worker will compare his effort and related achievement with the effort and achievement of some other employee in the organization, and will use the comparison to seek parity or equity.

equivalent four-wire system. a transmission system using frequency division to obtain full duplex operation over only one pair of wires.

erase-on-allocate. in computer usage, a technique that applies an erasure pattern whenever a new area is created in a file for data. The new area is erased with the erasure pattern so that subsequent attempts to read the area (for the purpose of unauthorized scavenging) will only yield the erasure pattern and not some valuable remaining data.

erector-set fraud. a criminal practice in which:

an automobile owner arranges for his automobile to be stolen; the owner collects from the insurance company; the automobile is stripped and the skeleton of it is abandoned so it can be found; the automobile owner buys the skeleton from the insurance company for little or nothing; and the owner then rebuilds the automobile with the same parts originally stripped from it.

ergonomics. the study of human characteristics for the appropriate design of the living and work environments. Ergonomics is based on the methodologies of anthropometry, physiology, psychology, engineering and their interrelationships.

ergotin tartrate. an ergot fungus poison used to induce abortion, but which also produces as side effects diarrhea, convulsions, headache, nausea and vomiting.

error in law. an error by the court in administering the law.

errors and omissions excepted. a notation often seen on invoices, especially those originating in Canada and England. It means that the company issuing the invoice reserves the right to correct any errors appearing therein.

erythroxylon coca. the coca plant which is cultivated in the Andean highlands of South America.

escorted entry. a situation in which visitors to a protected area are required to be escorted and kept under surveillance.

escutcheon plate. a surface-mounted cover plate, either protective or ornamental, containing openings for any or all of the controlling members of a lock such as the knob, handle, cylinder or keyhole.

Espionage Act. an act that provides criminal penalties for unlawfully accessing and disclosing information.

ethchlorvynol. the generic name of a depressant sold legally as Placidyl. The Controlled Substances Act lists it as a Schedule IV drug.

ethinimate. a drug classified as a Schedule IV Controlled Substance.

etonitazene. an opiate classified as a Schedule I Controlled Substance.

etorphine. an opium derivative classified as a Schedule I Controlled Substance.

etoxeridine. an opiate classified as a Schedule I Controlled Substance.

eupnea. in polygraphy, regular breathing as represented in the inked tracing of the pneumograph component.

euthanasia. mercy killing, such as assisting in or hastening the death of a terminally ill person, with or without the person's consent.

evaluation. the process of determining the value, credibility, reliability, pertinency, accuracy and use of an item of information, an intelligence product, or the performance of an intelligence system.

evasive action. in computer usage, a system's responsive behavior to break-in attempts whenever they seem to be in progress. Typically, when a system suspects that an unauthorized user is attempting to log in, the evasive action consists of locking out all login attempts by the offender for a limited period of time.

event code. a dedicated signal generated by a digital communicator for the purpose of identifying the nature of the alarm circuit to the central station. Event codes may differentiate between fire, intrusion, a supervised opening, or a supervised closing.

evidence. anything which tends to prove a fact in question in a court of law.

evidence tape. tape specially designed to reveal tampering or breaking. It is used to seal containers in which evidence is placed for safekeeping.

examination before trial. a legal procedure which permits one litigant to make the other answer questions under oath before the actual trial of the case.

exception. a statement made by a counsel in a trial, objecting to a ruling by a judge. The statement is made for the trial record so as to permit appeal on the ground that the ruling was incorrect.

exceptional clearance. an investigative technique in which a criminal's methods of operation are related to other, uncleared crimes.

exception principle. a principle of management in which only exceptional results, good or bad, are brought to the attention of decision-makers.

excessive bail. a sum of money set as bail that is far higher than would be expected under the circumstances of the crime, and in excess of the amount which would reasonably assure the defendant's appearance at subsequent proceedings involving him. Excessive bail is prohibited by the Eighth Amendment to the United States Constitution. Determination of whether bail is excessive is sometimes made by a higher court, which may decrease, confirm, or increase the bail or allow the accused to be released on his own recognizance.

exclusion area. a Department of Defense term that describes any area containing one or more nuclear weapons or components.

exclusionary rule. a rule which states that any evidence collected during an illegal search will not be accepted in court.

exclusive jurisdiction. a jurisdiction in which the Federal Government possesses all the authority of the state, and in which the state concerned has not reserved to itself the right

to exercise any authority concurrently with the United States, except the right to serve civil or criminal process relating to activities which occurred off the area.

exculpatory clause. a clause in a contract that frees one or more parties from fault or guilt.

excusable homicide. the intentional but justifiable killing of another person or the unintentional killing of another by accident or misadventure, without gross negligence.

ex delicto. arising from a tort.

execute. to put to death by legal means. Also, to carry out or do something, such as to execute a search warrant.

execute only access. a security feature of a computer system in which an authorized user is allowed to run files, but not read them.

executive action. in espionage, a violent action including assassination or sabotage.

executive action group. a small group or team of government-sponsored experts who specialize in the removal, by assassination or other means, of unfriendly foreign leaders.

executive clemency. the sovereign prerogative to extend mercy, exercised in the United States by the President, for federal and military offenses, and within the states by the governor, for violations of the state penal law. Examples of executive clemency include amnesty, commutation of sentence, pardon, and reprieve.

executive system. in computer usage, the basic system program that ensures orderly execution of all computer actions.

exemplar. a sample the origin of which is known. For example, handwriting samples taken directly from a suspect by an investigator are called handwriting exemplars.

exemplary damages. a sum assessed by the jury in a tort action (over and above the compensatory damages) as punishment in order to make an example of the wrongdoer and to deter like conduct by others. Injuries caused by willful, malicious, wanton, and reckless conduct subject the wrongdoers to exemplary damages. Also called punitive damages.

ex gratia. as a matter of favor.

exhibitionism. sexual gratification obtained through exhibiting the genitals to an involuntary bystander.

exigent circumstances. a situation requiring immediate action which permits certain latitude with regard to arrest, search and seizure.

exit alarm. an alarm activated upon the opening of a secured exit door. The alarm is usually announced at the door in the audible mode.

exit button. a button serving as an electrical switch that releases the lock on an exit door from a protected area. It is typically used in access control systems where an access card is required for entry, but not for departure.

exit delay. an amount of time allowed an authorized individual to arm an alarm system and exit the premises without causing the alarm to activate.

ex officio. an act done by a person merely by virtue of the office he or she holds.

exonerate. to remove blame from a person.

expanded metal. a type of fencing material made from a rigid piece of metal that has been split and drawn into an open mesh pattern.

ex parte. on one side only; by or for one party.

expectancy theory. a management theory which holds that an employee's beliefs will influence the performance goals selected by the employee and the extent of effort made to attain them. For example, if an employee believes that punctuality will result in a promotion (and the employee desires a promotion), the employee will strive to be punctual.

expense padding. falsification of expense reports or vouchers. This is typically done by dishonest employees who claim reimbursement for non-existent or inflated expenses.

experience curve. a graphic depiction showing that the costs of producing a unit drop as an organization gains experience in making the unit.

expert evidence. testimony given in relation to some scientific, technical or professional matter by a person judged to possess expert knowledge in the matter.

expert testimony. opinion or conclusions given by a witness who has certain unusual qualifications to interpret evidence bearing on a disputed issue. The principal function of an expert witness is to render necessary assistance to the court in the interpretation of evidential facts which have been presented to it. Certain inferences as to material issues may be drawn from those facts, but special training or experience is required to draw the proper inferences. The witness is typically skilled in a particular art, trade or profession or possessed of special knowledge derived from education and/or experience not within the range of common experience, education or knowledge.

expert witness. a person who possesses expert knowledge in a particular subject that is not generally understood by ordinary persons.

exploitation. the process of acquiring information from any source and taking full advantage of it.

explosimeter. a device which detects and measures the presence of gas or vapor in an explosive atmosphere.

explosion. a violent bursting or expansion as the result of the release of great pressure. It may be caused by an explosive or by the sudden release of pressure, as in the disruption of a steam boiler. An explosive produces an explosion by virtue of its very rapid self-propagating transformation into more stable substances, accompanied by the liberation of heat and the formation of gas.

explosion-proof device. any device, such as a contact switch, enclosed in an explosion-proof housing to help prevent possible sparking in a potentially volatile environment.

explosive. any chemical compound or chemical mixture that, under the influence of heat, pressure, friction or shock, undergoes a sudden chemical change (decomposition) with the liberation of energy in the form of heat and light and accompanied by a large volume of gas.

explosive ordnance. a Department of Defense term meaning munitions containing explosives, nuclear fission, or fusion materials and biological and chemical agents. Included in the term are bombs and warheads; guided and ballistic missiles; artillery, mortars, rocket and small arms ammunition; mines, torpedoes and depth charges; pyrotechnics; clusters and dispensers; cartridges and propellant-actuated devices; electro-explosive devices; clandestine and improvised explosive devices; and all similar or related items or components explosive in nature.

explosive ordnance disposal. the detection, identification, field evaluation, rendering safe, recovery, evacuation, and disposal of explosive ordnance which has been fired, dropped, launched, projected, or placed, in such a manner as to constitute a hazard to operations, installations, personnel, or material. It also includes the rendering safe and/or disposal of items which have become hazardous or unserviceable by damage or deterioration when the disposal of such items is beyond the capabilities of personnel normally assigned the responsibility for routine disposition.

explosives classifications. classifications established by the US Department of Transportation in which: Class A explosives are materials that possess a detonating hazard (e.g., dynamite, nitroglycerin, picric acid, lead azide, fulminate of mercury, black powder, blasting caps and detonating primers); Class B explosives are materials that possess a flammable hazard (e.g., propellant explosives); and Class C explosives are materials which contain restricted quantities of Class A and/or B explosives.

explosives detector. a device that detects components of explosive devices or explosive compounds by radiographic analysis, by analyzing chemical emissions, or by other methods.

explosive sensitivity. the ease with which an explosive will react to heat, shock or friction.

explosives taggants. small granules added to commercial explosives during manufacture. The taggants are intended to provide investigative leads in criminal bombing cases. A typical taggant is smaller than a grain of sand and will have several layers of different colors. One layer might be sensitive to magnets to aid in retrieval from bomb debris; another layer might be sensitive to ultraviolet light to aid in visual detection at the crime scene; and other layers might contain codes that reveal the manufacturer, lot number and other details useful in identifying the purchaser.

ex post facto. after the fact.

ex post facto law. an unconstitutional law that makes an act a crime when the crime was committed before the law existed.

exposure of person. as used in criminal law, the intentional exposure in a public place of the naked body or the private parts so performed as to shock the feelings of chastity or to corrupt the morals of the community.

expunge. the sealing or purging of arrest, criminal or juvenile record information.

extenuating circumstances. particular characteristics of an offense or an offender that partially or entirely excuse the offender or serve to reduce the gravity of the crime.

exterior private area. the ground area outside a single family house, or a ground floor apartment in the case of a multiple dwelling, which is fenced off by a real barrier, is available for the use of one family, and is accessible only from the interior of that family's unit.

exterior public area. the ground area outside a multiple dwelling which is not defined as being associated with the building or building entry in any real or symbolic fashion.

exterior semi-private area. the ground area outside a multiple dwelling which is fenced off by a real barrier and is accessible only from the private or semi-private zones within the building.

exterior semi-public area. the ground area outside a single family house or multiple dwelling, which is accessible from public zones, but is defined as belonging to the house or building by symbolic barriers only.

extort. to gain by wrongful methods; to obtain in an unlawful manner; to compel surrender of money or property by threats of injury to person, property or reputation.

extortion. unlawful demanding or receiving of favors, money or property through the use of fear or force or the authority of office. Blackmail, ransom demands and threats are forms of extortion.

extract. a verbatim portion or combination of portions of an official document.

extractor mark. a mark observable on or near the rim of a fired shell caused by an extractor. An extractor mark is an important identifying characteristic to a firearms examiner.

extradite. to return a fugitive to the place from which he fled.

extradition. the surrender upon request by one jurisdiction to another of an individual accused or convicted of an offense in the requesting jurisdiction.

extraordinary coverage. an arrangement between a credit insurance company and a policy holder to increase the amount of insurance on certain customers.

extrasystole. in polygraphy, a characteristic formation sometimes observed in the cardiographic tracing. It results from a premature contraction of the heart. The cause may be a double heartbeat, as in the case of a cardiac disorder, or a short, emotional surge.

extremis. the state of a person who is near death and beyond hope of recovery.

eyewitness. one who has been present at a crime while it was being committed, or shortly before or after. An eyewitness is usually called to testify as to what he saw or heard.

eyewitness identification. the identification of a defendant in a police lineup or in court. The person making the identification is usually the victim or someone who witnessed the act and the person identified is the person who committed the act.

F

fabricated evidence. evidence manufactured or arranged so as to intentionally deceive.

face plate. the part of a mortise lock through which the bolt protrudes and by which the lock is fastened to the door.

facility clearance. a type of security clearance issued in the DoD Industrial Security Program.

facility code. a code used in alarm or access control equipment that identifies the customer or location of the equipment. For example, a central station operator might use facility codes to identify subscribers being served by the central station system.

fact finder. the individual or group with the obligation and authority to determine the facts in a case. In a jury trial, the jury is the fact finder and is charged with accepting the law as given to it by the judge.

factor analysis. any of several methods of analyzing the intercorrelations among sets of variables.

fail safe. a feature of an alarm system that announces a mechanical breakdown in the system or to any of its component parts.

fail safe data protection. the copying of data and programs that reside on disk to magnetic tape.

fail safe lock. a type of lock that automatically opens when a power failure occurs. Typically, a fail safe lock will have an electrically released strike plate or a solenoid operated bolt.

fail secure lock. a type of lock that automatically locks when a power failure occurs, as opposed to a fail safe lock.

Fair Credit Reporting Act. an act that provides criminal penalties for unlawfully accessing or disclosing information pertaining to consumers. The act requires that a credit applicant be advised if a consumer report may be requested and be told the scope of the possible inquiry. Should the applicant's request for credit be declined because of information contained in that report, the applicant must be given the name and address of the reporting agency.

fair preponderance. the measure of evidence required in a civil case for the plaintiff to prevail over the defendant. This is to be distinguished from the requirement in a criminal case that the defendant be found guilty beyond a reasonable doubt.

fallout. the process of precipitation to earth of particulate matter from a nuclear cloud, also applied in a collective sense to the particulate matter itself. Although not necessarily so, such matter is generally radioactive.

false alarm rate. the number of false alarms per installation per month or year.

false alarm ratio. the ratio of false alarms to total alarms, usually expressed as a percentage.

false arrest. the detention of a person by another who claims to have official authority which is in fact invalid.

false entry. an entry in an official record intentionally made to represent what is not true or does not exist, with intent to deceive or defraud.

false imprisonment. to unlawfully restrain a person's freedom of movement.

false negative. an intrusion incident in which a qualified individual is excluded by access control screening criteria; the outcome of a drug test in which a drug abuser is mistakenly identified as a non-abuser.

false positive. an intrusion incident in which an unqualified individual is accepted by access control screening criteria; the outcome of a drug test in which a non-abuser is mistakenly identified as a drug abuser.

false pretense. a designed misrepresentation of existing fact or condition for the purpose of obtaining another's money or goods.

false representation. a representation which is untrue, willfully made to deceive another to his injury.

false statement. a statement more than merely untrue or erroneous and made with intention to deceive.

false token. a false document or a sign of the existence of a fact. An example is counterfeit money.

false witness. one who is intentionally rather than merely mistakenly false.

falsify. to counterfeit or forge; to tamper with as in falsifying a record or document.

fatigue. structural failure of a material caused by repeated or fluctuating application of stresses, none of which is individually sufficient to cause failure.

fault. a signal that indicates an abnormal line condition or an alarm.

feasance. the doing of an act; a performing or performance.

fecal matter identification. a crime laboratory technique for identifying persons through the microscopic examination of fecal matter. Several studies have concluded that a person can be matched to fecal matter; for example, feces found at a crime scene.

Federal Bureau of Investigation. the general enforcement agency for federal crimes whose enforcement authority is not assigned to another federal agency, such as the Internal

Revenue Service. The FBI is also charged with domestic security responsibilities. It compiles and publishes annual statistics on crime.

Federal Communications Act of 1934. an act which in part provides that "no person not being authorized by the sender shall intercept any wire or radio communication and divulge its existence, contents, substance, purport, effect, or meaning," to any person.

Federal Coordinating Officer (FCO). a person appointed by the President of the United States to coordinate the overall federal response to a major nuclear disaster or emergency.

Federal Crime Insurance Program. a federally administered program under which pooling insurance companies write crime insurance for those unable to secure it in the open market.

federal exclusionary rule. a US Supreme Court ruling that any evidence obtained through an unlawful search and seizure by the police is inadmissible in court.

Federal Fair Credit Reporting Act. an act that regulates the consumer reporting industry.

federal judicial circuit. the United States is geographically divided into twelve judicial circuits, in each of which there is a United States Court of Appeals with appellate jurisdiction over the United States district courts within that circuit.

federal response center. an on-site focal point for coordinating the federal response to a nuclear weapon accident or significant incident.

federal sector. a general term meaning the agencies of federal government.

felonious assault. assault with a deadly weapon.

felony. a criminal offense punishable by death, or by incarceration for a period of which the lower limit is prescribed by statute, typically one year or more.

felony murder. an unlawful killing of a person while committing or attempting to commit another felony, such as robbery. In felony murder, specific intent to kill need not be proved, since it is implied from the intent of the felony associated with the murder.

fence. a metal pin that extends from the bolt of a lever lock and prevents retraction of the bolt unless it is aligned with the gates of the lever tumblers. Also, a receiver of stolen goods.

fence ribbon. a barbed metal tape, similar to barbed wire, used for perimeter protection.

fence sensor. any of the several varieties of vibration, taut-wire, and electret cable sensors designed for installation on fences.

fencing. receiving stolen goods; receipt, handling, and sale of stolen goods as a business.

fenethylline. the name of a stimulant drug regulated as a Schedule I Controlled Substance. A commercial product called Captagon contains fenethylline, but Captagon is not marketed in the U.S.

fentanyl. an opiate classified as a Schedule II Controlled Substance.

ferroresonant regulator. a device that provides regulation for AC line loads ranging from 15 VA to 15,000 VA. It compensates continuously for incoming voltage fluctuations by raising and lowering output voltage. Also called a constant voltage transformer.

feticide. destruction of the fetus; the act by which criminal abortion is produced.

fetishism. the pathological displacement of erotic interest and satisfaction to a fetish, such as the derivation of sexual pleasure by possessing or wearing undergarments of the opposite sex.

fetters. physical restraints attached to a person to hinder movement. Leg irons and manacles are types of fetters.

fiber burning test. a crime laboratory procedure in which a piece of fiber evidence is observed as it is exposed to flame. The smell and whether the fiber burns, melts, forms beads or will not burn are identification indicators.

fiber optic system. a transmission system that uses light-transmitting fibers. A fiber optic system that transmits light but not images is called a noncoherent system. A fiber optic system that transmits images is called a coherent system. The image resolution capability is a function of the size and number of fiber optic links. Optic fibers are extremely fine and thousands of them may be combined into what is called a "bundle." Because they do not emit electromagnetic emissions they are difficult to detect and interdict electronically, thereby making them desirable for use in high-security data transmission systems.

fidelity bond. a bond that will reimburse an employer for loss due to the dishonest acts of a covered employee.

fidelity loss. a property loss resulting from a theft in which the thief leaves no evidence of entry.

field. in security alarms, the space or area under the influence of a force such as electricity or magnetism.

field citation. a procedure used in lieu of arrest in which a police officer is empowered to issue summonses for most misdemeanors and some minor felonies. The procedure is intended to unburden overcrowded jails and channel criminal justice resources to more important purposes.

field disturbance sensor. any type of sensor

that uses disruption of a radiated or ambient energy field to initiate an alarm.

field expandable. a term describing equipment that can be readily expanded or modified at the point of installation rather than at the place of manufacture.

field inquiry. a procedure used by police on patrol to inquire into the activities of a person believed to be involved in a criminal act. The person stopped is asked questions and may be searched if there is reason to believe he is armed. Also called stop and frisk or investigatory stop.

field interview. a conversation held at the area where an unfamiliar individual is encountered by a police or security officer. The officer courteously attempts to learn the individual's purpose for being in the area.

field of view. the image area transmitted by a lens. This area is a function of the lens focal length and the distance from the lens to the subject or area viewed.

field sensor testing. activating sensors located in the field from the central station for the purpose of verifying correct operation.

fighting words. words which tend to incite a breach of the peace.

filing. the initiation of a case in court by formal submission to the court of a document alleging the facts of a matter and requesting relief.

film pirate. a person who sells or uses film produced by another without recording its sale or use so that revenue is unreported or untaxed and royalties unpaid.

filter. as used in security communications, an electronic circuit element which reduces interference and unwanted signals.

financial audit. an examination of those accounting records and practices which have material impact upon the financial condition of the enterprise.

financial modeling system. a computer program that displays financial output data based on the calculations of input data according to a predetermined model. "What if" calculations are performed in which the output data will change in value depending on a change in value of input data.

financial statement. the disclosure of the financial results of a firm's operations. It involves the balance sheet, profit and loss statement, and associated information.

find. the discovery of a bug, wire tap or other electronic eavesdropping device.

finding. a conclusion of a court as to an issue of fact; for example, that the defendant is or is not competent to stand trial.

fingerman. a person who provides information on a truck marked for hijacking. He supplies a description of the truck, cargo, plate number, road route, departure time, schedule of stops, arrival time, and similar details of interest to the hijackers.

fingernail scrapings. residue scraped from under the fingernails of a suspect or deceased victim. The residue may contain traces of skin, hair, fibers, soil and similar materials connected to a crime scene or suspect.

fingerprint pattern area. that part of the loop or whorl in which appear the cores, deltas and ridges used in making a fingerprint classification.

fingerprint reader. a high-security identification or access control device that identifies persons by finger or palmar prints. The system uses a central computer, an optical scanner, and a data base of prints obtained from authorized persons. A person using the system places his thumb, fingers or palmar side of the hand on a light-sensitive plate. The impression is read by the optical scanner and compared against the person's file print. An approve/disapprove decision is made by the computer.

fingerprint ridge count. the number of ridges intervening between the delta and the core.

fingerprint type lines. the two innermost ridges which start parallel, diverge, and surround or tend to surround the fingerprint pattern area.

fink. a strikebreaker or other person who hires out to help an employer obtain information about unhappy employees; an informant.

firearm frame. that part of a firearm which provides housing for the hammer, bolt or breechblock and firing mechanism, and which is usually threaded at its forward position to receive the barrel. Also called the receiver.

firearms identification. a crime laboratory function which seeks to associate particular bullets, cartridge cases or shotshell casings to a particular weapon to the exclusion of all other weapons.

fire basket. a container, usually of heavy wire, used to carry small pieces of fire fighting equipment. It is sometimes also used as a stretcher.

fire blanket. a fireproof or flameproof heavy cover used to smother fires.

fire bomb. an incendiary device, typically homemade, which when thrown will produce fire upon impact. A fire bomb usually consists of gasoline and a wick in a glass container. The wick is ignited, and the bomb is thrown. When the glass container breaks, a flash explosion occurs. Also called an incendiary bomb or a Molotov cocktail.

fire brigade. an organized group of employees, usually in an industrial setting or a privately owned fire department, who are trained and practiced in basic firefighting operations.

fire cabinet. a cabinet that typically contains a length of fire hose, a nozzle and standpipe connection.

fire cart. a cart for transporting to a fire scene needed equipment such as extinguishers, hoses, ropes, gloves, air packs, and similar items.

fire door. a door tested and rated for resistance to various degrees of fire exposure and utilized to prevent the spread of fire through horizontal and vertical openings. Fire doors remain closed normally or are closed automatically in the presence of fire.

fire extinguisher. a device having characteristics essential for extinguishing flame. Fire extinguishers may contain liquid, dry chemicals or gases. They are tested and rated to indicate their ability to handle specific classes and sizes of fires. The Class A extinguisher is used for ordinary combustibles such as wood, paper and textiles, where a quenching/cooling effect is required. The Class B extinguisher is used for flammable liquids and gases such as oil, gasoline and paint. The Class C extinguisher is used for fires in electrical wiring and equipment. The Class D extinguisher is used for combustible metals.

fire point. the lowest temperature at which a flammable liquid, when exposed to a source of heat and in the presence of sufficient air, will give off sufficient vapors and continue to burn. This point is usually a few degrees above the flash point.

fire resistance rating. the time in minutes or hours that a given material or assembly has withstood a fire exposure as established in accordance with specified test procedures.

fire resistant glass. glass plate having an ability to remain intact in its frame during a fire. This characteristic helps reduce the amount of oxygen available to fuel the fire.

fire-resistive. a term applied to properties of materials or designs that are capable of resisting the effects of any fire to which the material or structure may be expected to be subjected.

fire-retardant. a term denoting a substantially lower degree of fire resistance than "fire resistive" and frequently refers to materials or structures which are combustible but which have been subjected to treatments or modifications to prevent or retard ignition or the spread of fire.

fire stair. any enclosed stairway which is part of a fire-resistant exitway.

fire stair door. a door forming part of the fire-resistant fire stair enclosure, and providing access from common corridors to fire stair landings within an exitway.

fire stop. a solid, tight closure of a concealed space which exists to prevent the spread of fire and smoke.

fire wall. a fire-resistant wall designed to prevent the horizontal spread of fire into adjacent areas. It is generally self-supporting and designed to maintain its integrity even if the structure on either side completely collapses.

firing chain. in bomb incident investigations, a chain of four elements necessary to produce an explosion. The four elements are: firing device, primary explosive, booster explosive and main charge. Also called the firing train.

firing device. an item that starts the basic firing chain typical of most explosions. A match, firing pin and safety fuse are types of firing devices.

firing pin marks. the imprints made on a cartridge case by contact with the firing pin of a firearm. These imprints help the firearms examiner to match a cartridge case with a particular firearm.

firmware. fixed software instructions in a computer.

first degree murder. the most serious and severely punishable crime of killing, usually defined as premeditated, deliberate, and with malice aforethought, or carried out while committing another felony.

first offender. a person who has been convicted for the first time and who therefore might be treated leniently. Although the accused may have committed previous crimes, he is officially categorized as a first offender if he has not been convicted previously.

fiscal year. any consecutive twelve months period selected by an entity as the basis of reporting operating results.

fissile material. in nuclear security, any material consisting of or containing one or more fissile radionuclides: plutonium-239, plutonium-241, plutonium-238, uranium-233, and uranium-235.

fixed assets. properties which are not easily converted to cash. Examples are real estate and heavy equipment.

fixed data. unchanging information entered or programmed into a computer or a device.

fixed evidence. items which cannot easily be removed, such as walls of a room, trees and utility poles. Also called immovable evidence.

fixed liabilities. long term liabilities; debts that have a maturation of more than one year.

fixed temperature sensor. a fire detection sensor that works like a thermostat. Typically, a detector sensitive to heat will cause electrical contacts to close when the temperature around it reaches a pre-set, fixed number of degrees. The bi-metallic strip type of detector operates a set of contacts when the sensing element bends due to the different coefficients of expansion of the two metals comprising the strip. A fusible-link type of detector consists of two conductors separated by a material that melts away at a predetermined temperature allowing the conductors to complete a circuit. Bi-metallic strips are restorable after activation, but fusible links require replacement.

flagging. a nervous shoplifter's habit of looking around just prior to the concealment act.

flagrante delicto. in the very act of committing.

flame arrester. a device used on vents for flammable liquid or gas tanks, storage containers, cans, gas lines, or flammable liquid pipelines to prevent flashback (movement of flame) through the line or into the container.

flame detector. a sensor that detects the light output from a flame. A photoelectric cell in the sensor responds to light pulses in the 10 Hz region. Flames produce emissions in the 8-12 Hz range.

flame propagation. the spread of flame, independent of the ignition source, throughout a combustible vapor area which may be in a container or across a surface.

flammable liquid burn pattern. in arson investigations, sharp lines of demarcation between areas of burn, usually on floors and walls, which suggest the flowing or splashing of an accelerant.

flaps well down. a term describing an undercover agent who is worried about his future and lying low.

flashback. a fragmentary recurrence of psychedelic effects long after a hallucinogen is eliminated from the body.

flash blinding. a security lighting technique in which an extremely intense burst of illumination is directed into the eyes of an intruder, resulting in a period of visual incapacitation.

flash money. marked money used in undercover operations to bait a criminal into action or to make controlled purchases of illegal drugs or stolen property.

flash paper. a chemically treated paper that self-destructs by rapid burning. It is used in illegal gambling operations.

flashpoint. the lowest temperature of a flammable liquid at which it gives off sufficient vapor to form an ignitable mixture with the air near the surface of the liquid or within the vessel used.

flex cuff. a nylon restraining strap applied to the wrists or ankles of a person in custody.

It is removed by cutting and is therefore limited to a single use. Flex cuffs are frequently employed in multiple arrest situations.

flicker effect. an effect which produces disorientation in some individuals when they are exposed to fluorescent lighting, usually when the exposure is long and the fluorescent lamp defective.

float glass. basic windowplate glass. It is generally unsuitable for security applications.

floating exchange rate. a system that allows currency values to fluctuate on foreign exchange markets in response to changes in trade and economic conditions.

floating game. an illegal card or dice game which moves from location to location in order to avoid detection.

floodlight. a luminaire designed to project its light in a well defined area. It is directional in character.

floodlight beam. the angular spread of light between two planes each of which equal 10 percent of the maximum candlepower within the beam.

floor anchor. a metal device attached to the wall side of a jamb at its base to secure the frame to the floor.

floor contact. a wide gap magnetic contact housed in a heavy metal case and primarily used to detect opening of an overhead door.

floor sensor. any type of sensor installed under, in, or upon a floor and designed to trigger an alarm when an intruder moves across the floor. Typically, a floor sensor operates on a weight or pressure principle.

Florence test. a micro crystal test in which a solution of iodine is added to a suspect seminal stain. If choline is present in the stain, characteristic crystals will form which can then be viewed microscopically.

flowchart. a pictorial representation of a system or program.

flow control sprinkler. a sprinkler that automatically opens and closes as heat conditions dictate.

fluorescein. a tracing powder used to mark objects likely to be touched by a culprit. The powder is invisible in small quantities, but will emit a bright yellow glow when exposed to ultraviolet light.

fluorescence microscope. a microscope that allows an examiner to view with ultraviolet light a sample treated with a fluorescent dye.

fluorescent examination. a crime laboratory technique in which fabrics and other materials are exposed to an ultra-violet or black light. If the item being examined contains a seminal stain, the stain will glow blue-white.

fluorescent lamp. a large, elongated bulb which provides a high light output over an extended light life. This lamp has a higher initial cost but a lower operating cost than the incandescent lamp.

fluorescent mercury vapor lamp. a lamp that produces a large amount of ultraviolet radiation, and has a thin coating of phosphor on the inside of the tube that fluoresces and gives off visible light. Its efficiency is approximately 62 lumens per watt. The fluorescent mercury vapor lamp is sensitive to surrounding air temperatures, with an ideal at 70 degrees to 80 degrees F., making it primarily an indoor lighting source. While it offers more wattage output and a longer life than the incandescent lamp, it is subject to a condition that results in flicker effect. The flicker effect can cause disorientation among some individuals, and the electromagnetic radiation given off by the fixture can cause interference with some electronic equipment.

fluorescent powder (or paste). a material used to mark an object in order to transfer a detectable amount to the body or property of a person who handles the object at a later time. An ultraviolet light is used to bring out the fluorescent markings.

flurazepam. the generic name of a depressant sold legally as Dalmane. It is a Schedule IV Controlled Substance.

flush bolt. a door bolt so designed that, when installed, the operating handle is flush with the face or edge of the door. Usually installed at the top and bottom of the inactive door of a double door.

flush door. a smooth-surfaced door having faces which are plane and which conceal its rails and stiles or other structure.

fob worker. a pickpocket who works from in front of his victim.

focal length. the distance from the optical center of a lens to the focal plane.

focal plane. the area behind a lens where the image is formed.

focal point. the point at which light rays, passing through a lens or reflected from a concave mirror, are concentrated; in fingerprint sciences, the delta or core located within the pattern area of a loop or whorl.

focus. the point at which light rays or an electron beam form a minimum size spot, thus producing the sharpest image.

foil. thin metallic ribbon usually used to protect glass in closed circuit protective loops. Also called foil tape.

foil connector. a terminal block for connecting the ends of a foil circuit to protective circuit wiring.

foil crossover. an insulated bridge over which foil tape is run when conductive material must be crossed.

foil take-off block. a device that terminates foil loops. Alarm circuit wires are connected to a foil circuit at the take-off block. Some types feature a cover to hide connections and prevent damaging the foil circuit leads.

foil take-off switch. a pair of metal contacts used in a foil circuit to make an electrical connection between a door or window and the corresponding door or window frame.

folk crime. a term sometimes applied to illegal activity that society does not stigmatize; an offense that does not incite a sense of outrage and that is generally thought of as less than criminal; for example, a parking violation.

foot bolt. a type of bolt applied at the bottom of a door and arranged for foot operation. Generally, the bolt head is held up by a spring when the door is unbolted.

footcandle. a unit of illumination. One footcandle equals the illumination on a surface all points of which are at a distance of 1 foot from a uniform point source of 1 candle. One footcandle equals one lumen per square foot.

footcandle chart. a chart showing lines of equal footcandles. It is useful for determining results from a particular fixture without making calculations. Also called an isofootcandle diagram or isolux chart.

footlambert. a unit of light measurement that applies to emitted or reflected light. A footlambert is equal to the amount of light reflected or emitted from a perfect diffusing surface at the rate of one lumen per foot.

foot pound. a unit of work; 1 ft-lb equals the work done in raising a mass of 1 pound vertically through a distance of 1 foot, against the force of gravity.

foot rail. an inconspicuous hold-up alarm device operated by foot action.

forbearance. giving up the right to enforce what one honestly believes to be a valid claim in return for a promise.

forced choice. a method for evaluating the effectiveness of an employee by forcing an informed person (such as a supervisor) to choose one phrase as more or less descriptive of the employee than another phrase.

forced entry. an unauthorized entry accomplished by the use of force upon the physical components of the premises; breach of an enclosed area usually through a door or window, using tools or muscle power.

force majeure. superior or irresistible force. Corresponds in a general way to "Act of God"; for example, an earthquake, or the sudden death of a person. If a party to a contract is prevented from executing it by a force majeure, he may not be held liable for damages.

forcible entry and detainer. the use of threat, force, or arms to gain possession of the real property of another and to retain it after surrender has been lawfully demanded. It is a remedy given to a landowner to evict persons unlawfully in possession of his land. A landlord may also use it to evict a tenant in default.

forcible rape. sexual intercourse with a female against her will, by force or threat of force.

forecasting. a management tool for long-range planning; an informed estimate about the future based on an analysis of past data and present and future trends.

Foreign Corrupt Practices Act. a law intended to discourage American businesspeople from bribing foreign officials in the conduct of their business affairs.

foreign government information. as used in federal government security, information that is (1) provided to the United States by a foreign government or governments, an international organization of governments, or any element thereof with the expectation, expressed or implied that the information, the source of the information, or both, are to be held in confidence; or (2) produced by the United States pursuant to or as a result of a joint arrangement with a foreign government or governments or an international organization of governments, or any element thereof, requiring that the information, the arrangement, or both, are to be held in confidence.

foreign intelligence. in Department of Defense security, specially caveated information: (1) on the capabilities, intentions, and activities of foreign powers, organizations, or their agents; (2) that concerns activities conducted to protect the United States and its citizens from foreign espionage, sabotage, subversion, assassination, or terrorism; and (3) that concerns methods used to collect foreign human, technical, or other intelligence, and methods and techniques of analysis that are designated by an intelligence community organization of the United States government to require a specific degree of protection against unauthorized disclosure, modification, or destruction for reasons of national security.

foreign national. a person not a citizen of, not a national of, nor an immigrant alien to the US.

forensic. relating to law, courts, or the judiciary.

forensic auditing. the application of accounting and audit disciplines to matters in litigation or debate.

forensic ballistics. the science of detecting and identifying lethal bullets and the firearms from which they were fired.

forensic chemistry. chemistry applied to questions of law.

forensic medicine. the application of medical knowledge to legal problems such as determining the cause of death.

forensic photography. a crime laboratory function which utilizes specialized photographic techniques to make visible latent evidence which is not otherwise visible to the unaided human eye. Forensic photography is typically used to examine alterations and obliterations to documents, laundry marks, and handwriting.

forensic psychiatry. psychiatric knowledge applied to questions of law, as in the determination of insanity. Forensic psychiatry is concerned with psychiatric advice or opinion on a crime, a defendant, or a convicted offender.

forensic science. the application of chemistry, physics and other sciences to the examination of physical evidence.

forensic serology. the study and examination of blood and other body fluids in a crime laboratory.

forfeiture. the loss of goods, property or rights, as punishment for a crime.

forfeiture proceeding. a court action aimed at depriving a defendant of rights or property, such as something taken by the police in a search and seizure.

forgery. the creation or alteration of a written document, which if validly executed would constitute a record of a legally binding transaction, with the intent of defraud by affirming it to be the act of an unknowing second person.

former jeopardy. a defense plea founded on the common law principle that a man cannot be brought into danger of his life or limb for the same offense more than once.

Formerly Restricted Data (FRD). information that has been removed from the Restricted Data category upon joint determination by the Departments of Energy and Defense that such information relates primarily to the military use of atomic weapons and can be adequately safeguarded as national security information. For purposes of foreign dissemination, however, such information is treated in the same manner as Restricted Data.

former testimony. testimony given by a witness at a prior legal proceeding which is admissible in a later trial.

Formosa plan. a plan for controlling drug addiction through the issuance of licenses to sell and use drugs in prescribed locations. The plan's name is derived from a system implemented in Formosa to control opium smoking.

formula quantity. in nuclear security, special nuclear material in any combination in a quantity of 5,000 grams or more.

FORTRAN. an acronym for Formula Translating system, a computer language closely resembling algebraic notation.

fortress prison. a maximum-security confinement facility with high walls, guard towers, armed personnel and similar features.

founded offense. a complaint in which the police determine that a criminal offense was committed.

fragging. the use of a fragmentation grenade by a subordinate to murder a military superior while in combat or in a combat-related situation.

fragile evidence. items that are easily destroyed, contaminated or will easily deteriorate. Fragile evidence is sometimes difficult to detect.

fragmentation. in bomb investigations, the scattering of the broken, jagged pieces of the bomb case.

franchising. selling by a corporation of its rights to market a service or product.

fraud. an element of certain offenses, consisting of deceit or intentional misrepresentation with the aim of illegally depriving a person of his property or legal rights; an act which involves bad faith, a breach of honesty, a lack of integrity or moral turpitude.

fraudulent concealment. the hiding or suppression of a material fact or circumstance which a party is legally or morally bound to disclose.

fraudulent conversion. receiving into possession money or property of another and fraudulently withholding, converting or applying the same to or for one's own use and benefit, or the use and benefit of any person other than the one to whom the money or property belongs.

fraudulent conveyance. a conveyance of property by a debtor for the intent and purpose of defrauding his creditors. Such conveyance is of no effect, and such property may be reached by the creditors through appropriate legal proceedings.

Frazier vs. Cupp. a case in which the U.S. Supreme Court upheld a conviction based in part upon a confession obtained by the police through trickery and deceit. The Court commented that "these cases must be decided by viewing the totality of the circumstances."

free basing. smoking cocaine after it is converted from its normal form to cocaine base. In its normal form (cocaine hydrochloride), the drug is water soluble to facilitate absorption by the membranes. Cocaine in the hydrochloride form can be converted to cocaine base with a few common chemicals and simple equipment. Because the chemicals are highly flammable, the process is dangerous.

Freedom of Information Act of 1966. an act that provides for making information held by federal agencies available to the public, unless it comes within one of the specific categories of matters exempt from public disclosure. The legislative history of the act (particularly the recent amendments) makes it clear that the primary purpose was to make information maintained by the executive branch of the federal government more available to the public. At the same time, the act recognized that records that cannot be disclosed without impairing rights of privacy or important government operations must be protected from disclosure.

free on board. a provision in a contract of sale which requires the seller to deliver the merchandise at a designated place, usually to a carrier. Also called F.O.B.

frequency distribution. a term used in the study of statistics. It represents a method of presenting accumulated data by reclassifying the data into subgroups and then presenting again the original facts in terms of these subgroups.

frequency division. as used in security communications, a means of splitting a channel into subchannels for more efficient use of the channel.

frequency division multiplexing. a signaling method characterized by simultaneous transmission of more than one signal in a communication channel. Signals from one or multiple terminal locations are distinguished from one another by virtue of each signal being assigned to a separate frequency or combination of frequencies.

frequency inverter. a voice scrambler that inverts the frequency content of speech. It is usually low cost with good tolerance to poor communication conditions, but is easily broken with an equivalent device and can be defeated by a trained listener.

frequency modulation. a type of radio and television broadcast in which the frequency of the carrier wave is modulated. It provides less distortion but it can be received only over a comparatively small distance.

frequency response. an expression of the capability of a device to transmit or receive a given range of frequencies.

fresh complaint. a complaint of a victim of a sexual offense made within a short time after the offense was committed. The statements of the victim made during a fresh complaint can be reported in court by witnesses as an exception to the hearsay rule.

fresh pursuit. immediate, in-sight pursuit of an escaping felon that permits a police officer to depart from his jurisdiction or to intrude on private premises.

fresnel diffraction. diffraction of light when the light source as well as the screen on which the phenomena are observed are at finite distances from the diffracting apparatus.

frisk. an external patdown search of a suspect's outer clothing for the purpose of discovering weapons.

front porch. in CCTV applications, that portion of the composite picture signal that lies between the leading edge of the horizontal blanking pulse and the leading edge of the corresponding synchronizing pulse.

frotteur. a person who derives sexual satisfaction from rubbing against the clothing or anatomical parts, usually the buttocks, of a person of the opposite sex. This deviance is practically unknown in females.

fruits of crime. material objects acquired by means and in consequence of the commission of crime. Swindled money, a stolen watch and illegally intercepted trade secret information are examples of fruits of crime.

f-stop. the dimensional ratio between a lens aperture and its focal length. For example, a 4-inch lens with an aperture of 0.5 inches equals a ratio of 8 to 1. This corresponds to an f-stop of f-8.

fugitive from justice. a person who is charged with a crime in one jurisdiction and flees to another jurisdiction.

fugitive print. a latent fingerprint that disappears after it has been developed through an iodine fuming process.

full-custody arrest. the taking of a person into physical custody for the purpose of (1) taking him before a judicial officer to answer for a crime, or (2) transporting him to a police facility to answer for a crime, where he will be locked up or will post bond.

full duplex. a multiplex system that can simultaneously transmit in both directions on a transmission line.

functional job analysis. a technique of work analysis that measures and describes a position's specific requirements. The technique produces a variety of component descriptions which can be used to accurately illustrate the specific and varied duties actually performed by an incumbent.

function key. a key on a keyboard or keypad that has a dedicated function, such as to acknowledge receipt of a signal. Depressing the function key causes the system to respond in some preprogrammed manner.

functus officio. a Latin term applied to an officer who has fulfilled the duties of an office that has expired and who, in consequence, has no further formal authority.

funding risk. the danger that depositors whose money is being lent will demand the return of their funds.

furethidine. an opiate classified as a Schedule I Controlled Substance.

furlough program. a community-based alternative to sentencing of an offender. The aim is to maintain the incarcerated offender's community ties through attendance at work, school and in the home.

fusible link. a device used in fire detection. The link will fuse when a pre-set temperature is reached. The fusion results in an alarm.

G

G-2. a US military intelligence unit.

gag rule. a colloquial term for any formal instructions from a competent authority, usually a judge, to refrain from discussing and/or advocating something.

gage. marijuana.

gain. an increase in voltage or power.

gain control. a device that regulates the gain of particular equipment.

gait pattern identification. an investigative technique in which measurements are made of a series of footprints. Because a person's gait is highly individual, footprints can be useful in connecting a suspect to a crime scene.

galvanic skin response. a change in the electrical resistance of the skin. It is one of three physiological changes measured by the polygraph instrument. Changes of body tissue polarization (neural discharge) and sweat gland activity or circulatory variations which occur as the result of work, emotion, or a combination of either, are recordable by the polygraph instrument. These changes are recorded on a polygraph chart by a pen attached to a galvanometer driven by the variations of electrical conductivity introduced into a Wheatstone Bridge.

galvanograph. a component of the polygraph instrument. It records a phenomenon known as the psychogalvanic skin response or electrodermal response.

ganja. an Indian hemp plant from which hashish is made. Also called ghang.

gaping stab wound. a wound inflicted perpendicular to the direction of tissue of fibers. Distortion of skin tension resulting from a separation of the tissue fibers gives the wound a gaping appearance.

garnishment. a proceeding which requires a person who owes money to a judgment debtor to pay the judgment creditor instead.

Gas Chromatograph Intoximeter. a breath testing device used by the police to determine alcohol concentrations in the blood of drivers suspected of being under the influence of alcohol.

gas detector. a sensor designed to detect and report the presence of gases or vapors.

gas neutralizer. a product used in riot control operations to neutralize the effect of tear gases. It is usually packaged as an aerosol spray and issued to police/security personnel.

gate. a notch in the end of a lever tumbler, which when aligned with the fence of the lock bolt allows the bolt to be withdrawn from the strike.

gelatin dynamite. a type of commercial dynamite made of nitrocotton (collodion cotton dissolved in nitroglycerin) and nitroglycerin gel. It is usually sticky and rubber-like in appearance.

Gel-Cel battery. a trade name for a type of gelled electrolyte battery that can be recharged.

general characteristics. in observation and description, the gross characteristics of people, e.g., sex, race, build, height, weight and age.

general circulation stair. an interior stairway in a non-elevator building which provides access to upper floors.

general criminal intent. an intent of the criminal to act contrary to the law with voluntariness and foresight of the consequences.

general intent. the state of mind characterized by recklessness or negligence rather than a specific criminal intent to do what is prohibited.

generalized anxiety disorder. a personality disorder characterized by diffused and generalized anxiety that is difficult to manage.

general operating procedures. written instructions which concern a security force as a whole and are applicable to all posts or patrols.

general series test. in polygraphy, a series of questions typically comprised of a combination of relevant, irrelevant and control questions.

genlock. a type of circuitry that synchronizes one or more devices to a standard reference signal.

geophone. an intrusion sensor usually sealed in an insulating material and mounted on a fence or underground. The sensor has a built-in audio capability that permits monitoring or annunciation at a manned location.

ghang. an Indian hemp plant from which hashish is made. Also called ganja.

ghosting. multiple images on a video screen caused by signal transmission echoes.

Gideon vs. Wainright. a case in which the U.S. Supreme court ruled in 1963 that the Sixth Amendment's guarantee of counsel requires the states to furnish free lawyers to poor defendants.

gigahertz. one billion cycles per second. Microwave frequencies extend from 1000 megahertz to values expressed in gigahertz.

Gilbert vs. California. a case in which the U.S. Supreme Court held that a suspect may not decline to provide a handwriting sample.

glare projected lighting. a technique that projects light into the face of the potential intruder, and protects the guard by keeping him in comparative darkness.

glass break detector. an electronic sensing device that detects the intermolecular frequencies generated by breaking glass. Other types of glass break detectors use contact microphones or piezoelectric circuitry.

glass-clad polycarbonate. a five-ply laminate with glass layers on both sides of a polycarbonate core, using elastic interlayers that allow for differences in expansion/ contraction. This product combines the impact resistance characteristics of polycarbonate with the fire and chemical resistance of glass.

glazed bricks. in arson investigations, bricks of a burned structure which bear a glossy appearance. Glazed bricks are indicators that the fire was enhanced by an accelerant.

glazing. any transparent or translucent material used in windows or doors to admit light.

glazing bead. a strip of trim or a sealant such as caulking or glazing compound, which is placed around the perimeter of a pane of glass or other glazing to secure it to a frame.

glitch. a problem in a system; a horizontal bar moving vertically on a television monitor; a defect in a tape that causes imperfect playback.

glutethimide. a depressant introduced in 1954 as a safe barbiturate substitute, but which has since been found to have no particular advantages and several disadvantages. One disadvantage is that the effects of the drug are of such long duration that it is exceptionally difficult to reverse overdoses, which often result in death. Glutethimide is sold as Doriden and is a Schedule III and IV depressant.

good behavior bond. a promise made to a court by a defendant to maintain good behavior for a specified period of time.

good faith exception. an exception to a rule based on the honest belief that the person was acting lawfully and properly. For example, an exception might be granted to allow certain illegally obtained evidence to be introduced at trial if the officer who obtained the evidence had acted in good faith.

Good Samaritan. a person other than a police officer who is not directly involved in a crime but who steps in to prevent injury, aid a victim, or apprehend the criminal.

good time. the amount of time deducted from time to be served in prison on a given sentence contingent upon good behavior or awarded automatically by statute or regulation.

goodwill. an intangible business asset. It refers to the value of a business which has been built up through the reputation of the business concern and its owners.

Grade AA System. a Grade A alarm signalling system which additionally provides line security.

Grade A System. a UL specification for an alarm signaling system that must respond to both an increase and a decrease in either resistance or current within certain limits.

Grade BB System. a Grade B alarm signalling system which additionally provides line security.

Grade B System. a UL specification for an alarm signaling circuit that must provide supervision of the protection circuit but does not have to conform to the full requirements of a Grade A System.

graft. coerced or voluntary payments made to influence public officials; for example, payments made to the police to overlook illegal gambling.

grain confetti. small paper taggants added to grain in storage for the purpose of identifying stolen grain and discouraging grain theft. Each paper taggant bears a code number indicating source and ownership.

grandfather file. a backup record preserved at a location different than the originating location. Grandfather files are almost always used when information is processed by a computer.

grand jury. a body of persons selected and sworn to investigate criminal activity and the conduct of public officials, and to hear evidence against an accused person for the purpose of determining if there is sufficient evidence to bring that person to trial.

grand master key. a key designed to operate all locks under several master keys in a system.

grant of probation. a court action requiring that a person fulfill certain conditions of behavior for a specified period of time, often with assignment to a probation agency for supervision, either in lieu of prosecution or judgment, or after conviction, usually in lieu of a sentence to confinement.

graphic annunciator. a mimic board or CRT display that has special graphics to delineate alarm zones or sensor locations. A graphic annunciator can present an overall picture of a system's status on a map or facility outline and depict the location and current reporting condition of each sensor.

graphologist. a person who analyzes handwriting or handprinting for the purpose of making conclusions concerning the personality or character of the writer.

gratuity. something given freely or without recompense, or something given in expectation of a return favor or consideration.

gravimetric analysis. in chemistry, a form of quantitative analysis by weighing the substances and precipitates obtained.

grazing. the consumption on store premises of edible or consumable merchandise by customers or employees. Popular grazing items are soft drinks, small food items, aspirins, hairspray and lipstick.

great grandmaster key. a key that will open locks of a lock system having more than one grandmaster key.

greening. making freshly harvested marihuana ready for smoking by drying it and filtering out debris.

green phosphor CRT. a cathode ray tube display having a green fluorescing hue. It is normally used for displaying data and graphics.

grey propaganda. propaganda which does not specifically identify a source; a mixture of distortions, half-truths and untruths.

grid. an arrangement of wire, screen or tubing placed over openings to provide protection from intrusion. An attempt to enter will break the grid, causing an alarm.

grid search. a search of an outdoor crime scene in which the area is divided into grids that are separately and thoroughly examined.

gross earnings. an accounting term which is arrived at by subtracting the cost of goods sold from the total sales.

gross negligence. the intentional failure to perform a duty in reckless disregard of consequences that may affect the life or property of another; the lack of even slight or ordinary care.

gross profit. net earnings before expenses.

ground fault. a malfunction of an alarm circuit caused by contact with electrical ground; the flowing of power from phase to ground through an external path not designed as a conductor.

ground fault interrupter. a device that automatically switches off power if there is a variance in current between the positive and grounding wires of more than a given limit.

ground loop. a conductive path formed by two or more grounded points in an electrical system. The conductive path renders all or part of the protective circuit ineffective.

ground wire. a conductor leading from a device to an earth ground connection.

group dynamics. the interactions among members of a group, particularly as they relate to employees and work processes.

grouted frame. a frame in which all voids between it and the surrounding wall are completely filled with the cement or plaster used in the wall construction.

growth share matrix. a square divided into quarters with productivity growth plotted on a vertical axis, and the competitors' share of the market plotted on the horizontal axis.

guard bar. a series of two or more cross bars, generally fastened to a common back plate, to protect the glass or screen in a door.

guardian. one who has the control or management of the person, property, or both, of another, who because of infancy, insanity or other reason is incapable of acting in his or her own behalf.

guard plate. a piece of metal attached to a door frame, door edge, or over the lock cylinder for the purpose of reinforcing the locking system against burglary attacks.

Guaiac Analysis. a crime laboratory test that seeks to determine the presence of blood on evidence.

guidance. the general direction of an intelligence effort, particularly in the area of collection.

guilt complex question. in polygraphy, a question pertaining to a purely hypothetical crime. It is used as a safeguard against misinterpreting the pertinent question responses of an innocent apprehensive person.

gun assembly weapon. in nuclear security, a weapon on which the rapid assembly of two subcritical masses of fissionable material produces a supercritical mass resulting in a nuclear explosion.

gunshot residue. residues deposited on the thumb, forefinger and web area of the hand when the hand is used to discharge a weapon. Deposits are also made on the face and neck area when a rifle or shotgun is fired. A residue frequently contains antimony and barium which are components of most primer mixtures. Also called primer residue.

Gutzedt Analysis. a crime laboratory test that seeks to determine the presence of arsenic.

H

habeas corpus. an order issued by a judge requiring that a prisoner be released from jail.

habitual offender. a person sentenced under the provisions of a statute declaring that persons convicted of a given offense, and shown to have previously been convicted of another specified offense, shall receive a more severe penalty than that for the current offense alone.

habituation. a condition resulting from repeated consumption of a drug. It is characterized by a desire to continue taking the drug, little or no tendency to increase the dose, and some degree of psychic dependence.

hacker enthusiast. a person who seeks to gain access to a computer system for the purpose of personal satisfaction as opposed to a criminal motive.

Hailey Bridge. the trade name of a device that processes voice-grade multiplex signals between a subscriber and a central station. It provides active bridging with up to 128 ports.

halation. a diffused region surrounding a bright image on a video display screen. Also called a halo.

Halcion. the trade name for a depressant drug known generically as triazolam. It is regulated as a Schedule IV Controlled Substance.

half duplex. as used in security communications, a multiplex system that can transmit in both directions on a transmission line but not at the same time.

halfway house. a community-located correctional institution in which offenders are supervised under minimum security and which provides therapy, vocational support, and other services. It is used to bridge the gap between prison and unconditional release.

hallucinogen. any one of the many varieties of drugs that affect the brain at the cellular level, causing distortions in space, time, color, sound, and feeling. A user is likely to engage in bizarre behavior and lose contact with reality. LSD is an hallucinogen.

halo effect. a bias in ratings arising from the tendency of a rater to be influenced in his/her rating of specific traits by general impressions of the person being rated.

halon. a non-corrosive, chemical agent used for extinguishing fires in areas containing computers and electrical equipment.

hand. the opening direction of a door. A right-handed door is hinged on the right and swings inward when viewed from the outside. A left-handed door is hinged on the left and swings inward when viewed from the outside. If either of these doors swings outward, it is referred to as a right-hand reverse door or a left-hand reverse door, respectively.

hand down. to announce or file an opinion in a legal cause; to announce a decision by a court upon a case or point reserved for consideration.

hand/finger attachment. in polygraphy, a spoon-like metal contact placed on an examinee's finger or hand for the purpose of detecting changes to the skin's resistance to electricity.

hand geometry. a technique of access control verification which analyzes relative variations in finger lengths. Typically, a person is enrolled in the system through a stored image of one hand. When seeking access, the enrollee places his hand on an imaging plate; a comparison is made of the stored and active images; and if the images match to a predetermined accuracy, access is granted.

handle. the total amount of money taken in during a specified time by a betting operation.

handset. the part of the telephone instrument used for talking and listening.

handshake. a tone produced by a digital receiver and transmitted to a digital communicator indicating that the receiver is ready to receive the communicator's transmission.

handshake verification. a technique for restricting access to a computer's dial-up ports. A person wishing access to a computer by phone dials a designated number and gives an identification code. If the code is correctly given, the call is transferred to a line that provides access. Also known as dial-up/ call back or return call verification.

handwriting analysis. a psychological tool sometimes used to evaluate the personality and character of job applicants. A term also used to describe the examination of questioned documents.

handwriting dynamics. a technique of access control verification which analyzes handwriting velocity, acceleration and pressure. The technique is also used for accepting or rejecting handwritings for forgery detection and deterrence purposes.

hand x-ray examination. a crime laboratory technique in which evidence is examined using x-rays ranging from 25 to 140 kilowatts. The technique is generally limited to gross metal objects. Soft x-rays (4 to 25 kilowatts) are generally used to examine paintings, fabrics, papers, inks, gunshot residues, and jewelry.

hanging. an extremely slow response of a computer system. When a terminal appears to be doing nothing, it is said to be hanging.

hanging ceiling. a ceiling separated from the floor or roof above by a dead air space. Also called a false ceiling or plenum.

hanging jury. a jury selected among persons who have declared their support for the death sentence.

happy light. a small light or LED on a digital communicator that indicates the unit is in communication with the receiver; any light on alarm equipment which indicates proper functioning.

harboring a felon. the crime of hiding or otherwise aiding an escaped or wanted felon for whom the police are searching.

hard copy. the output of a printing device. A computer printout is hard copy.

hard copy printer. an automatic printing machine, sometimes resembling a typewriter, which produces intelligible symbols in a permanent form.

hardened cable. land line encased in a protective shielding such as metal or concrete for the purpose of resisting unauthorized access.

hardened container. a container, usually used for shipping, that by its construction and strength provides protection against unauthorized access and may also reveal intrusion attempts.

hardware. physical equipment such as mechanical, magnetic, electrical or electronic devices used in the configuration and operation of an ADP system. Types of ADP hardware are: general and special purpose digital, analog, and hybrid equipment; components used to create, collect, store, process, communicate, display or disseminate information; auxiliary or accessorial equipment such as data communications terminals, source data automation recording equipment, and data output equipment; and electrical accounting machines. Hardware is also used in a general sense in reference to physical equipment employed in any protective system. Examples would be locks, containers, and intrusion detection devices.

hardwire. a circuit evidencing direct current continuity; the use of wire rather than radio signals to communicate between two points; to connect two or more points with wire.

harmonica bug. an audio amplifier and microphone connected to a telephone line through an audio-tone sensitive relay which is activated by telephoning the bugged premises and sounding the coded tone.

Harrison Process. a technique in which photographic film is pressed against latent fingerprints. When the film is developed, the fingerprint impression is revealed.

hash. a slang name for hashish; in security communications, an electrical noise.

hashish. the resinous secretions of the cannabis plant, which are collected, dried, and then compressed into a variety of forms, such as balls, cakes, or cookie-like sheets. It is a hallucinogen and usually smoked. Hashish is also called hash and THC. It is a Schedule I substance.

hashish oil. a dark viscous liquid yielded through a process of repeated extraction of cannabis plant materials. It has a high percentage of THC content and is typically smoked by adding it to tobacco. Hashish oil is a Schedule I substance.

hasp. a fastening device which consists of a hinged plate with a slot in it that fits over a fixed D-shaped ring, or eye.

Hatch Act. a collective popular name for two federal statutes passed in 1939 and 1940. The 1939 act restricted the political activities of almost all federal employees, whether in the competitive service or not. The 1940 act extended the restrictions to positions in state employment having federal financing.

hatchway. an opening in a ceiling, roof or floor of a building which is large enough to allow human access.

hazard analysis. a process for determining loss exposure and loss potential by comparing loss history against applicable standards.

hazard control. a means of reducing the risk due to exposure to a hazard. Such means may include: ergonomic designing of work stations and equipment; arranging, safetyguarding and interlocking of equipment; barricading of pedestrian and vehicular traffic routes; controlling exposure to toxic materials; wearing protective gear; and using hazard annunciators.

hazardous waste. in nuclear security, any materials designated as hazardous by the Environmental Protection Agency.

head end. the primary transmission or receive source in a system, especially in a cable television system.

headhunter. a slang term for executive recruiter.

hearing. a proceeding in which arguments, witnesses, or evidence are heard by a judicial officer or administrative body.

hearing sensor. a sensor device that reacts to changes in sound.

hearsay. testimony about what another person said. A dying declaration is one kind of hearsay that is acceptable in court.

hearsay evidence. evidence of a statement which is made other than by a witness. Hearsay cannot be entered into evidence unless the maker of the statement can be cross examined.

heart of the typewriter. the spacing mechanism of a typewriter which when examined by a questioned documents expert will reveal whether or not certain documents were typed on that particular machine.

heat blanket. a thermostatically controlled electric blanket designed to keep electronic circuitry warm in cold environments.

heat detector. a sensor device that detects the presence of heat, without the simultaneous presence of smoke or fire. There are two types of heat detectors for fire prevention purposes: fixed temperature and rate-of-rise. The infrared motion sensor is technically a heat detector in the sense that it alerts to heat changes caused by a person or object entering a protected area. Heat detectors are also called thermal sensors.

heat of passion. as used in criminal law, a state of violent and uncontrollable rage engendered by provocation. The heat of passion argument is often used to seek a reduction in the charge against a defendant.

heat sensing detector. a device that operates either by a rapid change in temperature or by a rise in temperature above a given level. When the temperature change occurs, an alarm is activated.

heavy burner. a chronic smoker of marihuana.

hebephrenic reaction. a schizophrenic reaction characterized by shallowness, distortion of fact and inane behavior.

heel of a padlock. that end of the shackle on a padlock which is not removable from the case.

helping interview. an interview that consists of a genuine dialogue between the interviewer and the interviewee; the interviewer is an empathic listener rather than an interrogator or recorder of information.

hemin crystal test. a laboratory test to determine the presence of blood in a stain or substance of unknown origin. If blood is present, hemin crystals form upon application of a reagent. It is a confirmatory test, i.e., it is used to confirm a test by a different procedure. It is also called a Teichmann test.

Henry System. a fingerprint classification system developed by Sir Edward Richard Henry.

Hering-Breuer reflex. in polygraphy, a reflex characterized by rhythmic control of normal breathing. Quiet, passive expiration is accomplished by relaxation of the external intercostal muscles.

hermaphroditic connector. an electrical cable connector that mates with any connector of the same design without regard to male or female configuration.

heroin. a narcotic drug synthesized from morphine. Pure heroin is a white powder with a bitter taste. It may vary in color from white to dark brown depending on impurities left from the manufacturing process. Pure heroin is almost always diluted, usually with sugars, starch, powdered milk and quinine. The chemical name for heroin is diacetylmorphine. Street names include horse, smack and Big H. It appears in the Controlled Substances Act as a Schedule I narcotic. Heroin produces high physical and psychological dependence.

hertz. a unit of electrical frequency, mostly used in Europe. One hertz equals one cycle per second.

Herzberg Theory. a management theory which holds that employees are motivated by feelings of achievement, the work itself, responsibility, advancement and personal growth as a contributing member of the organization.

hesitation marks. cutting or stabbing marks on the body of a suicide or attempted suicide victim. The marks indicate the victim's hesitating attempts at self-destruction.

hidden agenda. unannounced or unconscious goals, personal needs, expectations and strategies that an individual brings with his/her participation in a group.

hidden key. in polygraphy, an item of evidence known only to the victim, perpetrator, investigator, and polygraphist. The polygraphist will use the key in testing suspects. Neutral responses to questions concerning the key are considered indicative of innocence. Deceptive responses suggest knowledge of the key, i.e., guilty knowledge.

hierarchy of needs. a management theory which holds that humans share certain needs, which when satisfied, no longer motivate. From lowest to highest, the needs are: basic physiological survival (food, water, shelter, etc.); security against danger; social esteem; independence; and self-actualization.

high accident frequency location. a place, intersection or length of roadway where an excessive number of traffic accidents have occurred over a given period of time.

high explosive. an explosive with a rapid burning rate. On detonation, a high explosive will have a shattering effect on objects in the immediate area. TNT, dynamite and nitroglycerin are types of high explosives.

high frequency. a band of the radio spectrum operating between 3-30 megahertz.

high-order explosion. an explosion characterized by an extremely rapid combustion, known as detonation reaction, occurring through the action of explosives such as dynamite, TNT, nitroglycerin, pentaerythritol-tetranitrate and various "plastic" explosives.

high pressure fog. a fine mist of water used in fighting fire. It is produced by water being forced by high pressure through a small capacity spray jet.

high-pressure sodium lamp. a security lamp having a long and dependable service life. When combined with the proper ballast, it will tolerate 40 to 50 percent dips in power. A power interruption of only one-twentieth of a second, however, can cause this type lamp to extinguish and begin its restrike sequence. Restrike is rated as instant, but the lamp will not be at the fully rated output until it has returned to its normal operating temperature. High-pressure sodium luminaires are an excellent choice for lighting systems to be used in conjunction with TV surveillance systems, both indoors and outdoors. They provide high efficacy, uniformity, and a short restrike. A possible disadvantage of high-pressure sodium is electromagnetic radiation, which could cause interference with electronic equipment or systems, including alarms.

high profile look. the distinctive appearance of security officers clothed in uniforms similar to that worn by law enforcement officers.

high-resolution monitor. a CRT display unit having a horizontal resolution greater than the standard 500-line monitor. When the number of lines of picture information is increased, the display is sharpened and the detail improved.

high risk commodity. an expensive consumer product with a high demand, such as money or cash, jewelry, furs, and electronic appliances.

high risk target. a person, object or place which, because of actual value, symbolic value or relative isolation, is more likely to be attractive or accessible to criminal action.

high-voltage transient. a momentary surge in AC line power, such as a lightning spike.

highwater marking. in computer usage, a technique for discouraging disk scavenging. In the truest sense, the system tracks the furthest extent that the owner of a file has written into the file's allocated area. It then prohibits any attempts at reading beyond the written area, on the premise that any information that exists beyond the currently written limit is information the user had intended to discard. Erase-on-allocate is a form of highwater marking.

highway. a major circuit pathway in an alarm system.

hijacking. taking control of a vehicle by the use or threatened use of force or by intimidation; or, taking a vehicle by stealth, without the use or threatened use of force, in order to steal its cargo.

histogram. a bar graph of a frequency distribution.

historical logging. the chronological recording of system events such as places entered, by whom and when, alarm activations, and similar occurrences needed to be known by security management.

hit. a momentary surge of voltage on a transmission channel.

hit and run. unlawful departure by the vehicle operator from the scene of a motor vehicle accident which resulted in injury to a person or damage to the property of another.

hit it. an order given during firefighting operations. It means to attack the source of fire with streams of water or other extinguishing agents.

hit man. a paid assassin; professional killer; hired gun.

hit slip. in a numbers operation, a slip of paper bearing the amount of money bet and the amount of the pay-off.

hit the ceiling. an order in firefighting operations to direct a stream of water so as to strike a ceiling at an angle and thereby deflect and distribute water onto the fire.

hold-back feature. a mechanism on a latch which serves to hold the latch bolt in the retracted position.

hold fast. in firefighting operations, an order to stay in position with a hose line; in military or law enforcement operations, an order to not give ground in the face of attack.

hold harmless clause. a clause in a contract that frees one or more of the parties from fault or guilt. One party assumes the liability inherent in a situation, thereby relieving the other party or parties of responsibility.

hold order. a notation on an inmate's file that another jurisdiction which has charges pending against him or in which he is due to serve time must be informed of his impending release.

hold-over till scheme. a scheme in which a dishonest clerk or cashier retains a portion of money taken in on a shift and when asked to explain the shortage will claim that the money was placed in the till for the next work shift.

hold-up alarm. an audible or silent alarm transmitted from the scene of a hold-up or other emergency for the purpose of summoning assistance.

hold-up switch. a switch used to trigger a hold-up alarm. A hold-up switch is usually located out of sight and capable of being triggered inconspicuously. Panic buttons, money clips and foot rails are types of hold-up switches.

hold-up till alarm. an alarm device placed in a till so as to register a silent alarm when money is removed during a robbery. A money clip is a type of hold-up till alarm.

Hollerith card. a type of access card having small holes which can be read by a light source or contact brushes. A Hollerith card is usually not suitable for security purposes.

hollow core door. a door constructed so that the space (core) between the two facing sheets is not completely filled. Various spacing and reinforcing materials are used to separate the facing sheets. Some interior hollow core doors have nothing except perimeter stiles and rails separating the facing sheets.

hollow metal. hollow items such as doors, frames, partitions, and enclosures which are usually fabricated from cold formed metal sheet, usually carbon steel.

hollow point. a type of bullet designed to expand on impact. In some jurisdictions the use of hollow point bullets is prohibited.

hollow steel door. a door generally stronger and more durable than standard wood doors. It is less susceptible to damage and deterioration, and provides good protection against forced entry.

Holmes-Rahe Social Readjustment Scale. a scale used to rate the probability of suicide. The scale rank orders a series of 43 stressful life events and applies to each event a value. A total of 200 or more points is indicative of a suicide candidate or of suicide in a questionable death case.

holographic document. a writing that is wholly in the handwriting of one person.

homemade napalm. an improvised incendiary comprised of gasoline in combination with soap, lye, castor oil, blood or salt.

Home Office. a British cabinet office that exercises limited jurisdiction over the police, operates the prison and aftercare systems, and organizes research and statistics on crime.

homerun. a wiring method in which each sensor is connected directly to the control panel instead of several sensors connected on a continuous circuit.

homicide. a killing of one person by another.

homing sequential switcher. a video switcher that automatically switches from camera to camera. It typically allows the dwell time to be varied, and has a manual override feature.

hook. that member of a team of pickpockets who removes items from the mark (victim).

hooked. addicted to drugs; swindled or conned.

hooker. a prostitute.

hooking. convincing a worker to spy on fellow union members, usually by means of bribery or blackmail.

hook switch. the switch on a telephone instrument that is turned on or off when the handset is lifted or returned.

hook-up. in firefighting operations, a connection between hose lines, pumpers and hydrants.

hophead. a narcotics addict.

hopped up. intoxicated by drugs.

horizontal footcandles. those footcandle values which are calculated or measured perpendicular to a horizontal surface. All horizontal footcandles are in the same plane for the same surface and can be added arithmetically when more than one source contributes light to the surface.

horizontal growth. corporate acquisition of other companies having related services.

horizontal merger. a merger of companies that are in the same general business line.

horizontal overcharging. the practice of charging an offender with separate offenses for each criminal act in which he/she allegedly participated, thus fragmenting the principal single offense into several component offenses.

horizontal sliding window. a type of window, composed of two sections, one or both of which slide horizontally past the other.

horizontal throw deadbolt lock. a lock with a deadbolt that enters a strike positioned on a side member of the door frame.

horse. a slang name for heroin.

horse parlor. a place where bets can be made on horse races; a bookie's joint.

horseshoe load. a fire hose wrapped in the form of a horseshoe-shaped loop.

hose dryer. an oven-like cabinet with racks for drying fire hose.

hose jacket. a temporary covering that can be clamped around a burst portion of fire hose to stop a leak.

hose reel. a reel of fire hose, typically hand-drawn, used for industrial fire protection.

hose roller. a device that fits over a roof projection, building cornice or window and operates as a pulley for hoisting hose or ladders.

hose strap. a short length of rope with a metal hook at one end. It is used to fasten hose line to banisters, railings and other fixtures so that the line will be stable.

hose tag. a metal plate or disc strapped to a hose line for the purpose of identifying the line as to its source of supply and its use during firefighting operations.

hose test. a test made periodically of hose to determine its condition according to certain minimum standards. Also called a hydrostatic test.

host computer. the main controlling computer in a system that has more than one computer. It typically coordinates the activities of peripheral computers that perform dedicated functions such as access control and intrusion detection.

hostile witness. a witness who manifests hostility or prejudice under examination to an extent that the party who has called him to testify will treat him as a witness for the opposite party.

hostility displacement. a displacement of pent-up feelings on objects less dangerous than those which initially aroused the emotions.

hot book. in a numbers operation, a writer who is a particular target of the police.

hot check. a stolen check; fraudulent check; a check knowingly passed without sufficient funds to cover it. Also called a rubber check.

hot check artist. a person who passes worthless checks. Also called a paper hanger.

hot line. a dedicated communication circuit; a telephone line used exclusively for transmitting emergency messages.

hot mike. activation of a telephone's microphone in the "hung up" position through the use of a third wire or similar component.

hot oil. oil produced in violation of state regulations or transported interstate in violation of federal regulations.

hot pursuit. the pursuit of a fleeing criminal by a law enforcement agency in which the chase is not significantly interrupted. The concept of hot pursuit allows jurisdictional lines to be crossed without prejudicing the legality of the arrest at the conclusion of the chase.

hot site. a fully-equipped computer backup site capable of performing critical data processing operations.

hot spot. an area in a radiation contaminated region in which the level of contamination is considerably greater than in nearby areas within the region.

hot sprinkler. a fire suppression water sprinkler maintained in a charged, or water-filled condition.

hot-stage microscopy. a crime laboratory method for examining the effect of heat on a sample. In fiber examinations, for example, the melting characteristics and relative melting points of various fibers are revealing as to their natural or polymeric properties.

hot stamping. a heat and pressure process for embossing credit cards.

hot surveillance. open tailing or bugging of a target for purposes of harassment or intimidation.

hot wire. a technique for starting a vehicle without the use of a key. Also, an electrical jumper wire used in the technique.

house arrest. restriction of an individual to a specific residence with limitations applied to visitors who may enter. House arrest is seldom employed in the United States.

housebreaking. a criminal activity in which a house (sometimes merely a structure) is entered by a forcible breaking. Housebreaking in some jurisdictions is synonymous with burglary.

household burglary. the unlawful entry or forcible entry or attempted forcible entry of a residence, usually, but not necessarily, attended by theft.

household larceny. the theft or attempted theft of money or property from a residence or its immediate vicinity.

house of assignation. a meeting place for performing illegal activity such as gambling, prostitution and drug abuse.

howler. an alarm annunciator which emits a howling sound.

"H" substance. in crime laboratory examinations, the water soluble substance in body fluids that would be secreted by a person of blood group O. However, it is thought that both A and B substances are made from H substance so that persons of groups A, B, and AB may also secrete some H substance as well.

huckster. a petty criminal; a con artist; a dishonest salesperson; a person who makes false claims for his products or services.

Hudgens vs. NLRB. a case in which the U.S. Supreme Court held that union pickets have no legal right to enter a privately owned shopping center for the purpose of advertising their strike against one of the retail stores leased from the owner of the center.

hung jury. a jury that is unable to agree on a verdict. In most states, unanimity is required. A retrial of the case before another jury may be made and would not constitute a violation of the protection against double jeopardy.

hush money. money used to purchase silence from a person in a position to report an illegal activity.

hydrant house. a small house containing a hydrant, hose, nozzles, wrenches and other firefighting equipment. It is frequently seen in an industrial setting.

hydrocodone. the generic name of a narcotic drug sold legally as Vicodin. The Controlled Substances Act lists it as a Schedule III narcotic.

hydrometrograph. an instrument for determining and recording the quantity of water discharged from a pipe in a given time.

hydromorphinol. an opium derivative classified as a Schedule I Controlled Substance.

hydromorphone. a highly abused semi-synthetic narcotic analgesic. It is sold in tablet and injectable forms and is a target of theft and acquisition by fraudulent means. Dilaudid is the trade name for hydromorphone which is a Schedule II narcotic.

hydrostatic pressure. the pressure exerted by water or another liquid at rest.

hydrostatic test. the test of a hollow part, such as a hose, for tightness by means of water, oil, or other liquid under pressure; a test made periodically of hose line, fire extinguishers and other equipment susceptible to leakage. The test seeks to insure that such equipment meets certain minimum standards of performance.

hydroxypethidine. an opiate classified as a Schedule I Controlled Substance.

hyoid bone. a U-shaped bone at the base of the tongue. A fractured hyoid bone is indicative of manual strangulation.

hypergolic. self-igniting. A characteristic of certain explosives in which detonation will result from a combining of chemicals contained in a bomb.

hypergolic initiation. an explosion or sudden burning that results when two or more chemicals are combined and consequently react upon one another.

hypernea. in polygraphy, rapid or deep breathing as represented in the ink tracings of the pneumograph component.

hypochondriasis. a neurotic reaction characterized by excessive concern about one's health in the absence of related organic pathology.

hypothetical question. a combination of assumed or proven facts and circumstances, stated in such form as to constitute a coherent and specific situation, upon which the opinion of an expert is asked at trial.

Ibogaine. a drug that appears in the Controlled Substances Act as a Schedule I hallucinogen.

identification reaction. an ego defense mechanism which causes an individual to identify with some other person or institution usually of a successful or illustrative nature.

Identi-Kit. a commercial identification device consisting of a series of photographic transparencies depicting varieties of facial features that can be overlaid to form a human face. An Identi-Kit operator (usually a trained police officer) assembles the transparencies in response to cues received from a witness. The facial likeness produced by the technique is used for suspect identification purposes.

idiot stick. a shovel.

"If" clause. a clause which terminates insurance coverage if certain conditions are created or discovered. An example is the concealment or misrepresentation provision of an insurance policy which renders coverage void if concealment or misrepresentation is discovered.

ignition jamming. a car theft technique in which a key blank is inserted in the ignition lock and then forcibly driven into the lock with the use of a hammer. The resulting damage allows access to the ignition wires.

ignition temperature. the lowest temperature of a flammable liquid required to initiate or cause self-sustained combustion in the absence of a spark or flame. This temperature varies considerably, depending upon the nature, size and shape of the ignition, surface, container, and other factors.

ignorance or mistake of fact. a legal defense that seeks to excuse an accused on the grounds that the wrongful act was committed by an honest mistake. For example, the defense might be employed if a homeowner injures a guest in his home who he has mistaken for a burglar.

ignorant end. the heavier end of any device such as a wrench or length of pipe.

illegal alien. one who has illegally entered a country of which he is not a citizen, or who, having entered legally, violates the terms of his visa, as by overstaying or by engaging in prohibited activities.

illegal search and seizure. an act in violation of the Fourth Amendment of the US Constitution.

illiquidity. the insolvency of a business. The term has special reference to the ease in which assets can be converted to cash without a loss. If a firm's current assets cannot be converted to cash to meet current liabilities, the firm is said to be illiquid.

illumination value. the amount of lumens per unit of area for any given surface, or the concentration of candelas at any point relative to the distance from the source. Illumination value is expressed in footcandles.

image intensifier. a device that uses fiber optics to increase the sensitivity of a television image pickup tube.

immaterial. in criminal law, not pertinent or of no significance to an issue.

immaterial question. in polygraphy, a question that is irrelevant or neutral to the issue being evaluated.

immigrant alien. a person who is lawfully admitted into the US under an immigration visa for permanent residence.

imminent danger. the appearance of threatened and impending injury as would put a reasonable and prudent man to his instant defense. The term is often used as a legal defense to charges of aggravated assault and homicide.

imminent danger citation. a citation issued by the Occupational Safety and Health Administration alleging that the cited place of employment has conditions or practices such that a danger exists which could reasonably be expected to cause death or serious physical harm immediately.

immovable evidence. evidence that cannot easily be collected and transported, such as a blood-spattered wall.

immunity. an exemption from a legal liability. Total or complete immunity means the individual receiving the immunity cannot be held liable for his acts. Qualified immunity refers to a partial grant of immunity to a person by reason of position or a particular activity.

impairing the morals of a minor. engaging in sex-related acts (except intercourse) with a minor; for example, taking obscene photographs of the minor or caressing the minor in a lewd manner.

impanel. to select jurors; the act of the clerk of the court in making up a list of jurors who have been selected for the trial of a particular cause.

impeach. to proceed against a public officer for crime or misfeasance, before a proper court, by the presentation of a written accusation called "articles of impeachment." In the law of evidence, to call in question the veracity of a witness, by means of evidence adduced for that purpose.

impeach a witness. to show that a witness cannot be believed under oath.

impedance. resistance to the flow of alternating current.

impedance matching. a circuit arrangement that adjusts the impedance of an AC load to the value appropriate for the operation of a given device. It is frequently used to match the relative impedance between a speaker and an amplifier.

impersonating an officer. pretending to be a police officer, an officer of the armed services, or an official of a federal, state, or local law enforcement agency, usually by wearing a uniform, showing an identification card or badge, and identifying oneself as an officer.

implied answer question. a question phrased so as to imply its answer. In interviewing, it is a type of question to be avoided since it defeats the purpose of determining what the interviewee knows. Also called a leading question.

implosion-type nuclear weapon. a type of nuclear weapon in which a subcritical configuration of fissionable material is compressed into a supercritical state by a centrally directed radial shock to produce a nuclear explosion.

impound. to take into custody of the law or of a court. A court will sometimes impound a suspected document, when produced at a trial, until a question affecting it is decided.

impression system. a technique to produce keys for certain types of locks without taking the lock apart.

inactive leaf. the leaf of a double door that is bolted when closed. The strike plate is attached to this leaf to receive the latch and bolt of the active leaf.

inadmissible. that which under the established rules of law cannot be admitted or received into evidence.

inadvertent intruder. in nuclear security, a person who might occupy a nuclear waste disposal site after closure and engage in normal activities, such as agriculture, dwelling, construction, or other pursuits in which the person might be unknowingly exposed to radiation waste.

incandescent lamp. a common glass light bulb in which light is produced by the resistance of a filament to an electric current. The incandescent lamp is usually reserved for emergency lights, spotlights, or augmentation. Because of instant restrike/restart capabilities, but rather limited watt output and service life, it is suitable for backup uses.

in camera. in chambers; in private. A cause is said to be heard in camera when the hearing is had before the judge in his private room or when all spectators are excluded from the courtroom.

incapacitation of criminals. keeping convicted criminals in prison as a means of preventing them from committing further crimes.

incendiary. one guilty of arson; one who maliciously and wilfully sets another's property on fire.

incest. unlawful sexual intercourse between closely related persons.

inchoate offense. an offense which consists of an action or conduct which is a step to the intended commission of another offense.

incidence of crime. criminality measured in a given population over a defined time span, as during a single day or a single year.

incised wound. a cut or incision on a human body; a wound made by a cutting instrument, such as a razor or knife.

included offense. an offense which is made up of elements which are a subset of the elements of another offense having a greater statutory penalty, and the occurrence of which is established by the same evidence or by some portion of the same evidence which has been offered to establish the occurrence of the greater offense.

income center. an element or unit within a business organization where income is accumulated and identified with a specific project or organizational entity. Also called revenue center.

incompetency. lack of ability, legal qualification, or fitness to discharge the required duty.

incompetent evidence. evidence which is not admissible under the established rules of evidence.

inconclusive. that which may be disproved or rebutted; not shutting out further proof or consideration. Applied to evidence and presumptions.

inconclusive opinion. in polygraphy, a term signifying that the polygraph was unsuccessful in determining if the examinee was truthful or untruthful. The inconclusive opinion usually results from a malfunction of the polygraph instrument, illness of the examinee during the test, or poor test construction due to insufficient information available to the polygraphist.

incontrovertible evidence. evidence which cannot be refuted.

incorrigible. a condition of a juvenile who is habitually delinquent, ungovernable, and unresponsive to rehabilitative efforts.

incriminate. to charge with crime; to expose to an accusation or charge of crime; to involve oneself or another in a criminal prosecution or the danger thereof; as in the rule that a witness is not bound to give testimony which would tend to incriminate him.

incriminating admission. an acknowledgment of facts tending to establish guilt.

incriminating circumstance. a fact or circumstance, collateral to the fact of the commission of a crime, which tends to show either that such a crime has been committed or that some particular person committed it.

incubation period. the period of time in which heat builds up sufficiently to generate a fire. An incubation period precedes a fire caused by a discarded cigarette or spontaneous ignition.

inculpate. to impute blame or guilt; to accuse; to involve in guilt or crime.

indecent assault. sexual assault not amounting to rape, sodomy or carnal abuse; uninvited sex-related touching of another.

indecent exposure. unlawful intentional or reckless exposing to view of the genitals or anus, in a place where another person may be present who is likely to be offended or alarmed by such an act.

indefinite sentence. a prison sentence for a range of time; for example, between one and ten years, or from one year to life.

indemnify. the act of compensating insured individuals for their losses; to restore the victim of a loss to the same position as before the loss occurred.

indemnity. an insurance contract to reimburse an individual or organization for possible losses of a particular type.

indented writing. impressions on a sheet of paper caused from writing made on an overlying sheet. The impressions or indentations can be made visible by a variety of crime laboratory techniques.

independent variable. the variable whose occurrence or change results in the occurrence or change of another variable; the hypothesized cause of something else.

indeterminate sentence. a type of sentence to imprisonment where the commitment, instead of being for a specified single time quantity, is for a range of time.

index crimes. eight particular crimes whose incidence is reported by the FBI as an index of the extent, nature, and fluctuation of criminality in the United States. The index crimes are murder and non-negligent homicide, forcible rape, robbery, aggravated assault, burglary, larceny-theft, motor vehicle theft, and arson.

indictment. a formal written accusation made by a grand jury and filed in a court alleging that a certain person committed a certain offense.

indirect approach. in criminal investigation, an interrogational approach that is explora-tory in nature, seeking to test the suspect's truthfulness in relation to facts known by the interrogator. The indirect approach is frequently used when interrogating a suspect whose guilt is uncertain or doubtful.

indirect evidence. circumstantial evidence; evidence of a collateral fact, that is, of a fact other than a fact in issue from which, either alone or with other collateral facts, the fact in issue may be inferred. It is a well settled rule in some jurisdictions that where the prosecution relies wholly upon circumstantial evidence to establish the guilt of the accused, the circumstances must be satisfactorily established and must be of such a character as, if true, to exclude to a moral certainty every other hypothesis except that of the accused's guilt.

indirect interviewing approach. a method of obtaining information in which the witness or interviewee is asked to "tell the story" and is allowed to speak freely, prompted only as needed and with a minimum of direct questions.

indirect loss. loss resulting from a peril but not caused directly and immediately by that peril. For example, loss of property due to fire is a direct loss, while the loss of rental income as the result of fire is an indirect loss. Also, a measure in dollars of costs associated with loss of reputation, goodwill, employee turnover and employee morale.

individual characteristics. marks made on an object as the result of its use. Such marks, commonly cuts, tears and uneven wearing, can be significant to the analysis of foot and tire prints, tool marks and similar forms of physical evidence.

induced AC. a condition caused when low-voltage wiring is placed near high-voltage wiring. The higher voltage line may interfere with the lower voltage line and may interfere with or damage microprocessor-based equipment.

inductance. the tendency of a circuit or component to oppose a change in current flow. Inductance is a function of the magnetic field associated with a flowing current.

induction tap. a wiretap that makes use of a coil placed around or near the telephone instrument or line.

inductive reasoning. a method of reasoning which starts out from specific cases, studies and analyzes them and reaches conclusions on the basis of the observations; an investigative process in which the investigator develops from observed facts a generalization explaining the relationships between the events under examination. The process moves by logical steps from the particular to the general.

inertia sensor. a sensor that causes an alarm condition when it has experienced a movement caused by shock or vibration. The term also refers to an intrusion detector capable of tolerating background vibration without loss of sensitivity to intrusion attempts.

in evidence. included in the evidence already adduced. The "facts in evidence" are such as have already been proven in the case.

in extremis. the state of a person who is near death, beyond the hope of recovery.

infamous crime. a crime for which an infamous punishment may be imposed such as to deprive a person of civil and political rights, or to imprison a person in the state penitentiary or at hard labor. The term infamous crime is generally synonymous with felony crime.

infanticide. the murder or killing of an infant soon after its birth.

inference. in the law of evidence, a truth or proposition drawn from another which is supposed or admitted to be true. A process of reasoning by which a fact or proposition sought to be established is deduced as a logical sequence from other facts already proved or admitted.

infiltration. the placing of an undercover operative within a targeted group or organization.

infinity bug. an audio amplifier and microphone connected to a telephone line through an audio-tone sensitive relay which is activated by telephoning the bugged premises and sounding a coded tone. Also called a harmonica bug.

informal social control. a crime prevention strategy that seeks to develop in a community a network of trust and interdependence built on social relationships of the community's residents. The sense of community cohesiveness exercises informal control of deviant behavior.

informant. a person who wittingly or unwittingly provides information. Also called a source.

informant card file. a file that lists information about informants such as personal data, reliability, specialties, payments made and tips on handling.

in forma pauperis. a request to waive the payment of legal fees on behalf of an indigent defendant.

information. a formal written accusation made by a prosecutor and filed in a court alleging that a certain person committed a certain offense; in intelligence parlance, raw data obtained from any source which, when processed, produce intelligence.

information access password. a password used to protect data stored in an electronic data processing system by associating a unique password with a particular file or data set. The password is presented to the system following logon when access to data is requested.

information overload. a constant flood of details that confronts the individual at a rate that exceeds the human ability to process and respond.

information security. the effort or the result of a system of administrative policies and procedures established for identifying, controlling and protecting information from unauthorized disclosure.

information sheet. a file or document containing such data as a subject's arrest record, charges preferred and case dispositions. Also called a rap sheet or criminal history sheet.

informer. a person who intentionally discloses information about persons or activities, usually for a financial reward or other consideration.

infraction. a violation of a state statute or local ordinance punishable by a fine or other penalty, but not by incarceration, or by a specified, unusually limited term of incarceration.

infrared. light waves that are too low in frequency to be seen by the human eye.

infrared analysis. a crime laboratory technique which uses infrared light to detect substances invisible to the human eye.

infrared card reader. a card reader that uses an infrared light source to read information encoded in an access control card. It operates on an optical density principle.

infrared examination. an investigative technique in which objects or events are examined while exposed to infrared radiation. Infrared differs from ultraviolet examination in that there are no fluorescent effects which can be seen by the unaided eye. The appearance of an object or event in the infrared is ordinarily studied through the medium of a photograph. Infrared is useful in examining evidence for tell-tale stains and in nighttime surveillance operations.

infrared fuse. a bomb fuse sensitive to minute increases in heat. The fuse functions when an influence from the target is exerted on a sensitive detecting device within the fuse itself.

infrared motion detector. a passive, low-power, area-protection device that detects a change in ambient temperature caused by movements of a body or objects within a protected zone. Sensor circuitry generates an alarm when a moving object causes a change in a radiated energy pattern covering the protected zone. For example, an intruder moving into a protected zone would introduce a heat change caused by the intruder's body heat. Also called passive infrared or PIR.

infrared scanning. a technique that uses an infrared imaging device to detect short circuits or hot spots in a building's wiring system.

infrared viewer. a device that makes infrared light waves visible to the human eye.

infrasonic sensor. a motion detector designed to sense a change in pressure such as that caused by the opening of a door or window.

in-house security. protective services provided to a company by its own employees.

initial appearance. the first appearance of an accused person in the first court having jurisdiction over the case.

initial footcandle. an illumination value assigned to a lamp or luminaire which takes into consideration the newness of the device.

initiator. that part of an explosive train used to ignite the explosive; the first charge in a firing train.

injunction. an order from a court telling a person or group not to do something; a writ of judicial process issued by a court of equity by which a party is required to do a particular thing or to refrain from doing a particular thing.

in loco parentis. in the place of a parent; instead of a parent; charged with a parent's rights, duties, and responsibilities.

inmate code. the code of the inmate subculture; the basis of prisonization, as in the practice of not informing and not cooperating with correctional specialists.

inmate self-government. the informal self-regulation of an inmate population, usually at the lower levels of decision-making, as in planning and organizing athletic and recreational programs.

inmate subculture. the mores, traditions and customs of an inmate population.

innocent agent. in criminal law, one who, being ignorant of any unlawful intent on the part of a principal, is merely the instrument of the principal in committing an offense; one who does an unlawful act at the solicitation or request of another, but who, from defect of understanding or ignorance of the inculpatory facts, incurs no legal guilt.

innocent passer. a person who passes an illegal instrument, such as counterfeit money or a bogus check, without guilty knowledge. For example, a store owner who accepts a fraudulent check and passes it along in good faith to a bank would be an innocent passer.

in order of seriousness. a custom of classifying crimes in order of their seriousness or gravity. For example, common law crimes might be placed into three categories: treasons, felonies, and misdemeanors. Under the custom, felonies might be further ordered into murder, manslaughter, or negligent homicide.

inorganic metallic poison. a class of poison which includes arsenic, mercury, lead, and other metals.

inorganic nonmetallic poison. a class of poison which includes cyanide, fluoride, iodine, acids, oxidants, and gases.

in parallel. a term that describes pieces of electrical apparatus so connected that the current divides between them and re-unites after passing through them.

in pari delicto. in equal fault.

in personam. a remedy where the proceedings are against the person, as contradistinguished from those against a specific thing; a legal proceeding, the judgment of which binds the defeated party to a personal liability.

input element. in security alarms terminology, a sensing instrument that monitors the status of a specific location. An intrusion detector is a type of input element.

input/output. punched cards, magnetic input/output, volumes, and other forms of processable information used for computer input or produced as computer output, as well as reports, listings, and other forms of hard copy output.

inquest. a judicial inquiry to determine the cause and manner of a violent, sudden, mysterious or suspicious death.

inquisitorial system. the system of criminal prosecution prevailing in most of continental Europe, Japan, and other countries, in contrast to the English and American adversary systems. In the inquisitorial system, a judicial officer is assigned to investigate, and adjudication is not limited to the facts adduced by the parties.

in rem. a legal proceeding, the judgment of which binds, affects, or determines the status of property.

insanity. such unsoundness of mental condition as, with regard to any matter under action, modifies or eliminates legal responsibility or capacity.

insanity defense. a legal defense which rests on the principle that a person who is insane at the time of committing a crime cannot be charged with the crime since an insane person is incapable of forming the requisite intent.

inscription. in law of evidence, anything written or engraved upon a metallic or other solid substance intended for great durability such as a tombstone, pillar, tablet, ring or medal.

in series. a term that describes pieces of electrical apparatus so connected that the same current flows in turn through each of them.

inside perimeter. a line of protection adjacent to a protected area, usually passing through points of access.

inside worker. a pickpocket who specializes in stealing wallets from inside coat pockets.

INS Master Index. a file maintained in the central offices of the Immigration and Naturalization Service. It contains names and descriptive data of persons admitted to or excluded from the US, as well as sponsors of record.

inspection ink. ink that is detectable by ultraviolet light. It is typically used to mark items for control and inspection.

instant circuit. an input on a control panel that produces an immediate alarm or trouble signal.

instructions to the jury. verbal and written instructions of a guiding nature given by the judge to the jury. The guidance explains the legal principles that should be applied to the facts of the case when the jury deliberates and reaches a decision.

instrumental analysis examinations. crime laboratory examinations which make use of instrumentation such as infrared spectroscopy, x-ray diffractometry, and emission spectrometry. Paints, plastics, explosives and dyes are typically analyzed by these techniques.

insufficient evidence. evidence that is not enough to constitute proof at the level required at a given point in criminal proceedings.

insurable interest. the required ownership or interest a person must have to be able to take out insurance.

intaglio process. a printing process in which the design is engraved into the surface of the plate. The ink used in intaglio printing is thicker and coarser than planographic printing ink. Under a stereoscopic microscope, the ink lines of the intaglio process appear to be mounds of ink piled on top of the paper and the grains of the coarse ink can be seen. The intaglio process is used in the printing of US currency and in placing characters on plastic credit cards.

intangible assets. elements of property in an established enterprise which represent customer goodwill, general reputation and other nonphysical assets.

integral frame. a metal door frame in which the jambs and head have stops, trim and backbends all formed from one piece of material.

integrated circuit. an electronic circuit element similar to a transistor but embodying many additional functional elements; a microminiature circuit frequently mounted in a DIP plug or printed circuit board.

intellectualization. an ego defense mechanism by which an individual achieves some measure of isolation from emotional hurt by cutting off or distorting the emotional charge which normally accompanies hurtful situations.

intellectual property. any idea, invention, design, program, work of authorship, and similar information or device generated or collected by or utilized in actual or anticipated business, research or development.

intelligence. the product resulting from the collection, evaluation, analysis, integration and interpretation of information obtained from covert and open sources.

intelligence collection plan. a plan for gathering information from available sources to meet an intelligence requirement.

intelligence cycle. the steps by which information is assembled, converted into intelligence, and made available to consumers. The cycle has four steps: direction, collation, processing and dissemination.

intelligence data base. all holdings of intelligence data and finished intelligence products at a given department or agency.

intelligence estimate. an appraisal of intelligence elements relating to a specific situation or condition to determine the course of action open to an adversary.

intelligent terminal. an input and output device that has freestanding logical capabilities.

intent. the state of mind or attitude with which an act is carried out; the design, resolve or determination with which a person acts to achieve a certain result.

interactive computer system. a computer system in which the user and the operating system communicate directly by means of a terminal.

interactive display terminal. a CRT display and keyboard that interfaces with a central processing monitor. An operator may enter data and command system functions via the keyboard. Prompting by the computer, with a response from the operator, is called interactive dialogue.

interchangeable core lock. a type of lock that permits replacement with a core having a different key.

interconnected bolt. a bolt in a lock that combines the features of a spring bolt and a deadbolt.

interest-rate risk. the danger that rates on banks' purchases will rise to make loans unprofitable.

interface. point of contact; the boundary between organizations, people, jobs and/or systems.

Interim Security Clearance. a Department of Defense security clearance based on the completion of minimum investigative requirements. It is granted on a temporary basis, pending completion of a full investigation.

interior common circulation area. an area within a multiple dwelling which is outside the private zones of individual units and is used in common by all residents and the maintenance staff of the building.

interior microwave motion detector. a microwave sensor designed specifically for indoor use. It usually consists of a single transceiver. Microwaves are transmitted into the protected area. A constant pattern of microwaves is reflected back. Movement within the protected area disturbs the constant pattern and a comparison circuit trips an alarm. Also called a monostatic microwave sensor.

interior private area. the interior of a single family house; the interior of an apartment in a multiple dwelling; or the interior of a separate unit within a commercial, public, or institutional building.

interior public area. an interior common-circulation area of common resident-use space within a multiple dwelling to which access is unrestricted.

interior semi-public area. an interior common-circulation area or common resident-use room within a multiple dwelling to which access is possible only with a key or on the approval of a resident via an intercom, buzzer-reply system.

interior zone. a protective zone established inside a perimeter zone. Also generally called a secondary zone or a trap zone.

interlocking directorates. the practice of overlapping memberships on corporate boards of directors.

interlocking strike. a strike which receives and holds a vertical, rotary, or hook dead bolt.

interlocutory appeal. a request, made at some point before judgment in trial court proceedings, that a court having appellate jurisdiction review a pre-judgment decision of the trial court before judgment is reached.

interlocutory decree. an interim decision of a court; a decision issued pending a final decree; a provisional court decision.

intermediate-acting barbiturates. a classification of barbiturates based on the time between administration and the onset of anesthesia. In this classification, barbiturates take effect within 15-40 minutes, with duration up to 6 hours. Pentobarbital (Nembutal), secobarbital (Seconal), amobarbital (Amytal), butabarbital (Butisol), talbutal

(Lotusate) and aprobarbital (Alurate) are intermediate-acting barbiturates.

intermittent sentence. a sentence to periods of confinement interrupted by periods of freedom.

intermodal freight. freight packaged in such a way that it is capable of being transported in more than one shipping mode, such as cargo that has been compartmentalized or containerized to allow movement by rail, vessel and truck.

internal accounting control. a plan of organization and the accompanying procedures and records that are concerned with the safeguarding of assets and the reliability of financial records.

internal control. a plan of organization and all of the coordinate methods and measures adopted within a business to safeguard its assets, check the reliability and accuracy of its accounting data, promote operational efficiency, and encourage adherence to prescribed managerial policies.

international law. a body of law derived from treaties, decisions of supranational courts (such as the Permanent Court for International Justice), and the charters of the League of Nations and the United Nations; legal precedents and procedures governing multinational corporations, import-export trade, and disputes between nations. In a limited sense, international law governs the conduct of a sovereign nation in matters not entirely internal.

Interpol. a body of police representatives from many countries organized for the purpose of gathering and sharing information about transnational criminal personalities and activities. Interpol also seeks missing persons and identifies unknown dead persons. Its headquarters is in Paris.

interrogation. a systematic effort to procure information by direct questioning of a person who is unwilling to provide the information; the extraction of information from a person suspected of having committed a crime or of a person who is reluctant to make a full disclosure. Interrogation involves a process through which the interrogator uses conversation, questioning, and observation as a means of eliciting truth. The process is adversary in nature and depends upon the application of logic, reasoning, and understanding without violence or coercion.

interrogation distance. the distance between an interrogator and the boundary of the subject's "personal space bubble." At this distance, the interrogator is said to be confrontational and mildly aggressive.

interrogator. in security communications, a central station transmitter and receiver.

interstate compact. an agreement between two or more states to transfer prisoners, parolees, or probationers from the physical or supervisory custody of one state to the physical or supervisory custody of another, where the correctional agency that first acquired jurisdiction over the person usually retains the legal authority to confine or release the prisoner.

interstitial environment. an urban area isolated by natural or social barriers in which criminal activity flourishes. A ghetto or slum is an interstitial environment.

interview. in criminal investigation, a structured process of obtaining information when the person being questioned is willing to provide the information. The person being interviewed usually gives in his own manner and words an account of the crime or provides details concerning a suspect or other person connected to the crime. In intelligence activities, an interview is the gathering of information from a person who knows that he is giving information, although not always with awareness of the true connection or purposes of the interviewer.

interview distance. the distance between the interviewer and the area just outside the interviewee's "personal space bubble." The interviewer who operates from this distance is said to be in a dominating, but not threatening or intimidating position.

intestate. without making a will. A person is said to die intestate when he dies without making a will, or dies without leaving anything to testify what his wishes were with respect to the disposal of his property after his death.

intimidation. an offense comparable to extortion, the essential difference being its application to all persons, not just those involved in public official transactions. A person commits intimidation when, with intent to cause another to perform or omit the performance of any act, he communicates to another a threat to inflict physical harm, or to make a criminal accusation, or to expose a person to hatred, contempt, or ridicule, or to bring about or continue a strike or boycott, etc.

intradermal injection. a method used by a drug abuser to administer a drug by scratching a hypodermic needle just beneath the skin.

intramuscular injection. a method used by a drug abuser to administer a drug by inserting a hypodermic needle into the muscle tissue.

intrascene dynamic range. the range over which a camera can produce light gradations within a scene from highlight to shadow.

intravenous injection. a method used by a drug abuser to administer a drug by inserting a hypodermic needle into a vein.

introjection. incorporation of external values and standards into the ego structure so that the individual is not at the mercy of external threats.

intruder barrier. in nuclear security, a sufficient depth of cover over radiation waste that inhibits contact with waste and helps to ensure that radiation exposures to an inadvertent intruder will be non-hazardous.

intrusion detection equipment. a combination of mechanical or electronic components that detect and annunciate an unauthorized entry or attempted entry into a protected area.

intrusion detection system. a system that combines the functions of sensing, controlling and annunciating so that intrusion attempts into areas covered by the system will be detected and reported with a minimum need for direct human observation.

intrusion switch. a type of sensor that operates on a mechanical or magnetic principle to detect an opening. This type of sensor has one contact installed on the door window or opening surface, and a second, immediately adjacent contact is installed on the fixed surface. When the contacts separate, due to an opening, an alarm is triggered.

inventory shrinkage. a common euphemism for losses due to employee pilfering or shoplifting.

investigative consumer report. as used in the Fair Credit Reporting Act, a report pertaining to a consumer's character, general reputation, personal characteristics or mode of living as derived through personal interviews with friends, neighbors or associates.

investigative monitoring. intercepting, listening to, or recording any telephone conversation by use of any electronic, mechanical, or other device without the advance consent of all of the parties to the conversation.

investigative survey. an in-depth probe or test check of a specific operation or activity, usually conducted on a programmed basis, to detect the existence of crime or significant administrative irregularities.

investigative vendor audit. an examination of the records of transactions between a purchaser and a vendor covering a specified period of time for the purpose of determining if the vendor overbilled or committed other irregularities.

investigatory stop. a procedure used by police on patrol to inquire into the activities of a person believed to be involved in a criminal act. The person stopped is asked questions and may be searched if there is reason to believe he is armed. Also, called stop and frisk or field inquiry.

invisible hinge. a hinge so constructed that no parts are exposed when the door is closed.

involuntary manslaughter. causing the death of another by recklessness or gross negligence.

iodic acid analysis. a method of testing for the presence of morphine in a substance.

iodine crystals. in fingerprint identification, a product that produces violet fumes when subjected to a small amount of heat. The violet color is absorbed by fatty and oily matter in fingerprint impressions, thereby making the impressions visible against their background surface.

iodine fuming cabinet. a large glass-walled box used in a crime laboratory to develop latent fingerprint impressions. The item bearing the impressions is placed inside the cabinet; iodine fumes are introduced; the fumes are absorbed by the impressions; and the impressions take on color, making them visible and photographable.

iodoform analysis. a method of testing for the presence of ethyl alcohol in a substance.

Ionamin. the trade name for phentermine, a commonly abused stimulant which appears in the Controlled Substance Act as a Schedule IV drug. Street names include speed, upper, black beauty, crank, meth, bam, and pink.

ionization detector. a device that operates by a small electric current passing through the air between two plates. Hydrocarbons and other products given off by a fire disturb the electric current and cause the alarm to activate.

ipso facto. by the fact itself.

irrelevant. not relevant; not relating or applicable to the matter in issue; not supporting the issue. Evidence is irrelevant when it has no tendency to prove or disprove the issue involved.

irrelevant question. in polygraphy, a non-threatening question intended to elicit a normal tracing on the test chart. Tracings of irrelevant questions are compared against tracings of relevant questions.

irresistible impulse. a legal defense by which an accused seeks to be fully or partially excused from responsibility on the grounds that although he knew the act was wrong, he was compelled to its execution by an impulse he was powerless to control.

isofootcandle diagram. a chart showing lines of equal footcandles. It is useful for determining results from a particular fixture without making calculations. Also called an isolux chart or footcandle chart.

isolation zone. in nuclear security, any area adjacent to a physical barrier, clear of all objects which could conceal or shield an individual.

isomethadone. an opiate classified as a Schedule II controlled substance.

isoquinoline alkaloids. one of two general categories of alkaloids extracted from opium. Alkaloids in this category have no significant influence on the central nervous system and are not regulated under the Controlled Substances Act. The other general category is the phenanthrene alkaloids, represented by morphine and codeine.

J

Jacob's ladder. a ladder made of rope, wire or chain and having wooden or metal rungs. It is a fire rescue tool.

jail. a short-term confinement facility, usually under the jurisdiction of a county or city government. It is used to house persons awaiting arraignment or trial when no bail has been set or when bail cannot be met. A jail also holds convicted misdemeanants and others sentenced to less than one year confinement, as well as prisoners awaiting transfer and occasionally material witnesses.

jailhouse lawyer. a prisoner who advises other prisoners on grounds for appeal and on other legal matters, not always with good or correct advice.

jamb anchor. a metal device inserted in or attached to the wall side of a jamb to secure the frame to the wall. A masonry jamb anchor secures a jamb to a masonry wall.

jamb peeling. a technique used in forced entry to deform or remove portions of the jamb to disengage the bolt from the strike.

jamb/strike. that component of a door assembly which receives and holds the extended lock bolt. The strike and jamb are considered a unit.

jamb wall. that component of a door assembly to which a door is attached and secured by means of the hinges. The wall and jamb are considered a unit.

jammer. a frequency generating oscillator that interferes with the operation of electronic audio surveillance.

jamming. the intentional transmission of interfering signals in order to disturb the reception of other signals.

jeopardy. the danger of conviction and punishment which the defendant in a criminal case incurs when a valid indictment has been found against him and a jury has been impaneled and sworn to try the case and render a verdict; charged with a crime before a properly organized and competent court. If acquitted, the charged person cannot be tried again for the same offense.

jet axe. the commercial name of an explosive device used by firefighters to blow holes in walls. The device has also been used by safecrackers to penetrate safes.

jeweler's mark. a small identifying mark placed at an inconspicuous place on an item of jewelry made or repaired by a jeweler. The mark can be important in an investigation.

jimmy. a pry bar; a burglar's tool.

jimmying. a technique used in forced entry to pry the jamb away from the lock edge of the door a sufficient distance to disengage the bolt from the strike.

jimmy pin. a sturdy projecting screw, which is installed in the hinge edge of a door near a hinge, fits into a hole in the door jamb, and prevents removal of the door if the hinge pins are removed.

jingle key. a key blank milled to fit a particular keyway. Raking and turning the jingle key in the keyway may cause the lock to open. Also called a try key.

jitter. the instability of a signal in terms of amplitude, phase, or both that is due to changes in the input power, mechanical affectations, or circuitry.

job analysis. the systematic study of a job to discover its specifications, frequently for the purposes of determining knowledge, skill and ability requirements, setting wages, and simplifying work procedures.

job hazard analysis. the breaking down into its component parts of any method or procedure to determine the hazards connected therewith and the requirements for performing it safely.

John Doe. a fictitious name frequently used to indicate a person in legal proceedings until his real name can be ascertained.

joint. a marihuana cigarette.

joint and several. an obligation or liability incurred, either under contract or otherwise, by two or more parties together and separately. The parties may be held jointly responsible or severally responsible.

Joint Nuclear Accident Coordinating Center (JNACC). a combined Defense Nuclear Agency and Department of Energy center for exchanging information in support of radiological assistance activities during a nuclear accident/incident.

joint stock company. a form of business organization created by an agreement of the parties. The agreement is commonly called the articles of association. A joint stock company is similar to the corporation in the following respects: (1) the ownership is represented by transferable certificates; (2) management is in the hands of a board of governors or directors elected by the members (shareholders); and (3) the business continues for its fixed term notwithstanding the death or disability of one or more of the members. It is unlike the corporation and like the partnership in that each shareholder is personally liable for the company's debts.

joint tortfeasors. two persons alleged to have committed the same tortious act with a common intent.

joint venture. an arrangement under which two or more individuals or businesses participate in a single project as partners.

Jones Act. a law that requires shippers to use American-flag vessels when shipping goods between US ports.

joule burn. a burn wound caused by high electrical shock. It is usually brown and has a shape corresponding to the object that made the contact.

joystick. a device having two potentiometers and a single toggle switch that moves on both the X and Y axes. It is used in alarm systems for controlling CCTV camera views and for creating video graphics.

judgment. the statement of the decision of a court.

judicial confession. a confession made during a court proceeding; an admission by a defendant while testifying; a guilty plea entered during a trial.

judicial knowledge. knowledge of that which is so notorious that everybody, including judges, knows it, and hence need not be proved.

judicial notice. the doctrine that a court will, of its own knowledge, assume certain facts to be true without the production of evidence in support of them. A court will usually take judicial notice of facts that are common knowledge.

judicial officer. any person exercising judicial powers in a court of law.

judicial sale. a sale authorized by a court that has jurisdiction to grant such authority. A judicial sale is conducted by an officer of the court.

juggler. a small time numbers game backer who holds all of the small bets, usually up to 25 cents, and lays-off all bets over that amount.

jumper. a piece of metal or short length of wire used to bypass or close a circuit. Jumpers or jump wires are used by automotive vehicle thieves and by persons who steal electric power. Also, a conductor used to temporarily connect two points.

jump out. to bypass one or more sensors in a protective circuit.

junction box. a protective enclosure for connecting circuit wires of an alarm system.

junk. a slang name for heroin.

jurat. a certificate of an officer or person before whom writing was sworn to; the clause written at the foot of an affidavit, stating when, where, and before whom such affidavit was sworn.

jurisdiction. the authority by which courts take cognizance of and try cases. Also, the territory, subject matter, or person over which authority may be exercised.

jury. a group of citizens impaneled to hear evidence and decide on the facts of a case in a court of law. A petit jury hears criminal cases and decides on the guilt or innocence of the defendant. A grand jury sits in private and decides whether a case should be brought to trial.

just cause. in employee relations, a good or fair reason for administering an adverse personnel action such as suspension or termination.

justifiable homicide. the intentional causing of the death of another in the legal performance of an official duty or in circumstances defined by law as constituting legal justification.

K

kalomein door. a door made by rolling two face panels of light steel around a wood frame and filling the interior cavity with injected plastic. It provides moderate protection against forced entry.

K book. the book used by a numbers writer.

kelly tool. an axe-like tool used by firemen to forcibly enter a structure.

Kelvin. a name meaning 1000 and sometimes used when referring to kilowatt-hours.

Kentucky Blue. marihuana grown in Kentucky; home grown marihuana; marihuana grown in the US.

ketobemidone. an opiate classified as a Schedule I Controlled Substance.

Kevlar. the trade name of a special woven cloth used in bullet-proof vests. It works by stretching upon bullet impact, spreading the bullet's energy, and stopping the bullet before it penetrates.

key blank. an uncut, pre-stamped key from which a key is made.

key cuts. the indentations cut into the shaft of a key blank.

keyed-alike cylinders. cylinders which are designed to be operated by the same key, but are not master-keyed cylinders.

keyed-different cylinders. cylinders requiring different keys for their operation.

key-in-knob lock. a lock having the key cylinder and the other lock mechanism, such as a push or turn button, contained in the knobs.

key extractor. a tool used to remove pieces of keys lodged in a keyway.

keyholing. the tumbling motion of an unbalanced bullet in flight. A characteristic elongated opening, similar to the shape of a key, can be seen at the entering point on a target struck by a tumbling bullet.

keying chirp. a sound that accompanies a code signal when the transmitter's frequency shifts slightly when the sending key is closed.

keyless system. an entry system that uses a keypad and an electric door strike. Pressing the correct sequential combination of push buttons on the keypad releases the lock to allow entry.

key measurement point. in nuclear security, a location where nuclear material appears in such a form that it may be measured to determine flow or inventory.

Keynesian economics. the economic theory, advanced by John Maynard Keynes, which holds that government intervention, through deficit spending, may be necessary to maintain high levels of employment.

key over-ride. a feature that allows an electrically operated lock to be released or engaged with a hand-operated key.

keypad. in computer usage, the small set of keys next to the main keyboard on a terminal.

key plate. a plate or escutcheon having only a keyhole.

key run. a route having key stations. A security or fire patrol follows the route and uses the key at each station to record the check-in time.

key station. a place along a route followed by a security or fire patrol. The station has a key which when inserted into the watchman's clock carried by the patrol will record the check-in time.

key stream. an electronic control signal that unscrambles a scrambled signal.

keyswitch. a switch operated by a key. Also called a lockswitch.

keyway. the longitudinal cut in the cylinder core, being an opening or space with millings in the sides identical to those on the proper key, thus allowing the key to enter the full distance of the blade.

kickback. money or something of value given to an employee by a vendor or contractor in exchange for a consideration. Also, money paid by an employee to a supervisor or third party in exchange for continued employment.

"kicked upstairs". removal of a person from a position where his or her performance is not thought satisfactory by promoting the person to a higher position in the organization.

kidnapping. unlawful transportation of a person without his consent, or without the consent of his guardian, if a minor.

kidnapping coverage. insurance against the hazard of a person being seized outside the insured premises and forced to return and open the premises or a safe therein or to give information which will enable the criminal to do so.

kidnap-ransom insurance. insurance written primarily for financial institutions and major corporations confronted with a kidnap-ransom threat. The insurance generally covers named employees for individual or aggregate amounts paid as ransom, with deductibles requiring the insured to participate in a percentage of any loss.

kiloton. the energy release of 1000 tons of TNT where 1 ton equals 2000 pounds and where the energy content of TNT is defined at 1100 calories per gram.

kinesic interview technique. an interview and

interrogational approach in which the subtle unconscious verbal and nonverbal behaviors of the interviewee are diagnosed and exploited.

kiosk. a protective housing or shield; a small booth used as a shelter for security guards; a teller or cashier enclosure.

kiss-off tone. a tone generated by a digital receiver telling a digital communicator that the emergency signal has been received. After the kiss-off, the communicator restores the telephone line for standard voice communications.

kite scheme. a scheme in which a criminal deposits money in a number of banks and then writes checks that exceed the total amount on deposit. The time required to transfer the cancelled checks affords the criminal an opportunity to substantially overdraw.

klaxon. an audible signaling device that emits a sound similar to a submarine's signal to dive.

kleptomania. in medical jurisprudence, a species of mania, consisting of an irresistible propensity to steal.

kneecapping. a form of torture performed by shooting a bullet or running an electric drill through a kneecap to cripple the victim for life.

knob and tube wiring. a method of electrical wiring in which wires are attached with porcelain knob insulators and porcelain tubes. This method is not used very frequently.

knob latch. a securing device having a spring bolt operated by a knob only.

knob shank. the projecting stem of a knob into which the spindle is fastened.

known solution peak of tension test. in poly-graphy, a test containing one relevant (hidden key) question pertaining to a known fact about which the examinee has denied knowledge. The relevant question is placed near the center of a group of similar but unrelated, non-relevant questions. The polygraphist compares the examinee's recorded reactions to both the relevant question and the non-relevant questions. The subject's response to the relevant or hidden key question may appear as a peak of tension in the polygrams.

known specimen. an article or material the origin of which is known. It is used as a standard of comparison with a comparable article or material of questionable origin. The character of the known specimen is determined by the circumstances of the investigation. Known specimens might be handwriting samples obtained from a suspected forger or pubic hair samples obtained from a suspected rapist.

known standard. in questioned document examinations, an original sample used to compare against unknown or questioned samples. Known standards include samples of typewriting from various typefaces/machines, watermarked papers, and checkwriter impressions.

knuckle. the enlarged part of a hinge into which the pin is inserted.

knuckling. a type of selvage obtained on a chain link fence by interlocking adjacent pairs of wire ends and bending the ends back into a closed loop.

kymograph. that component of the polygraph instrument which moves the polygram (chart paper) beneath and in contact with inked pens at a set rate of speed.

L

LAAM. levo-alpha-acetylmethadol, a synthetic compound closely related chemically to methadone. It is used in the treatment of narcotic addicts, and is regulated under the Controlled Substances Act as a narcotic.

labeling theory. a theory of deviance that focuses on the process by which some people are labeled deviant by others (and thus take on deviant identities), rather than on the nature of the behavior itself.

labor racketeer. a broad term that applies to a union leader who uses his/her office as a base for unethical and illegal activities.

labor spy. a union member who spies on union activities on behalf of management.

L Access. an access authorization granted by the Nuclear Regulatory Commission. It is based on a National Agency Check or National Agency Check and Inquiry conducted by the Office of Personnel Management.

lacing. a network of very fine wire placed in a concealed fashion around a protected object or at a point of entry such as a skylight or cellar window. If the lacing is broken, an alarm results.

lag. image retention in the form of a trail that occurs in a video image when the camera or an object in view moves quickly. Also called sticking or trailing.

laissez-faire economics. an economic theory, advanced by Adam Smith, which holds that the economic system develops and functions best when left to market forces, without government intervention.

lambert. a unit of measurement for luminance equal to the amount of light emitted or reflected from a perfect surface of one square centimeter.

laminate. a product made by bonding together two or more layers of material.

laminated glass. a type of glass fabricated from two layers of glass with a transparent bonding layer between them. Also called safety glass.

laminated padlock. a padlock, the body of which consists of a number of flat plates, all or most of which are of the same contour, superimposed and riveted or brazed together. Holes in the plates provide spaces for the lock mechanism and the ends of the shackle.

laminated safety glass. glass consisting of two layers of plate bonded with a plastic interlayer. When smashed, glass pieces tend to remain connected to the interlayer thereby reducing the hazard of flying glass.

laminate sensor. a sensor consisting of a thin lamination of metallic foil layered between paper or some other nonconductive substance. The laminate is attached to a surface such as a wall surrounding a protected area and electrified. A penetration of the laminate will cause an alarm.

lapping. an embezzlement technique in which a payment on account is diverted to the embezzler's use. To cover the shortage, a succeeding receipt is credited to the shorted account.

larcenous intent. an intent to knowingly take and carry away the goods of another without any claim or pretense of right, with intent wholly to deprive the owner of them or to convert them to personal use.

larceny. unlawful taking of property from the possession of another; the taking and carrying away of the personal property of another with intent to deprive the owner of it permanently.

large-scale integrated. a term relating to densely integrated circuits used to perform a large number of tasks. LSI technology has led to the development of many types of miniaturized and compact electronic devices used in security.

laser. a device that generates an intense single-color light beam or frequency.

laser identification. a property identification system in which a laser beam applies to high value items microscopic identification numbers too tiny to be seen by the naked eye. A high value item, such as a diamond, can be marked for ownership purposes without damage to the diamond.

laser intrusion detection. a beam-break sensor that operates on the same principle as the photoelectric sensor except that the beam source is generated by a low-power laser. Interruption of the laser beam between transmitter and receiver causes an alarm.

last clear chance. a doctrine on which recovery for injury due to negligence is based. In those states where contributory negligence by the plaintiff defeats his right to recovery, this theory may be used as an exception if the defendant, the person causing the injury, had sufficient notice of the danger to which the plaintiff was exposed and had sufficient opportunity to avoid the accident but did not do so.

latch bolt. a bevelled, spring-actuated bolt which may or may not include a dead-locking feature.

latching. in security communications, a technique for storing an event such as the momentary breaking of a perimeter circuit. The fact of the momentary break will remain readable until the alarm has been reset.

latent. any hidden or not visible print that must be specially developed for it to be seen.

latent fingerprints. fingerprints which are invisible but detectable by several techniques.

Lattes Crust test. a crime laboratory method used to determine what blood group antibody or antibodies of the A, B, O system are present in a dried stain. Also called a blood group agglutinins test.

law of crimes. a branch of public law which exists to protect the community as a whole against harms affecting fundamental areas of social life such as public peace, health, safety, welfare, morality, and authority. Law of crimes seeks to protect the individual's person, habitation and property. Also called criminal law.

layered security. a physical security approach that requires a criminal to penetrate or overcome a series of security layers before reaching the target. The layers might be perimeter barriers; building or area protection with locks, CCTV and guards; and point and trap protection using safes, vaults and sensors.

lay off. the protection a bookie affords himself by placing bets with other bookies in order to reduce the chance of a large loss.

lead azide. a type of primary explosive.

leader line. a fire hose attached to the end of a larger hose; a hose line attached from pump to nozzle as opposed to a line supplying the pump.

leading question. one which instructs a witness how to answer or puts into his mouth words to be echoed back. A question is a leading one when it indicates to the witness the real or supposed fact which the examiner expects and desires to have confirmed by the answer. The general rule is, subject to well defined exceptions, that leading questions may not be used in the direct examination of a witness, although they may be used in cross-examination.

lead number. in a numbers operation, the first digit of the three-digit winning number. It is most commonly associated with single-action betting.

lead styphenate. a type of primary explosive.

leaf door. an individual door, used either singly or in multiples.

leaf hinge. the most common type of hinge, characterized by two flat metal plates or leaves, which pivot about a metal hinge pin. A leaf hinge can be surface mounted, or installed in a mortise.

lease automatic custody transfer. automatic measurement and transfer of oil from a producer's tanks to a pipeline.

leased line. a dedicated telephone line leased to a customer for specific communications use.

legal. an intelligence officer who holds a legitimate embassy post or is attached to another legitimate organization.

legal aid. a system of providing counsel and other legal assistance to indigent defendants through a private or semipublic agency supported by governmental, philanthropic, or other funds.

legal liability. the responsibility an individual bears for his actions (or inactions), given his obligations to perform a duty or prevent an action or occurrence that is recognized as being a matter that is proper to be heard by and enforced by the courts.

legalization. the rescission of a statute so as to legalize previously illegal or criminal activity. Repeal of Prohibition is an example of legalization.

legging. a shoplifting technique in which merchandise is placed under the dress of the shoplifter and held in place between the upper thighs.

lemonade. poor quality drugs.

Leritine. the trade name of a commonly abused narcotic regulated by the Controlled Substances Act.

lesser included offense. a crime less grave than the one charged but not requiring a separate charge for a guilty verdict, because the less serious offense is automatically implied by the more serious one. For example, a person charged with murder may also be found guilty of inflicting bodily harm.

letter of credit. a letter issued by a bank on behalf of a buyer of merchandise. The letter allows the seller to draw funds from the bank up to a stipulated amount.

levels of proof. the degrees of certainty required at different stages in the criminal justice process.

leverage. a financial method applied with anticipation that the asset acquired will increase in return so that the investor will realize a profit not only on the investment but also on the borrowed funds, with the borrowed funds being predominant.

lever handle. a bar-like grip which is rotated in a vertical plane about a horizontal axis at one of its ends, designed to operate a latch.

lever lock. a key operated lock that incorporates one or more lever tumblers, which must be raised to a specific level so that the fence of the bolt is aligned with the gate of the tumbler in order to withdraw the bolt. Lever locks are commonly used in storage lockers, and safety deposit boxes.

lever switch. a mechanical intrusion detection sensor activated by movement of the surface upon which it is mounted. When an opening occurs, the lever is moved and an alarm is triggered. A lever switch is usually surface mounted.

lever tumbler. a flat metal arm, pivoted on one end with a gate in the opposite end. The top edge is spring loaded. The bitting of the key rotates against the bottom edge, raising the lever tumbler to align the gate with the bolt fence. Both the position of the gate and the curvature of the bottom edge of the lever tumbler can be varied to establish the key code.

levomethorphan. an opiate classified as a Schedule II Controlled Substance.

levomoramide. an opiate classified as a Schedule I Controlled Substance.

levophenacylmorphan. an opiate classified as a Schedule I Controlled Substance.

levorphanol. an opiate classified as a Schedule II Controlled Substance.

lewd and lascivious conduct. a statutory term describing prohibited behavior deemed to be perverse and depraved.

Lexan. the commercial name of a type of bullet-resistant glazing material.

lex talionis. harsh retaliation for a criminal act. Literally translated, the term means "law of the claw."

liaison files. files containing information on various official contacts, to include name, telephone, organization, specific area of value and remarks on the personal characteristics of the individual.

libel. any statement made in writing which is defamatory and injures the reputation of an individual in the community.

Librium. one of the most widely prescribed and highly abused depressant drugs. Prolonged use of excessive doses may result in physical and psychological dependence. A common mode of abuse is to ingest the drug with alcohol. Librium appears in the Controlled Substances Act as a Schedule IV barbiturate. Street names include barb, downer, blue, yellow jacket, and sleeping pill.

licensed material. a term used by the Nuclear Regulatory Commission to describe special nuclear material used, stored or transferred under licenses issued by the NRC.

lid. a measure of marihuana.

lie detector. any one of the devices variously called the polygraph, voice stress analyzer and psychological stress analyzer.

lien. a hold or claim which one person has upon another's property as security for some debt or charge.

life style inquiry. an investigation to factually determine the sources and amounts of income of a particular person and to compare known income against the person's evident living and spending habits.

lifting box. a box used to shoplift. It has a concealed opening in the bottom which permits it to be placed over the item targeted for theft. When the box is lifted, the item is captured inside the box. Also called a booster box.

light bulb bomb. an incendiary device made by drilling a small hole in a light bulb and filling it with a highly combustible material. The light bulb is placed in a socket. When the light switch is activated, the electrical arc in the bulb will ignite the combustible.

light emitting diode. a diode that creates light when energized. LEDs are used extensively as visual annunciators.

light-intensity cutoff. the threshold at which a reduction of light intensity in a photoelectric alarm sensor will trigger an alarm.

lightning spike. a momentary surge in AC line power caused by lightning. A lightning spike can cause voltage to exceed the normal level by 1,000 percent or more.

light source. a device, such as a lamp, which produces visible energy. It is distinguished from devices which reflect or transmit light, such as a luminaire.

limited partnership. a partnership in which the liability of one or more special partners for debts of the firm is limited to the amount of the partner's investment in the business. Special partners have no voice in the management of the partnership. They merely invest money and receive a certain share of the profits. There must be one or more general partners who manage the business and remain liable for all its debts.

line amplifier. a device that compensates for line loss, generally a broadband amplifier. A line amplifier permits extension of an audio signal across a greater distance.

line balance. the degree to which the individual conductors in a cable are similar in their electrical characteristics with respect to each other, to other conductors, and to ground.

line break. a trouble condition in an alarm circuit transmission line caused by a broken wire or wires.

line carrier transmitter. a device that transmits signals over existing AC power wiring. It may be used to transmit between structures sharing a common power system.

line dip. a short-term decrease in line voltage, usually resulting from a short-circuit or a sudden increase in electrical load on the line. Also called a voltage dip or sag.

line holdout. a circuit that prevents two alarms from reporting at the same instant on a McCulloh loop.

line of demarcation. in arson investigations, the boundary between charred and uncharred material. On floors or rugs, a puddle-shaped line of demarcation indicates a liquid fire accelerant. In the cross section of wood, a sharp, distinct line indicates a rapid, intense fire.

line of sight. in firearms, a straight line from the shooter's eye, through the sighting device of the weapon, to the target.

line seizure. the temporary and exclusive use of a telephone line by a digital communicator or tape dialer.

line smoke detector. a general term describing a type of smoke detector that generates a beam of light transmitted between a sender and a receiver mounted at extreme ends or sides of a protected area. Interruption of the beam by smoke particles causes an alarm.

line spike. a temporary increase in line voltage that lasts less than a full cycle (16 milliseconds).

line supervision. a means of determining that a transmission line is functional.

line surge. a temporary increase in line voltage that lasts at least one cycle (approximately 16 milliseconds). A line surge is the opposite of a line dip, voltage dip or sag.

line transient. a momentary surge or dip on an AC power line, frequently caused by the shutdown or startup of motor driven equipment sharing the same line. Also called a voltage transient.

lineup. a group of people placed together in a line for viewing by a witness or victim for the purpose of identifying the perpetrator of a crime; a line or parade of suspects and criminals in custody for the purpose of allowing law enforcement officers to familiarize themselves with habitual offenders.

lintel. a horizontal structural member that supports the load over an opening such as a door or window.

lip (of a strike). the curved projecting part of a strike plate which guides the spring bolt to the latch point.

liquidated damages. an amount the parties to a contract have agreed upon that shall be paid in satisfaction of a loss resulting from a breach of contract. The amount must be in proportion to the actual loss, otherwise the agreement is unenforceable.

liquidity. a term used to describe the solvency of a business and which has special reference to the degree of readiness in which assets can be converted into cash without a loss. If a firm's current assets cannot be converted into cash to meet current liabilities, the firm is said to be illiquid. Also called cash position.

liquid sulphur. a mixture of melted sulphur and iron filings used as a substitute for plaster of paris when making finely detailed casts

of foot and tire prints, tool marks and similar impressions.

lis pendens. a notice filed in the office of the county which advises that a lawsuit is pending against the owner of the designated property and involves that property.

listening post. a location where an eavesdropper monitors receiving equipment during bugging operations.

lithium battery. a battery that offers high-energy density, long shelf life, and higher cell voltages than the carbon-zinc type battery. Lithium batteries are of three types: electrolyte-organic, inorganic, and solid state.

livor mortis. a condition in a dead person produced by the settling of blood into the dependent areas. It usually appears as purple blotching of the skin where the blood has settled. Also called lividity or post mortem lividity.

load. the amount of power required by a circuit or device in operation.

load-bearing wall. an integral part of a structure which helps support the floors or roof and is relatively permanent.

load center. the electrical distribution center for a structure, either the main center or a branch center. A load center is typically equipped with circuit breakers instead of a main switch and fuse box.

load up. a fraudulent practice in which a party obtains goods on credit and then declares bankruptcy.

Local Agency Check. a Department of Defense review of the criminal, subversive and intelligence files of police departments, county and parish sheriff's offices, and other law enforcement agencies. It may also include other offices such as the Bureau of Vital Statistics, court records, credit agencies and other state or local records repositories.

local alarm system. a system in which the alarm signal is annunciated in the immediate vicinity of the protected area.

Local Files Check. a review of records maintained at the Department of Defense installation of assignment (conducted before requesting a personnel security investigation, granting a security clearance or granting information access) to determine the existence or absence of unfavorable information or to verify information provided by an applicant for a security clearance.

local non-interfering coded station. a fire alarm device that when actuated transmits four or more rounds of coded alarm signals and which cannot be silenced or turned off until the minimum number of signals have been transmitted.

lock and load. a command given to shooters

immediately prior to aiming and receiving the command to fire.

lock box. a housing for a key that is used to reset a fire alarm panel or other alarm system; a locked box where keys are stored.

lock clip. a flexible metal part attached to the inside of a door face to position a mortise lock.

lock edge. the vertical edge or stile of a door in which a lock may be installed. Also called the leading edge, the lock stile and the strike edge.

lock edge door. a door which has its face sheets secured in place by an exposed mechanical interlock seam on each of its two vertical edges. Also called a lock seam door.

locked password. in computer usage, a password that cannot be changed by the account's owner.

locking dog. that part of a padlock mechanism which engages the shackle and holds it in the locked position.

lock pick. a tool or instrument, other than the specifically designed key, made for the purpose of manipulating a lock into a locked or unlocked condition.

lock rail. the horizontal member of a door intended to receive the lock case.

lock record bar. that part of a polygraph instrument which prevents the inked pens from moving when the blood pressure cuff is inflated.

lock reinforcement. a reinforcing plate attached inside of the lock stile of a door to receive a lock.

lock seam. a joint in sheet metal work, formed by doubly folding the edges of adjoining sheets in such a manner that they interlock.

lockswitch. a switch that can only be operated with a key. Also called a keyswitch.

lockup. a short-term confinement facility or jail; the holding cells in a police station.

locus delicti. the place of the crime or tort.

logical access. access to the information content of a record stored in a computer system.

log in. to enter a computer system. When a user logs in, he/she types an account name and password in response to the appropriate prompts. If the name and password match an account on the system, the user will be permitted access to that account.

log off. to exit from a computer system.

logon. an access routine that requires a computer system user to log on by entering a user ID and password.

logon restricted. a security feature of a computer system which requires an authorized user to log on at specified workstations only.

loiding. a burglary attack method in which a thin, flat, flexible object such as a stiff piece of plastic is inserted between the strike and the latch bolt to depress the latch bolt and release it from the strike. The loiding of windows is accomplished by inserting a thin stiff object between the meeting rails or stiles to move the latch to the open position, or by inserting a thin stiff wire through openings between the stile or rail and the frame to manipulate the sash operator of pivoting windows. The term is derived from the word celluloid. Also called knifing and slip-knifing.

Lombrosian. a term pertaining to the criminological views postulated by Cesare Lombroso (1836-1909) and to adherents of the positivist school of criminology, particularly as they relate to a belief that some people are born criminals and others (called criminaloids) are born with criminal tendencies or predilections.

long-acting barbiturates. a classification of barbiturates based on the time between administration and the onset of anesthesia. In this classification, barbiturates take effect within 1 hour and have a duration time of up to 16 hours. Phenobarbital (Luminal), mephobarbital or methylphenobarbital (Mebaral), and metharbital (Gemonil) are long-acting barbiturates.

long bone measurement. a technique for estimating the height of a deceased person by measuring the length of a skeleton's long bones. These data are correlated to a standard scale and an estimate of height made.

longitudinal study. research involving the collection of data at two or more points in time, usually in relation to the same individuals.

long-range gunshot wound. a wound caused when the muzzle at time of discharge is more than 24 inches from the victim.

long-term liabilities. liabilities or expenses that will not mature within the next year.

long throw deadbolt lock. a lock having a deadbolt longer than five-eighths of an inch. It is resistant to forced entry attempts.

look-alikes. tablets, capsules and powders whose physical appearances mimic prescription drug products and are sold to naive drug buyers.

lookup file (or table). written procedures placed in close proximity to a security officer or other person responsible for monitoring alarm panels. The lookup file contains step-by-step instructions relating to coded signals received at the panels.

loop. a closed circuit with protective devices connected in a series; in fingerprint science, a pattern in which one or more ridges enter on either side of the impression, recurve, touch or pass an imaginary line drawn from the delta to the core, terminate or tend to terminate on or toward the same side of the impression from whence such ridge or ridges entered; one of the three basic groups of fingerprint patterns, the other two being the arch and whorl. The loop pattern has two sub-groups: the radial loop and ulnar loop.

loop system. a type of alarm system that has a number of sensors installed at intervals on a pair of wires looped throughout a large protected area and tied into a central station.

loose joint hinge. a hinge with two knuckles. The pin is fastened permanently to one and the other contains the pinhole. The two parts of the hinge can be disengaged by lifting.

loose pin hinge. a hinge having a removable pin to permit the two leaves of the hinge to be separated.

loss event. an occurrence that produces an actual loss, measurable by some standard, such as dollars, and not speculative in nature, such as a loss resulting from a poor investment decision. Examples of loss events include crime, accident, war and natural disaster.

loss event criticality. the impact upon an organization imposed by a single loss event or the cumulative impact of losses resulting from recurrence of the same event. For example, the criticality of a single loss resulting from a robbery of a convenience store can be measured in the average amount of dollars kept in the register. The criticality of loss resulting from shoplifting in the store can be measured by the average shoplifting loss times the number of shopliftings that occur over a given period of time.

loss event profile. a listing of the kinds of threats or risks confronting a particular asset or organization.

louvered window. a type of window in which the glazing consists of parallel, horizontal, moveable glass slats. Also called a jalousie window.

lower flammable explosive limit. the limit at which a low concentration of flammable vapor in a given space is susceptible to explosion.

low explosive. an explosive with a slow burning rate. On detonation a low explosive exerts a "pushing" effect, which propels objects as opposed to shattering them.

low frequency. a band of the radio spectrum operating between 30-300 kilohertz.

low-order detonation. an incomplete detonation of an explosive charge.

low-order explosion. an explosion characterized by a slow expansion over a relatively wide area into a combustion known as deflagration. Most explosives of this type have a pushing rather than shattering effect. Damage is characterized by twisting and tearing.

low-pressure sodium lamp. a lamp that produces a highly monochromatic yellow light which offers poor color discrimination but provides good contrast on uneven surfaces. The low-pressure sodium lamp reliably starts, has an excellent service life, and high efficiency. It has a long initial warmup (8-10 minutes) and at the end of the service life requires a higher operating current. This type of lamp works well with black and white CCTV and records well on film.

low profile look. the subdued appearance of security officers clothed in civilian-style dress, such as blazers and slacks.

LSD. an abbreviation of the German expression for lysergic acid diethylamide. It is an hallucinogenic drug produced from lysergic acid, a substance derived from the ergot fungus which grows on rye or from lysergic acid amide, a chemical found in morning glory seeds. LSD can cause illusions, poor perception of time and distance, intense psychotomimetic episodes, psychosis, and possible death. It is orally administered, and known by a wide variety of street names such as acid and microdot. LSD appears in the Controlled Substances Act as a Schedule I drug.

lumen. the quantity of luminous flux intercepted by a surface of one square foot, all points of which are one foot from a uniform source of one candela.

lumen maintenance factor. a multiplier which corrects for the decreased lumen output from a luminaire over a given period of time. The decrease is due to aging of the lamp and dirt accumulation on the fixture.

luminaire. a device or fixture containing a light source and means for directing and controlling the distribution of light from the source.

luminaire efficiency. the percentage of lamp lumens which are contained in the beam.

Luminal. the brand name of a commonly abused barbiturate.

luminance. the amount of light emitted from a surface, whether from a direct source or reflected. Luminance is not relative to distance, being a property of the object viewed. It is expressed in footlamberts.

Luminol. the trade name of a chemical used to detect invisible traces of blood by making them glow for a brief period. Luminol reacts even with blood traces that remain after an object has been washed. The luminescing reaction is typically photographed for evidentiary purposes.

luminous efficiency. a measure of the efficiency of a light source. It describes how much visible energy is produced per watt of power input, and is measured in lumens per watt. Also called efficacy of light source.

luminous readers. invisible marks placed on the backs of playing cards by a dishonest gambler. The marks are visible when viewed through special glasses.

lush worker. an unsophisticated pickpocket who steals from intoxicated or sleeping persons in trains, buses, waiting rooms, and parks.

lux. a metric unit of measurement for light. One lux equals one lumen per square meter.

lycopodium powder. a yellowish fingerprint powder made from spores. It is regarded as being especially effective when mixed with aluminum powder.

lysergic acid. a substance derived from the ergot fungus which grows on rye. It can be used to make LSD and is a Schedule III drug.

lysergic acid amide. a chemical found in morning glory seeds which can be used to produce LSD. It is a Schedule III drug.

lysergic acid diethylamide. an hallucinogen classified as a Schedule I Controlled Substance. It is the technical name of LSD. Also called blotter, purple haze, orange sunshine, acid, microdot, goofies, Snoopy, Mickey Mouse, Donald Duck, window pane, unicorn, and blue star.

Mace. the commercial name of a spray used in riot control operations. It causes dizziness, nausea and tears.

maceration. a softening and separating of skin tissue caused by extended immersion in water. Maceration produces problems when fingerprint and palmar surface impressions need to be obtained from drowning victims.

macerator. a machine used to destroy heavy paper by a chewing and pulverizing action. It is used to render unreadable sensitive documents no longer needed.

machine gun. any weapon which shoots, is designed to shoot, or can be readily restored to shoot, automatically more than one shot, without manual reloading, by a single function of the trigger.

made. the exposure of a surveillant or undercover operative. Also called blown or burned.

Mafia. a group of Italian-dominated organized crime leaders and their followers that originated in Sicily.

magistrate. a lower-court judge, sometimes called a justice of the peace, municipal judge, or police judge. He is usually assigned to arraignments, preliminary hearings, bail settings, and dispositions of minor offenses.

magnesium ribbon. a product used for developing latent prints. When the ribbon is burned, a white film attaches to an object passed above the burning. When the object is dusted, the powder remains attached to latent prints.

magnetic contact. a device that activates when the magnetic field set up between two contact points is broken. For example, one contact is mounted on a window with a corresponding contact on the window sill. When the window is opened, the contact is broken and an alarm is activated.

magnetic disk. a device for storing computer data. The data are recorded on the magnetic surface of the disk.

magnetic drum. a device for storing computer data. The data are recorded on a cylinder having a surface coated with a magnetic material.

magnetic fuse. a bomb fuse sensitive to minute variations in the earth's magnetic field. The fuse functions when an influence from the target is exerted on a sensitive detecting device within the fuse itself.

magnetic ink. printing ink that is impregnated with magnetic particles capable of being sensed by a magnetic reader.

magnetic input/output. mag cards, cassettes, diskettes, and other mountable magnetic storage media.

magnetic keycard. a plastic card containing thousands of magnetic bits or particles which can be arranged to match the required pattern set up in a card reader.

magnetic lock. a type of door lock consisting of an electromagnet and strike plate. The electromagnet is mounted in the door frame opposite the strike plate, which is mounted in the door. When current is applied, the strength of the magnet holds the door locked. Magnetic locks operate on low voltage and consume little power.

magnetic limpet mine. a bomb device containing TNT. It is of military origin and is a favored tool of terrorists.

magnetic sandwich card. an identity card which has been die cut from three-layer stock. The middle layer is gamma ferric oxide (a magnetic plastic material) and is magnetized in a pattern of dots. A card reader electronically examines the dot pattern.

magnetic spot card. a type of magnetic keycard having a barium ferrite core on which a code is fixed by the polarity of magnetized spots arranged in a readable pattern.

magnetic stripe card. a type of access card having a data-encoded stripe on one face.

magnetic tape recorder. a device that records sound on magnetic tape.

magnetometer. an instrument for measuring the magnitude and direction of magnetic fields.

maid master. a sub-master key typically used for gaining access to areas that require daily cleaning and maintenance.

mailbox. in computer usage, a software data structure used for general communications between users of the system. Also called a bulletin board.

mailbox key. a type of key that is held by the lock mechanism when the mechanism is in the open position.

mail cover. a practice in which the exterior surfaces of mail moving to and from a subject are examined or copied.

mail fraud. any scheme in which the US postal system is used to defraud another. Mail fraud is prohibited by 19 USC, Section 1341.

main charge. a quantity of high explosives detonated by a booster explosive. It is the fourth and final element in the basic firing chain of most explosions. The more common materials used as a main charge are TNT, dynamite and plastic explosives.

mainline. to inject a drug, typically heroin, into a vein.

mainliner. a person who injects illegal drugs into the veins.

maintained footcandles. an illumination value assigned to a lamp or luminaire which takes into consideration wear and tear, dirt and similar factors.

maison keying. a specialized keying system, used in apartment houses and other large complexes, that enables all individual unit keys to operate common-use locks such as the main entry and laundry room.

major case prints. recordings of all the friction ridge detail present on the palmar surfaces of the hands and full inner surfaces of the fingers. Major case prints are obtained by inking and then simultaneously pressing the full flat surface of the hand from fingertips to wrist joint. They are used for elimination and identification purposes in major cases.

malachite green. a dye stuff used to mark an object so that a detectable amount will be transferred to the body or property of a person who handled the object.

mala fides. bad faith; the opposite of bona fides.

mala in se. wrongs in themselves; acts morally wrong; offenses against conscience.

mala in se crime. a crime so inherently wrong in nature that it may be said to be bad or evil in itself. Mala in se crimes include murder, rape, robbery, and arson.

mala prohibita. prohibited wrongs or offenses; acts which are made offenses by laws.

mala prohibita crime. a crime that is not necessarily wrong in itself, but is said to be wrong because it is prohibited by statute. Examples would be illegal parking and fishing without a license.

malfeasance. the commission of some act which is unlawful.

malice. a mental state accompanying a criminal act that is performed wilfully, intentionally, and without legal justification.

malice aforethought. a knowledge of such circumstances that according to common experience there is a clear and strong likelihood that death will follow a contemplated act. Malice aforethought is usually coupled with an absence of justification for the act.

malicious. done with an evil heart or mind, cruelty or reckless disregard of the consequences.

malicious arrest. an unreasonable arrest done under the color of authority.

malicious mischief. the common law crime of injuring the property of another. If fire or an explosive is used, the offense is arson.

malicious prosecution. the institution of judicial proceedings, civil or criminal, against another, maliciously and without probable cause.

malum in se. an act considered wrongful by its very evil character based on principles of nature and morality.

malum prohibitum. an act which is not inherently immoral or wrongful, but becomes so because it is expressly forbidden by law.

management audit. any comprehensive examination of the administrative operations and organizational arrangements of a company or government agency which uses generally accepted standards of practice for the purposes of evaluation.

management by exception. a management control process that has a subordinate report to an organizational superior only upon the occurrence of exceptional or unusual events that call for decision-making on the part of the superior.

management by objectives. an approach to managing in which the subordinate and the superior agree on measurable goals to be accomplished by the subordinate (or team) over a set period of time.

management development. any conscious effort on the part of an organization to provide a manager with skills that he might need for future duties, such as rotational assignments or formal educational experiences.

management information system. any formal process in an organization that provides managers with facts they need for decision-making.

management science. an approach to management dating from World War II that seeks to apply the scientific method to managerial problems. Because of its emphasis on mathematical techniques, management science as a term is frequently used interchangeably with operations research.

managerial grid. a graphic gridiron format which has an X axis locating various degrees of orientation toward production and a Y axis locating various degrees of orientation toward people. Individuals scoring themselves on the grid can place themselves at one of 81 available positions that register their relative orientations toward production and people.

managerial psychology. generally, all those concepts of human behavior in organizations that are relevant to managerial problems.

mandamus. a court order that compels the performance of an act.

mandatory prosecution. a system of criminal procedure that denies or limits the prosecutor's discretion not to prosecute. It is used in several European countries.

mandatory sentence. a statutory requirement that a certain penalty shall be set and carried out in all cases upon conviction for a specified offense or series of offenses.

mandatory supervised release. a conditional

release from prison required by statute when an inmate has been confined for a time period equal to his full sentence minus statutory good time if any.

manic depressive reaction. a psychotic reaction characterized by prolonged and alternating periods of euphoria/overactivity and depression/underactivity.

manicure. remove stems and undesirable residue from marihuana by filtering or screening.

manslaughter. the unlawful killing of a human being, without malice aforethought.

mantrap. a double door booth arrangement that allows a person to enter at one end. The person undergoes an access identification routine inside the booth and if the routine is satisfied the lock on the booth door at the end is released. The booth can be engineered so that both end doors lock as soon as an individual enters.

manual override. a feature of an access control system which allows for manual shutdown during emergencies or in other circumstances not covered by automatic programming.

manual station. a fire alarm initiating device that transmits an alarm signal when manually operated. Sometimes called a pull station.

Mapp vs. Ohio. a landmark case that resulted in a judicially created rule of law generally called the exclusionary rule. The exclusionary rule prohibits admission of illegally obtained evidence in state and federal courts.

marbling. a preserving treatment applied to the edges of account books. An examination of the marbling pattern may be revealing as to whether pages had been removed or substituted.

march time signal. an audible signal having pulses that sound continuously at a rate between 108-120 per minute. The march time rhythm of the signal encourages orderly evacuation and is therefore commonly used in school buildings.

marginal analysis. any technique that seeks to determine the point at which the cost of something (for example, an additional employee) will be worth the cost or pay for itself.

marihuana (or marijuana). an hallucinogen, usually smoked. It is classified as a Schedule I Controlled Substance. Also called pot, grass, reefer, herb, weed, Columbian, hemp, joint, Mary Jane, sinsemilla and Acapulco gold.

Marihuana Tax Act. A federal statute which requires persons authorized to deal in marihuana to register and pay an occupational tax. Exempted from the act are legal sales of marihuana for medicinal purposes.

mark down. a technique in which dishonest employees of a retail operation will mark down price tickets on items purchased by them or their accomplices.

market. the number of people and their total spending (actual or potential) for products or services within a business firm's geographic limits of distribution ability.

market share. the percentage of sales compared to the sales of competitors in total for a particular product line.

marking for identification. marking evidence at the time of seizure or collection in order to connect the evidence to a particular crime and to demonstrate that fact in court.

mark switch. a switch on a polygraph instrument which when activated instantly places a mark on the GSR tracing. The mark is used to note outside noises or other distractions that occurred during the test. Also called an event marker.

martial law. the exercise of military power to preserve order and insure public safety in domestic territory in times of emergency when a civil government is unable to function or its functioning would itself threaten the public safety.

masquerade. to gain unauthorized access to a computer system by impersonating an authorized user's access identification routine.

mass spectrograph. an apparatus for determining the relative masses of isotopes of an element, and for sorting electrically charged particles in general. A small amount of the substance to be studied is gasified, and the gas is admitted into a vacuum tube where its molecules are ionized by electrons emitted by a thermionic cathode and accelerated. The various types of ions so formed are sent through a combination of electric and magnetic fields which deflects them to different degrees according to their masses, and those of different mass are brought to focus at different places.

master code. a code which serves merely to distinguish a fire signal from all other signals in a fire alarm system.

master code card. an access control card that operates any card reader within a system; a special card which when inserted in a self-contained reader sets the code for all cards in the system.

master coded system. a system in which a common coded alarm signal is transmitted for not less than four rounds, after which the annunciator may be manually or automatically silenced.

master combination. a universal code for unlocking digital mechanical locks. It serves the same function as a master key.

master disc tumbler. a disc tumbler that operates with a master key in addition to its own change key.

master key system. a method of keying locks which allows a single key to operate multiple locks, each of which also operates with an individual change key. Several levels of master keying are possible: a single master key is one which operates all locks of a group of locks with individual change keys; a grand master key operates all locks of two or more master key systems; and a great grand master key operates all locks of two or more grand master key systems. Master key systems are used primarily with pin and disk tumbler locks and to a limited extent with lever or warded locks.

master pin. a segmented pin, used to enable a pin tumbler to be operated by more than one key cut.

master-servant rule. the rule that employers are obligated to protect the public from the acts of their employees. Courts can hold employers liable for torts committed by employees in the course of their employment.

master timer. a device that develops basic timing signals for a terminal.

match bomb. an incendiary device consisting of a lighted cigarette placed between the cover of a pack of safety matches and the matchheads. When the cigarette burns down and reaches the matchheads, a small fire is produced. The match bomb is typically surrounded by highly combustible materials. The match bomb is typically used when the arsonist wants to be well away from the area when ignition occurs.

matchhead bomb. an explosive device consisting of matchheads packed tightly into a fragmentable container, such as a short length of pipe capped at both ends and drilled to allow insertion of a fuse.

matching network. an arrangement of equipment and circuits that couple an audio signal to a reporting line.

material access area. in nuclear security, any location which contains special nuclear material, within a vault or a building, the roof, walls, and floor of which each constitute a physical barrier.

material evidence. any evidence, physical or testimonial, which is relevant to the substantial matters in a dispute, or which has a legitimate and effective influence or bearing on the decision of a case.

material inside information. a term used in federal securities law as relates to the purchase or sale of a company's securities, such as its common stock, by persons possessing information not known to the public. Information may be considered "inside" or "nonpublic" if it has not been included in the company's Security and Exchange Commission filings, in a press release, or widely reported in the media. Information is considered "material" if it could be expected to affect the investment decision of a reasonable investor or the market price of the company's publicly traded securities.

material question. in polygraphy, a question which when posed to a guilty subject causes a response recordable by the polygraph instrument. Also called a relevant or pertinent question.

matrix. a section of alarm receivers and transmitters that code, decode, or annunciate signals.

matrix organization. any organization using a multiple command system whereby an employee might be accountable to one superior for overall performance as well as to one or more other superiors for specific projects. A contract security guard company can be said to operate on the matrix concept.

maximum allowable pressure. the greatest pressure that may safely be applied to a structure or vessel.

maximum footcandles. the highest illumination value at any point on a lighted surface.

maximum permissible dose. that radiation dose identified as the limiting cumulative dose permitted to be received over a specific period of time by persons exposed to radiation.

maximum security. security measures observed in a custodial institution where utmost efforts are made to prevent escapes. In maximum security institutions, the freedom of inmates and of visitors is restricted more than in other prisons and correctional facilities.

maximum sentence. the maximum penalty provided by law for a given criminal offense, usually stated as a maximum term of imprisonment or a maximum fine.

mayhem. intentional inflicting of injury on another which causes the removal of, or seriously disfigures, or renders useless or seriously impairs the function of, any member or organ of the body.

McCulloh Loop. the original multiplex circuit used for security applications. It consists of a series connection of many subscribers via telephone lines. Analogous to party line operation for ordinary telephone service.

mean time between failures. a statistical figure representing the average time between component or equipment failures.

mean time to failure. a statistical figure representing the average time between initial startup and the first failure of components or pieces of equipment for a given grouping of identical devices.

mean time to repair. a statistical figure representing the average time between component or equipment failure and the completed repair of the unit.

measure of dispersion. any statistical measure showing the extent to which data are concentrated or spread out from a measure of central tendency.

measures of variability. measures that show the extent to which a distribution of scores is clustered or spread.

mechanic. that member of a pickpocketing team who does the actual taking from the victim. A "stall" distracts the victim as the mechanic "lifts" and passes the "poke" to a third member of the team.

mechanical fuse. a fuse in which some form of mechanical energy is utilized to cause the fuse to function. In its simplest design, it consists of a striker (firing pin) held away from a detonator by a retaining spring until some external force is applied. When sufficient force is exerted to overcome the retaining spring, the striker is allowed to impinge on the detonator, initiating the firing train.

mechanical imprints. the imprints and markings made on a cartridge case by contact with the firing pin, breechface, extractor and ejector. These imprints assist the firearms examiner to match a cartridge case with a particular firearm.

mechanical initiator. any mechanical device used to initiate a bomb's detonator. A mouse trap and coil spring are common types of mechanical initiators.

mechanical lock. a lock that operates solely on mechanical principles. All locks are mechanical to some degree, but many require electrical or electronic circuitry to operate. A true mechanical lock uses springs and rotating cams which are purely mechanical in nature.

mechanical stability. the ability of an explosive to withstand mechanical force such as jolting and shaking.

mechanical switch. a switch in which the contacts are opened or closed by means of a depressable plunger.

mechanic's lien. a claim created by law for the purpose of securing priority of payment of the price or value of work performed and materials furnished in erecting or repairing a building or structure and as such attaches to the land as well as the building and improvements.

medical fraud. an unlawful practice by medical professionals in which kickbacks are received from laboratories, pharmacies and similar businesses for services or products unnecessarily recommended to patients, or the unlawful practice of billing an insurance carrier for services or products not provided to patients.

medical jurisprudence. medical knowledge applied to legal questions; the application of principles and practices of the different branches of medicine to the elucidation of doubtful questions in a court of justice. Also called forensic medicine.

medium frequency. a band of the radio spectrum operating between 300 kilohertz and 3 megahertz.

medium risk commodity. a relatively expensive consumer product with medium resale potential and of interest to thieves and professional fences. Examples are electric typewriters, calculators, musical instruments, power tools, automotive parts and apparel.

medium security. security measures observed in a correctional institution or detention facility where freedom of inmates and visitors is restricted and efforts are made to prevent escapes, but to a lesser extent than in institutions housing more dangerous criminals.

megahertz. one million hertz. It is abbreviated MHz.

megaton. the energy release of a million tons of TNT.

memorandum for record. a written record made for the purpose of formalizing the pertinent facts of an event.

mens rea. a guilty mind; a guilty or wrongful purpose; a criminal intent.

mental retardation. significantly subaverage general intellectual functioning which exists concurrently with deficits in adaptive behavior, and manifested during the developmental period.

menu. a list of optional computer functions or operations appearing on a video display terminal. The operator may select one option at a time.

Mepergan. a trade name for a synthesized or manufactured opiate used medically to relieve pain but which also has a high potential for abuse.

meprobamate. a drug classified as a Schedule IV Controlled Substance.

mercury battery. a mercuric-oxide type battery that is relatively inexpensive and suitable for compact circuitry applications. It has a high energy density, but a comparatively short shelf life.

mercury fulminate. a type of primary explosive.

mercury switch. a switch that opens or closes a circuit by the movement of a drop of mercury between contact points.

mercury switch bomb. a bomb that will explode when an electrical circuit has been opened or closed by the action of a mercury switch. A bomb of this construction is designed to detonate when moved.

mercury vapor lamp. a lamp that emits a blue-green light caused by an electric current passing through a tube of conducting illuminous gas. It is more efficient than the incandescent lamp of comparable wattage, and is used for interior and exterior lighting, especially where people work.

merger. the absorption of one corporation by another, including all of its assets.

mescaline. an hallucinogen derived from the peyote cactus. It is classified as a Schedule I Controlled Substance.

metal detector. a device used to detect the presence of metallic objects. It operates by creating a balanced magnetic field between transmitting and receiving coils. The movement of a sufficient volume of metal through the field causes an imbalance which triggers an alarm. Sensitivity is a function of coil characteristics.

metal foil. a thin strip of metal usually installed on glass. A break in the foil results in an alarm.

metal fracture examination. a crime laboratory examination which seeks to determine if a piece of metal was or was not broken from an object such as a knife or screwdriver.

metal halide lamp. a lamp that emits a harsh yellow-colored light caused by an electric current passing through a tube of conducting illuminous gas, usually sodium, phallium, indium or mercury.

metallurgy examination. a crime laboratory examination which seeks to determine if two metals or metallic objects came from the same source or from each other. The examination is based on surface and microstructural characteristics, mechanical properties and composition.

metal-mesh grille. a grille of expanded metal or welded metal wires permanently installed across a window or other opening in order to prevent entry through the opening.

metal oxide varistor. in an access control system, a device installed on a relay control line and/or incoming power source for the purpose of neutralizing excess electrical impulses.

metazocine. an opiate classified as a Schedule II Controlled Substance.

methadone. an opiate classified as a Schedule II Controlled Substance. It is a synthetic narcotic which prevents withdrawal symptoms and the craving to use other opiates.

methadone maintenance. a type of drug detoxification program which uses methadone, a substitute for heroin and other opiates. Patients being treated in a methadone maintenance program are not inclined to seek and buy illegal drugs, which are often associated with crime.

methamphetamine. a commonly abused stimulant drug. It is classified as a Schedule III Controlled Substance. Also called crank, go fast, speed and crystal.

methane. a light, gaseous, flammable paraffin hydrocarbon that is the chief component of natural gas and an important basic hydrocarbon for petrochemical manufacture.

methaqualone. a commonly abused narcotic drug.

methohexital. a drug classified as a Schedule IV Controlled Substance.

methyldesorphine. an opium derivative classified as a Schedule I Controlled Substance.

methylene blue. a dye stuff used to mark an object so that a detectable amount will be transferred to the body or property of a person who handled the object.

methylhydromorphine. an opium derivative classified as a Schedule I Controlled Substance.

methylphenidate. a stimulant classified as a Schedule III Controlled Substance.

methylphenobarbital. a drug classified as a Schedule IV Controlled Substance.

methyprylon. a depressant classified as a Schedule III Controlled Substance.

metric ton. a measurement equal to 1000 kg or 2204.6 lb avoirdupois.

microcomputer. a small computer with limited memory and functions appropriate for small to mid-sized computerized security systems.

microphonic cable. an intrusion sensor installed underground and which reacts to pressure at ground surface.

microprocessor-based sensor. a motion detector, usually ultrasonic or passive infrared, which is enhanced by a microprocessor. In the ultrasonic type, the microprocessor memorizes the environment to detect true point-to-point motion. In the PIR type, the characteristics of intruder motion are stored in memory and matched against detected motions.

microprocessor controller. a device that drives the computer program stored in the read only memory (ROM) and the random access memory (RAM). The program contains access authorization data such as areas allowed for entry and time frames for entry.

microscope photometry. a crime laboratory technique for comparing samples on the basis of light absorption. By measuring the light absorption of two samples at all wavelengths, an examiner can identify differences which are indistinguishable to the human eye.

microtaggants. tiny magnetized particles mixed with or attached to high-theft items. In addition to being magnetized (to facilitate detection of their presence), microtaggants are coded to provide valuable investigative leads. They are usually added to paints used in marking items, but have also been mixed with animal feed and fertilizers.

microwave motion detection. a means for detecting intrusion by the use of radio frequency transmitting and receiving equipment.

microwaves. radio frequencies generally higher than 1000 megahertz.

microwave sensor. an active intrusion sensor that detects the movement of a person or object through a pattern of microwave energy. Microwave sensors which use the Doppler Effect to recognize movement within a protected area (monostatic sensors) are most effective for indoor applications. Microwave sensors employing the beam break principle (bistatic) are often used in outdoor applications.

Middle East connection. a phrase describing the flow of narcotics from Iran and Turkey through local laboratories via Iranian and Turkish traffickers to distributors in Europe, Canada, the US and Mexico.

military jurisdiction. an area within which various individuals, organizations, agencies, or some other instrumentality of the armed forces of the United States exercises the broad police powers of government rather than civilian individuals, organizations, agencies, or other groups normally empowered to do so. The exercise of military jurisdiction is always closely circumscribed and is normally based on either constitutional provisions or international law, including the law of war.

military law. the jurisdiction exercised by the military establishment over its own members and those connected with it, under certain conditions, to promote good order and discipline. It is that body of federal statutes enacted by Congress, as implemented by regulations of the President and the armed services and interpreted through custom and usage, governing the organization and operation of the armed services in peace and war.

military offense. an offense applicable within the military environment but which has no parallel offense in the civil environment. Absent without leave, desertion and improper wearing of the uniform are military offenses.

mill finish. the original surface finish produced on a metal mill product by cold rolling, extruding or drawing.

mil spec. an abbreviated way of saying that a component or piece of equipment meets or exceeds military specifications.

mineralogy examination. a crime laboratory examination of materials that are mostly inorganic, crystalline or mineral in character. A mineralogy examination is intended to connect a suspect person or objects to a crime scene, prove or disprove an alibi, produce investigative leads or substantiate a theorized claim of events. Materials commonly examined include glass, building materials, soil, debris, industrial dusts, safe insulations, ores, abrasives and gems.

minicomputer. a medium-capacity computer that in scope and function falls between a microcomputer and a mainframe computer.

minimum footcandles. the lowest illumination value at any point on a lighted surface.

minimum-maximum term. a sentence in which the convicted person cannot be released before serving a minimum period, less time off for good behavior, or kept in prison longer than the maximum period, less time off for good behavior. In between the minimum and maximum, the prisoner is eligible for parole.

minimum security. security measures observed in a correctional institution or detention facility where relative freedom is granted to prisoners and visitors, congruent with the concept of involuntary detention, and where lesser emphasis is placed on preventing escapes.

Minnesota Multiphasic Personality Inventory. a paper and pencil test that measures degrees of hypochondriasis, depression, hysteria, psychopathic deviation, masculinity-femininity, paranoia, psychasthenia, schizophrenia, hypomania and social introversion. This test is widely used in personnel selection and counseling procedures.

Minor Derogatory Information. as used in Department of Defense security, information that by itself is not of sufficient importance or magnitude to justify an adverse action in a personnel security determination.

Miranda rights. the set of rights which a person accused or suspected of having committed a specific offense has during interrogation, and of which he must be informed prior to questioning, as stated by the US Supreme Court in deciding Miranda v. Arizona and related cases.

Miranda vs. Arizona. a case in which the U.S. Supreme Court ruled that whenever the police are about to interrogate someone who is in their custody, or who has "otherwise been deprived by the authorities of his freedom in any significant way," that person must be given the following warnings: (1) that he has a right to remain silent, and that he need not answer any questions; (2) that if he does answer questions his answers may be used as evidence against him; (3) that he has a right to consult with a lawyer before or during the questioning of him by the police; and (4) that if he cannot afford to hire a lawyer one will be provided for him without costs.

misapplication. improper, illegal, wrongful or corrupt use or application of funds.

miscarriage of justice. a gross error in the outcome of a criminal case, generally applied to the conviction and punishment of an innocent defendant.

misdemeanor. an offense usually punishable by incarceration for a period of which the upper limit is prescribed by law in a given jurisdiction, typically limited to a year or less.

misfeasance. the improper performance of a lawful act.

misprision. failure in the duty of a citizen to try to prevent a crime, or having knowledge of a crime, fails to reveal it to the proper authorities.

misprision of a felony. receiving or offering to give a monetary or other consideration in return for a promise not to prosecute or aid in the prosecution of a criminal offender. Also known as compounding a crime.

missing person. a person reported missing who is under 18 or who, being 18 or over, is seriously affected mentally or physically, or is absent under circumstances that indicate involuntary disappearance.

mistake of fact. a defense based on the grounds that a defendant did not know certain essential facts, that he could not have been expected to know them, and that there could be no crime without such knowledge.

mistake of law. a defense, rarely allowed, offered by an accused that he did not know his act was criminal or did not comprehend the consequences of his act.

mistrial. a trial terminated or declared void before a verdict is reached, because of some procedural defect, impediment, or error that will prejudice a jury, or because the jury has not been able to agree on a verdict. When there is a mistrial, a new trial can be held without double jeopardy, unless the defendant has objected to the mistrial and an appellate court holds that the mistrial was improperly declared by the trial judge, i.e., that the mistrial was neither necessary nor required by the interests of justice.

mitigating circumstances. circumstances that do not constitute a justification or excuse of an offense, but which may be considered as extenuating or reducing the degree of moral culpability. Also called extenuating circumstances.

mixed media communications. a manner of transmitting data through a combination of media such as radio, optical link, telephone lines and common twisted wire pair.

M'Naghten rule. the rule laid down by the House of Lords after the 1843 verdict of "not guilty by reason of insanity" in the case of Daniel M'Naghten. The rule stated that the perpetrator of the crime is not to be held criminally responsible if, at the time of the act, he suffered from a disease of the mind either making him unable to know the nature of the act he was committing or, if he did know it, making him unable to realize that what he was doing was wrong.

mnemonic code. a code that assists the memory by grouping characters to resemble original words.

mobile assistance team. a defensive team of USAF personnel who perform specialized antiterrorism services in response to a specific need. Team members are typically AFOSI special agents, security policemen, civil engineers, communications specialists and others as the team's mission may dictate.

Model Arson Law. a statute recommended by the National Fire Protection Association which has been adopted in many states.

Model Penal Code. a statute recommended in 1962 by the American Law Institute which has been adopted in many states.

Model Sentencing Act. a sentencing proposal drawn up in 1963 by the Advisory Council of Judges of the National Council on Crime and Delinquency.

model statute. a proposed statute, recommended to a legislature for adoption, which can serve several jurisdictions.

modem. a device that modulates (or converts) signals for sending over communications facilities and demodulates (or reconverts) signals being received. The term is derived from modulator and demodulator.

modified general question technique. in polygraphy, a testing approach consisting of a series of relevant, non-relevant and control questions asked in a planned order.

modulated wave. a wave of which either the amplitude, frequency or phase is varied in accordance with another wave. A combination of two or more waves which results in the production of frequencies not present in the original waves, these new frequencies being ordinarily made up of sums and differences of integral multiples of the frequencies present in the original waves.

modulator. electronic circuitry used to impress information on a carrier by instantaneously varying its amplitude (AM) or frequency (FM).

modus operandi. a characteristic pattern of behavior repeated in a series of offenses that coincides with the pattern evidenced by a particular single person, or by a particular group of persons working together.

modus operandi file. a file that records information concerning the distinct techniques applied in crimes of various types and the criminals or groups known to have applied those techniques.

moisture detector. a sensor that causes a contact closure when sufficient moisture creates an electrical bridge. It is used in equipment cabinets and electrical conduits.

mold. in criminal investigation, a negative impression of an object. Details on the mold will be reversed when the mold and object are viewed together. A mold is used to make a cast, which is a positive representation of the object.

Molotov Cocktail. a bottle or other breakable container containing a flammable liquid into which has been placed a wick or similar igniting device, and which bottle or container when ignited and thrown will cause a fire or explosion.

money clip. a hold-up sensor designed to trigger an alarm when paper money is removed from its special clip causing a contact closure. The clip is typically kept in the drawer of a cash register.

monitor. in CCTV applications, a device that displays on the face of a picture tube the images detected and transmitted by a television camera; an instrument that reports the performance of a control device or signals if unusual conditions appear in a system; to electronically watch, check and/or receive signals from an alarm system.

monitoring. the act of listening-in or eavesdropping on telephone lines or room conversations.

monitoring by exception. an electronic alerting system which annunciates only when an undesirable act takes place.

monitoring station. the place at which security officers or other designated persons monitor security system annunciators or alarm receivers.

Monroe Effect. the concentrating of explosive force through the shape of the charge.

montage synthesizer. a device that creates composite photographs of criminal suspects. It consists of a montage mounting unit, a television camera, and a television monitor. Photographs selected by a witness from a mug shot file are placed on the mounting unit and viewed through the monitor. The camera synthesizes up to four photographs at a time and adjusts for skin tone and texture, allowing any feature mix of gender and racial characteristics. When the victim is satisfied that the composite likeness corresponds to the suspect's likeness, a photograph is taken from the monitor screen.

moot point. a point or issue not settled by judicial decision. Frequently, a moot point is an abstract question which does not arise upon existing facts or rights in a case.

moral holidays. occasions when enforcement of the laws is relaxed and the police are indulgent, as during many athletic events, election celebrations, fraternal conventions, the Mardi Gras, and New Year's Eve.

moral offense. a general descriptor for a crime that offends morals or public health. Examples of moral offenses are sodomy, adultery, bigamy, prostitution, desertion, gambling, and drug abuse.

morals squad. a police unit dealing with prostitution, gambling, pornography and other offenses deemed detrimental to the morals of a community. Also called a vice squad.

moral turpitude. a legal term describing a crime found shocking to the sense of decency or to the morals of a community; a showing of conduct contrary to justice, honesty, modesty or good morals.

morbid criminal propensity. a natural inclination or uncontrollable impulse to engage in unlawful behavior.

morning-glory seeds. a source of an hallucinogen used by American Indians and others.

morning report. a report of activities that occurred in the previous 24 hours.

morpheridine. an opiate classified as a Schedule I Controlled Substance.

morphine. a commonly abused narcotic drug. Also called morph, morpho and cube.

morphine methylbromide. an opium derivative classified as a Schedule I Controlled Substance.

morphine methylsulfonate. an opium derivative classified as a Schedule I Controlled Substance.

morphine-N-oxide. an opium derivative classified as a Schedule I Controlled Substance.

mortise cylinder. a cylinder whose core may be removed by the use of a special key.

mortise bolt. a bolt designed to be installed in a mortise rather than on the surface. The bolt is operated by a knob, lever or equivalent.

mortise lock. a lock designed for installation in a mortise, as distinguished from a bored lock and rim lock.

Mosaic Code. the law of the Old Testament, particularly as expressed in the Ten Commandments.

motherboard. the primary electronic printed-circuit board in a piece of equipment. It usually interfaces with one or more secondary circuits.

motion. an oral or written request made by a party to an action, before, during or after a trial, that a court issue a rule or order.

motion detection alarm. a system that works on the principle that any motion in an area will upset an established balance and cause an alarm to be given. A motion detection alarm is usually based on the use of ultrasonic or radio frequency sound waves.

motion for a new trial. a motion by a defendant alleging certain errors committed in the course of his trial. If the trial judge agrees, the conviction is set aside and the defendant may be tried again by a new jury and usually before a different judge. A defendant may also seek a new trial on the grounds of newly discovered evidence favorable to him.

motion-initiated bomb. a bomb engineered to explode when it is moved. It is usually constructed so that movement brings objects or elements into contact, e.g., hypergolic chemicals or contact wires. The motion-initiated bomb is a type of booby trap.

motion to quash an arrest warrant. a motion made before trial by an arrested person alleging that the warrant was defective. If the motion is granted, the arrest is declared illegal and any evidence obtained incident to the arrest cannot be used at trial. However, if the circumstances under which the arrest was made would have justified an arrest without a warrant, the arrest may still be valid and seized evidence admissible.

motion to quash the indictment. a motion by a defendant which questions the legal sufficiency of an indictment. If the court agrees with the motion, the indictment is deemed invalid. The prosecutor can appeal the ruling and/or seek a proper indictment. A subsequent indictment would not violate the constitutional protection against double jeopardy.

motion to suppress evidence. a motion made by the defense attorney, in the absence of the jury, to suppress from introduction into evidence any evidence obtained in violation of the defendant's constitutional rights. Usually such rights are related to the 4th, 5th and 6th Amendments (search and seizure, self-incrimination, right to counsel and right of confrontation with witnesses).

motive. the reason why something is done. The motive for robbery, for example, would be to get possession of property owned by someone else.

moulage-agar. a colloidal substance of the compound agar used to make finely detailed

casts of foot and tire prints, tool marks and parts of the human body.

movable evidence. evidence that can be easily collected and transported, such as handguns, knives and documents.

movement control center. in nuclear security, an operations center which is remote from transport activity and which maintains periodic position information on the movement of strategic nuclear material, receives reports of attempted attacks or thefts, provides a means for reporting these and other problems to appropriate agencies and can request and coordinate appropriate aid.

moving coil microphone. a microphone having a moveable conductor in the form of a coil. Electric output results from motion of the coil in a magnetic field at an audio frequency rate.

mugging. a type of strong-arm robbery in which the offender approaches the victim from behind, usually suddenly and with stealth.

mug shot. a police-file photograph of a criminal's face, full-view and side-view.

mullion. a movable or fixed center post used on double door openings, usually for locking purposes; a vertical or horizontal bar or divider in a frame between windows, doors or other openings.

multicoupler. a device which connects several receivers to one antenna. Also called a signal splitter.

multilevel security mode. a mode of operation that provides a capability for various levels and categories or compartments of data to be concurrently stored and processed in an automated data processing system and permits selective access to such material concurrently by users who have differing access privileges and need-to-know rights.

multipath. the possible routes for a single beam of rf energy between two points caused by many reflecting surfaces.

multiple dwelling. a building or portion of a building designed or used for occupancy by three or more tenants or families living independently of each other.

multiple personality. a rare dissociative disorder characterized by a division of the personality into two or more complete behavior organizations, each well-defined and highly distinct from the others.

multiple points of origin. in arson investigations, two or more unconnected points where fire started. Since accidental fires have only one point of origin, the existence of multiple starting points is strongly indicative of arson.

multiple reference. the practice of establishing at least two identifiers when determining the identity of an unidentified corpse. Tattoos, scars and dental work are examples of identifiers.

multiplexing. a signal method that uses wire path, cable carrier, or radio carrier or combinations of these. It is characterized by the simultaneous and/or sequential transmission and reception of multiple signals in a communications channel including means for positive identification of each signal.

multipurpose dry chemical. a fire extinguishing agent consisting of ammonium phosphate as the base powder plus additives.

mummification. a process in which the tissues of the body become dehydrated. The process requires a hot, dry climate, devoid of the moisture required by bacteria. In this process the skin will have a leathery appearance. Infants killed immediately after birth are sterile, limiting bacterial organisms to those that enter from outside the body. Also, the small size of an infant body permits mummification to progress more rapidly than is the case with an adult body.

muntin. a structural member of a sash which extends either horizontally between the stiles or vertically between the rails to support individual panes of glazing material when the sash incorporates two or more panes.

murder. intentionally causing the death of another without reasonable provocation or legal justification, or causing the death of another while committing or attempting to commit another crime.

murder board. a panel of specially selected persons charged to review a briefing, presentation or public release.

Murphy game. a confidence game wherein money is taken from a customer, often by a pimp, to pay a prostitute who does not show up.

muscle power attack. the use of brute, physical strength to defeat a physical barrier, usually in connection with a forced entry through a window or door.

mushroom button. a button shaped like a mushroom which is typically used for emergency purposes, such as to shut off power equipment or summon help.

mushroom tumbler. a type of tumbler used in pin tumbler locks to add security against picking. The diameter of the driver pin behind the end in contact with the bottom pin is reduced so that the mushroom head will catch the edge of the cylinder body at the shear line when it is at a slight angle to its cavity.

Mutt and Jeff technique. an interrogation technique in which a first interrogator presents himself to the subject as being harsh and unsympathetic. A second interrogator takes the side of the subject and seeks to gain his confidence by being kind and sympathetic.

myrophine. an opium derivative classified as a Schedule I Controlled Substance.

N

name index file. a file that contains cross-indexing data on subjects, victims, witnesses, organizations, etc. This type of file is usually a locator file that assists in identifying larger records concerning the person or organization under investigation.

name position bond. a type of fidelity bond which covers losses caused by the dishonesty of only those employees holding positions specifically named in the bond.

name schedule bond. a type of fidelity bond which covers losses caused by the dishonesty of only those employees specifically named in the bond.

Napoleonic Code. the code of laws adopted in France by the regime of Napoleon Bonaparte in 1810 and revised in 1819. The Napoleonic Code became the basis for the criminal code in most continental European and Latin American countries.

narcoanalysis. memory analysis with the assistance of a narcotic such as sodium amytal. The technique usually seeks details concerning a traumatic experience so that associated emotional problems can be treated. It can also be used for criminal investigation purposes when the victim is unable to recall details.

narcotic analgesic. a drug used clinically to decrease pain. Morphine and other alkaloids of opium are narcotic analgesics.

narrow band FM. a special form of FM modulation where the deviation caused by the modulation process about the main carrier is less than normal.

National Agency Check. a Department of Defense personnel security investigation consisting of a records review of certain national agencies, including a technical fingerprint search of the FBI files. Also called an NAC.

National Agency Check and Inquiry. a Department of Defense personnel security investigation conducted by the Office of Personnel Management, combining an NAC and written inquiries to law enforcement agencies, former employers and supervisors, references and schools.

National Automobile Altered Numbers File. a collection of specimens of altered vehicle identification numbers found on stolen cars, trucks and heavy equipment. The file is maintained by the FBI Laboratory so that comparisons can be made to identify recovered stolen vehicles, and possibly link them with known commercial theft rings.

National Crime Information Center. a computerized information system operated by the FBI for the handling and exchange of documented police data used by law enforcement agencies at local, state and federal levels.

National Crime Survey Program. a statistical program administered by the Bureau of Justice Statistics (formerly the National Criminal Justice Information and Statistics Service of LEAA) with data collected by the Bureau of the Census. It provides information on the extent to which persons 12 years of age and older and households have been victimized by selected crimes. Data are collected on the incidence of crimes, and circumstances under which the events occurred, the effects on the victim, and whether or not incidents were reported to the police.

National Defense Area. an area established on non-federal lands located within the United States, its possessions or territories, for the purpose of safeguarding classified defense information, or protecting Department of Defense equipment and/or material. Establishment of a National Defense Area temporarily places such non-federal lands under the effective control of the Department of Defense and results only from an emergency event. The senior Department of Defense representative at the scene defines the boundary, marks it with a physical barrier, and posts warning signs. The land owner's consent and cooperation is obtained whenever possible; however, military necessity dictates the final decision regarding location, shape and size of the area.

National Electrical Code. a standard electrical code published by the National Fire Protection Association. It is frequently referred to as "code" or "the code."

National Fire Protection Association. an organization that creates and promotes standards for fire protection and fire prevention equipment.

National Fraudulent Check File. a collection of checks, writings and other documentary materials maintained by the FBI Laboratory for use in identifying individuals involved in fraudulent check schemes and in determining if questioned documents originated from the same source.

National Labor Relations Board vs. Weingarten. a case in which the US Supreme Court upheld a National Labor Relations Board ruling that a denial of an employee's request to have a union representative present at an "investigatory interview" that the employee reasonably believed might result in disciplinary action constitutes an unfair labor practice.

national security. as used in federal government security, the national defense and foreign relations of the United States.

National Security Area. an area established on non-federal lands located within the United States, its possessions, or territories, for the purpose of safeguarding classified and/or restricted data information, or protecting Department of Energy equipment and/or material. Establishment of a NSA temporarily places such non-federal lands under the effective control of the DOE and results only from an emergency event. The senior DOE representative having custody of the material at the scene defines the boundary, marks it with a physical barrier, and posts warning signs. The landowner's consent and cooperation is obtained whenever possible; however, operational necessity dictates the final decision regarding location, shape, and size.

National Vehicle Identification Number Standard File. a collection of VIN plates from each factory of the major manufacturers of U.S.-made automobiles. The file is maintained by the FBI Laboratory for the purpose of comparing suspected counterfeit VIN plates against the standards on file.

NATO Classified Information. military, political, and economic information circulated within and by members of the North Atlantic Treaty Organization, whether such information originates in the organization itself or is received from member nations or from other international organizations.

NCIC Agency Identifier. a nine-character code identifying specific law enforcement and criminal justice agencies in the United States and Canada. Assigned by NCIC, these identifiers designate originators of NCIC records and other law enforcement or criminal justice agency transactions.

near contact gunshot wound. a wound caused when the muzzle at time of discharge is approximately two inches or less from the victim.

necessity. the defense of justification of an otherwise criminal act on the ground that the perpetrator was compelled to commit it because a greater evil would have ensued had he failed to do so. Thus, one could plead necessity if he committed arson to destroy official documents that would otherwise have fallen into the hands of a wartime enemy.

necrophilia. sexual intercourse with a dead body; literally, love of the dead; morbid perversion which seeks sexual gratification from mutilation of the dead.

necropsy. examination of a dead body; an autopsy.

needle habit. the habit of taking drugs by injection. The habit usually follows a progression: intradermal injection (scratchings just under the skin); subcutaneous injection (skin popping); intramuscular injection (piercing into the muscles); and intravenous injection (piercing into the vein).

need-to-know. in federal government security, a determination made by a possessor of classified information that a prospective recipient, in the interest of national security, has a requirement for access to, or knowledge, or possession of the classified information in order to perform tasks or services essential to the fulfillment of an official United States government program. Knowledge or possession of, or access to classified information is not afforded to any individual solely by virtue of the individual's office, position, or security clearance.

negative impression tool mark. a mark made when a tool is pressed against or into a receiving surface.

negative pressure phase. the second phase of a blast wave in which air pressure rapidly decreases to a point less than normal creating a suction effect.

negative proof of arson. a method of proving in court the incendiary origin of a fire by eliminating every potential accidental or natural cause for the fire.

negligence. the doing of that thing which a reasonably prudent person would not have done, or the failure to do that thing which a reasonably prudent person would have done in like or similar circumstances. It is the failure to exercise that degree of care and prudence that reasonably prudent persons would have exercised in similar circumstances. Negligence cases are usually filed under state tort laws.

negligent manslaughter. death resulting from failure to use ordinary care, or from being culpably careless and imprudent.

neoclassicism. a trend in the history of criminal justice and criminology that flourished in the early nineteenth century in Europe. It modified the views of the classical school of criminology by introducing the concepts of diminished criminal responsibility and less severe punishment because of the age or mental condition of the perpetrator.

net luminaire utilization. the percentage of lamp lumens utilized on the area to be lighted.

net present value. a financial indicator that takes cash flow and discounts it at the service organization's cost of funds.

net quick assets. the difference between allowable current assets and changeable current liabilities. This figure is referred to as the working capital. For example, a businessman must have adequate working capital in order to meet operating costs.

net worth. the owner's equity in a given business represented by the excess of the total assets over the total amounts owing to outside creditors (total liabilities) at a given moment in time. Also, the net worth of an individual as determined by deducting the amount of all his personal liabilities from the total value of his personal assets.

neurasthenia. weakness, chronic fatigue, lack of enthusiasm, numerous bodily complaints.

neurosis. any condition in which a person develops some maladaptive behavior as a protection against unconscious anxiety.

neurotic depressive reaction. a psychoneurotic reaction characterized by persistent dejection and discouragement.

neutral density card. a photographer's tool for checking the density of colors in photographs. A crime scene technician may use it to verify that colors of objects photographed at a crime scene have been faithfully recorded.

neutral density filter. a glass or plastic material tinted grey for the purpose of reducing the amount of light entering a lens. A neutral density filter does not affect the color tone of the light. A filter can be mounted on the front or rear of a lens. It is used where a camera is subject to bright light or high reflectivity.

neutral question. in polygraphy, a question that is not pertinent to the issue for which a subject is tested. It is used to identify the "normal" pattern of reaction to non-threatening issues. Neutral questions are also called non-crucial, immaterial, non-pertinent and irrelevant questions.

neutron activation analysis. an analysis to determine chemical elements in a material by bombarding it with neutrons to produce radioactive atoms whose radiations are characteristic of the elements present. The technique has many forensic applications; for example, to determine the presence of lead, antimony, and barium in residue taken from the skin of a person believed to have fired a gun. Also called activation analysis.

newly discovered evidence. evidence of a new and material fact, or new evidence in relation to a fact in issue, discovered by a party to a cause after the rendition of a verdict or judgment therein; any new evidence, whether the facts existed at the time of the trial or not.

Newvicon. the trade name for a very sensitive video-image pickup tube that uses a cadmium and zinc-telluride target. The Newvicon is similar to a silicon tube because it uses a fixed target voltage. When used for low light situations, it provides good resolution and minimal burn-in and lag.

next best evidence. evidence used when the best or better evidence is lost or inaccessible. For example, next best evidence would be oral testimony and/or a copy of an original document that cannot be found.

NHSB National Register Service. a computerized record maintained by the National Highway Safety Bureau which identifies persons whose licenses to drive have been denied, terminated or temporarily withdrawn.

Nicad battery. the trade name of a battery with low-temperature and discharge characteristics and a relatively long and trouble-free operational life. The electrodes are made of nickel and cadmium, hence the name Nicad.

night latch. an auxiliary lock having a spring latch bolt and functioning independently of the regular lock of the door.

night vision device. any type of viewing device that employs infrared or low-light technology to produce discernible images of objects that are in near total darkness. Light levels as that provided on a dark night by a single star are sufficient for some night vision devices to produce images.

nihilist. a person devoted to the destruction of the present political, religious, or social institutions.

ninhydrin. a solution used to develop latent fingerprint impressions. A color reaction is produced when ninhydrin contacts with amino acids in the perspiration content of fingerprints.

nitric acid lift technique. a technique for collecting gunpowder residue from the skin of a suspect. Swabs moistened with a solution of nitric acid are used as the collecting agent. The swabs are later analyzed in the crime laboratory.

nitrocotton. collodion cotton dissolved in nitroglycerin.

nitroglycerin. a highly explosive substance that usually appears as an odorless, oily and milky liquid. Aging destabilizes nitroglycerin, causing it to turn yellow and eventually take on a greenish tint. Destabilized nitroglycerin is extremely hazardous. Also called nitro.

nitroglycerin/ammonium nitrate. a type of commercial dynamite made from a combination of nitroglycerin and ammonium sulfate. It is a gelatinous substance that may be sticky and rubber-like in appearance.

no bill. a determination by a grand jury that not enough evidence was found to warrant charging the defendant with a crime. Similar terms include "not found" and "not a true bill."

no deception indicated. an opinion reached by a polygraphist based on an interpretation of polygrams. Also called NDI.

noise. an undesirable electrical disturbance affecting performance of a circuit or electrical system.

noise generator. a device used to cover up voices in a room for the purpose of defeating electronic surveillance. The noise produced is generated randomly and from several alternating frequencies so as to defeat a filter applied to clean up a recording of conversations.

no-knock entry. a police procedure permitted in some jurisdictions to avoid giving suspects time to destroy evidence, escape, or prepare to resist.

nolle prosequi. a formal entry upon the record by the prosecuting officer in a criminal case, by which he declares that he "will no further prosecute" the case, either as to some of the counts, or some of the defendants, or altogether.

nolo contendere. a Latin term meaning "I will not contest it." It has the same legal effect as a plea of guilty, so far as regards all proceedings on the indictment, and on which the defendant may be sentenced.

nominal voltage. the voltage of a fully charged battery cell when providing rated current to a circuit.

non-breakglass station. a manual fire alarm station in which the operation of the station does not require the breaking of a glass plate or rod.

non-coded system. a system in which a continuous alarm signal is transmitted for a predetermined, minimum length of time, after which the fire alarm system may be manually or automatically silenced.

non compos mentis. not of sound mind; insane. A general term that embraces all varieties of mental derangement.

non-delay impact fuse. a bomb fuse designed to function upon impact with a hard surface, prior to its complete penetration or ricochet.

nondirective interviewing. an interview in which the interviewer does not guide the discussion, but says only enough to encourage the interviewee to express himself freely.

non-emotional offender. a person who commits crimes without regard to the nature of the crime or the effect of it on the victim. A person who kills for financial gain is considered a non-emotional offender.

non-encrypting transformation. a method for protecting information so sensitive it should not be available in a plaintext form after its initial generation and distribution. A non-encrypting transformation converts plaintext data into ciphertext in such a way that the process is computationally infeasible to reverse or absolutely irreversible. Also called non-reversible transformation and one-way encryption.

nonfeasance. nonperformance of some act which ought to be performed; omission to perform a required duty; neglect of duty.

Nonimmigrant Index. a file maintained by the Immigration and Naturalization Service which contains names and descriptive data of persons admitted to the US for temporary periods of time, and who must eventually depart.

non-negligent manslaughter. the intentional killing of another in the heat of passion or as a result of provoked anger.

non-removable hinge pin. a type of hinge pin that has been constructed or modified to make its removal from the hinge difficult or impossible.

non-secretor. a person whose blood may be grouped but whose body fluids may not be grouped due to low concentrations of group specific substances.

non-significant code. a code that provides for the identification of a particular fact but does not yield any further information, e.g., random numbers used as codes.

non-simultaneous transmission. half duplex, or one-way transmission at a time over a pair. Also referred to as duplex.

nonvolatile memory. a feature of a system having memory components that retain all memory when power is entirely absent. Equipment with nonvolatile memory provides a critical advantage in high-security applications or when reprogramming requires a considerable effort.

no opinion. a conclusion rendered by a polygraphist when an examination cannot be completed and that future testing is projected to be unproductive or unwarranted. A no opinion conclusion can result from uncooperative behavior by the examinee, a lack of emotional response, or the presence of extreme, erratic responses.

normal distribution. a bell-shaped, symmetrical distribution in which mean, median, and mode are the same.

normally closed. the condition of a circuit or switch that is in a no-fault state. The circuit is complete and current is able to flow. A break in the circuit triggers an alarm.

normally open. the condition of a circuit or switch that is in a no-fault state. The circuit is open and current is unable to flow. Closing the circuit completes a current path and an alarm condition is initiated.

nose loading. in transportation security, the practice of placing high-value cargo in the forward end of a truck, with bulky low-value cargo behind it in a blocking fashion.

no significant reaction. in polygraphy, the absence of a strong deceptive pattern in the polygrams of a tested person.

notary public. a public officer authorized to attest and certify, by his hand and official seal, certain classes of documents, to administer oaths and do other official acts.

notched bullet. a lead bullet which has a portion removed by cutting or filing and which will flatten out upon contact.

not guilty by reason of insanity. the plea of a defendant or the verdict of a jury or judge in a criminal proceeding that the defendant is not guilty of the offense charged because at the time the crime was committed the defendant did not have the mental capacity to be held criminally responsible for his or her actions. A plea or verdict of "not guilty by reason of insanity" differs from other not guilty pleas and verdicts in that the claim or finding is not based on what the defendant is alleged or determined to have done, but rather on the issue of whether he or she possessed the mental capacity to be held responsible for a criminal act. A verdict of "not guilty by reason of insanity" differs from a court finding that a defendant is incompetent to stand trial which concerns only the defendant's mental fitness at the time of trial, and is not related to the question of guilt.

notice. a formal communication, as to the defendant in a lawsuit, advising him of what further action is intended.

notice of alibi. information that the defense is required to give to the prosecution before a trial if a defense of alibi will be made, that is, if the defense will contend that the accused was elsewhere at the time of the crime. Such a notice is necessary so that the prosecution may investigate before the trial and be prepared for cross-examination and rebuttal.

no true bill. the decision by a grand jury that it will not return an indictment against the person accused of a crime on the basis of the allegations and evidence presented by the prosecutor. A grand jury finding of no true bill after a complaint has been filed in lower court may be a defendant disposition, terminating criminal justice jurisdiction over the defendant in those jurisdictions where the felony trial phase is initiated by the filing of a grand jury indictment. A grand jury, after its consideration of a case, can decide: to issue an indictment; not to issue an indictment; or to ignore felony charges, but refer the case back to the prosecutor for further prosecution on misdemeanor charges.

NRC-U special nuclear material access authorization. an access authorization based upon a National Agency Check and full-field background investigation conducted by the Office of Personnel Management.

Nuclear Accident and Incident Control Team. an Army team organized to minimize and prevent the loss of life, personal injury, hazardous effects, and destruction of property, to secure classified material, and to enhance and maintain the public's confidence in the Army's ability to effectively respond to a nuclear accident or incident.

nuclear contribution. explosive energy released by nuclear fission or fusion reactions, as part of the total energy released by the accidental explosion of a nuclear weapon. Any nuclear contribution equivalent to 4 or more pounds of TNT is considered significant, and would add beta and gamma radiation hazards to other radiological and toxic hazards present at a nuclear weapon accident site.

Nuclear Emergency Search Team. a Department of Energy asset which has specialized equipment for conducting radiation survey and detection, field communications, explosive ordnance damage support, bomb/weapon diagnostics, hazard prediction, damage mitigation, and decontamination.

nuclear incident. in nuclear security, any occurrence within the US causing bodily injury, sickness, disease, or death, or loss of or damage to property, or for loss of use of property, arising out of or resulting from the radioactive, toxic, explosive, or other hazardous properties of source, special nuclear, or byproduct material.

nuclear radiation. particulate and electromagnetic radiation emitted from atomic nuclei in various nuclear processes. The important nuclear radiations, from the weapons standpoint, are alpha and beta particles, gamma rays, and neutrons. All nuclear radiations are ionizing radiations, but the reverse is not true.

nuclear round. a nuclear weapon (warhead section) and the associated missile and/or propellant required to deliver the weapon on a target.

nuclear safing. the prevention of a nuclear yield in the event of accidental detonation of the HE of a high explosive assembly weapon or ignition of the propellant of a gun assembly weapon.

nuclear weapon. a general name given to any weapon in which the explosion results from the energy released by reactions involving atomic nuclei, either fission or fusion, or both.

nuclear weapon preinitiation. the initiation of

the fission or fusion chain reaction in the active material of a nuclear weapon at any time earlier than that at which the designed compression or degree of assembly is attained.

Nuclear Weapon Security Program. a Department of Defense program which places certain requirements on defense contractors involved with nuclear weapons. Among the requirements are security clearances and personnel reliability screening for persons holding positions categorized as critical or controlled.

nuclear weapon significant incident. an unexpected event involving nuclear weapons or radiological nuclear weapon components which does not fall in the nuclear weapon accident category but results in evident damage to a nuclear weapon or radiological nuclear weapon component to the extent that major rework, complete replacement, or examination or recertification by the Department of Energy is required, immediate action is required in the interest of safety or nuclear weapons security, adverse public reaction (national or international) or premature release of classified information may result, and that the incident could lead to a nuclear weapon accident.

nuclear yield. the energy released in the detonation of a nuclear weapon, measured in terms of the kilotons or megatons of trinitrotoluene (TNT) required to produce an equivalent energy release.

nuisance alarm. a false alarm; an alarm caused by equipment failure or a fault not related to an actual security violation.

numbers game. an unlawful game of chance in which money is wagered on the occurrence of a chosen number and in which a winner is usually paid at odds. In a numbers game, a person usually bets however much money he chooses on a single number. Any number of people can bet on the same number. The amount to be won is variable, depending on factors such as the amount of the person's bet, the total amount of all bets on the winning number, etc. The winning number is not randomly selected from the numbers bet on, but consists of a set of digits taken from an external source, such as the last three digits of the day's pari-mutuel gross receipts.

numerical evaluation. in polygraphy, any of several valid systems which apply numbers or number values to physiological responses graphically represented on polygrams.

O

oath. a solemn affirmation, declaration or other promise made under a sense of responsibility to God for the truth of what is stated.

obiter dictum. an observation, casual opinion, comment or remark not pertinent to a question or case at hand made by the presiding judge.

objection. an attempt to exclude evidence or testimony because it is improper. One lawyer might object to another lawyer's question to a witness, or to the answer given by a witness.

object protection. a class of protection for objects such as safes, vaults, files, cabinets or things of value that can be removed from a protected area.

object test. in polygraphy, a preliminary test intended to evaluate an examinee's reactions to a known lie. The examinee is asked to take and conceal on his or her person one object from a group of objects. The examinee is told to deny having taken the object when the question is asked during the object test. The deception pattern of the examinee is used by the polygraphist as a base of comparison with relevant questions in a subsequent test.

obscene matter. materials that appeal to prurient interest of the average person, applying contemporary standards of the community; materials that depict or describe sexual conduct in a patently offensive way; materials that lack serious literary, artistic, political or scientific value.

obsessive compulsive reaction. a psychoneurotic reaction characterized by persistent irrational thoughts and repetitive compulsions.

obstruction of justice. interference by act or omission with the proper performance of a judicial act; for example, an arrest or a lawful search, by such means as destroying records or giving false information.

occupational dose. in nuclear security, exposure of an individual to radiation in a restricted area or in the course of employment in which the individual's duties involve exposure to radiation.

oersted stripe. a type of magnetic stripe affixed to an access card.

offenses against public authority. a general descriptor for crimes affecting public authority and government. Examples include escape, perjury, resisting arrest, obstructing justice, misconduct in office and criminal contempt.

offenses against the public peace. a general descriptor for crimes affecting social order. Examples include breach of peace, unlawful assembly, public nuisance, riot, affray, disorderly conduct, vagrancy and drunkenness.

official records and business entries. a term relating to the admissibility of certain documents as an exception to the hearsay rule. Such a document is an official statement in writing made as a record of fact or event by an individual acting in the performance of an official duty, imposed upon him by law, regulation, or custom, to know or ascertain through appropriate and trustworthy channels of information the truth of the matter and to record it. The document may be admissible to prove the truth of such a matter.

offset pivot. a pin-and-socket hardware device with a single bearing contact, by means of which a door is suspended in its frame and allowed to swing about an axis which normally is located about 1.9 cm (3/4 in.) out from the door face.

ohm. the practical unit of electric resistance. One ohm is defined as the resistance which allows one ampere of current to flow through a conductor at one volt potential.

Ohm's law. the law stating that the current in an electric circuit is directly proportional to the electromotive force in the circuit. Ohm's law does not apply to all circuits. It is applicable to all metallic circuits and to many circuits containing an electrolytic resistance. Ohm's law was first enunciated for a circuit in which there is a constant electromotive force and an unvarying current. It is applicable to varying currents if account is taken of the induced electromotive force resulting from the self-inductance of the circuit and of the distribution of current in the cross-section of the circuit.

oiled block. a wooden or metal block coated with a thin film of oil. It is applied by a forger to paper to imitate a watermark.

old boys' network. a colloquialism referring to men who went to school together or belong to the same clubs who tend to help each other in the business world as the occasion arises.

omission. a failure to act that constitutes a crime when it involves nonperformance of an action the person is under a duty to perform as required by the law.

one-way encryption. a method for protecting information so sensitive it should not be available in a plaintext form after its initial generation and distribution. A one-way encryption converts plaintext into ciphertext in such a way that the process is computationally infeasible to reverse or is in fact absolutely irreversible. Also called privacy transformations or non-reversible transformations.

one-way screw. a screw specifically designed to resist being removed, once installed.

on-line. a peripheral device or piece of equipment that is part of a functional system, or a device connected to, and interacting with, a functional system.

on-line card access system. a system of card reader mechanisms attached to a computer.

"on the nod". the feeling experienced by a drug user going back and forth from alertness to drowsiness.

open bomb. a bomb in which all of the component parts are visible to the naked eye. Also called a straight bomb.

open circuit alarm. an alarm signal produced by opening or breaking an electrical circuit. Also called a break alarm.

open court. the time period during which a court is in session hearing cases.

open-end questioning. an interviewing technique in which the respondent is asked to tell what he knows in his own words and with minimum interruptions. The initial, prompting question is general as opposed to a question that can be answered with a yes or no response.

open head sprinkler. a fire sprinkler that activates upon the operation of a valve. It does not have a fusible link or other device that maintains the head in a closed position.

opening signal. a signal, transmitted from a protected premises to a central station or other monitoring location, which informs that the alarm system has been disarmed by an authorized person.

opening statements. statements made by the prosecuting and defense attorneys in which each outlines what he intends to prove during the trial. The purpose is to acquaint jurors with both sides of a case so it will be easier for them to follow the evidence as it is presented.

open system. any organism or organization that interacts with its environment.

open till pilferage. a technique used by a dishonest employee to steal from a cash register. The employee keeps the cash register drawer open, accepts payments for sales without ringing up the transactions, and steals the cash in excess of the registered ringups.

open to the jury. a part of the procedure of a civil or criminal trial in which each side has an opportunity to present his position to the jury and outline what he intends to prove.

operating system. as relates to computer software, an assemblage of programs or routines that control a computer's functions. It includes program execution and processing

times for the central processing unit, memory, and hardware input/output.

operational audit. an examination of a unit or phase of operations of the enterprise to assure that the activities being performed are consistent with expressed policy and generally recognized good practice.

operational control. the plan of organization and the procedures and records that are concerned with the decision process leading to management's authorization of transactions. Such authorization is a management function directly associated with the responsibility for achieving the objectives of the organization and is the starting point for establishing accounting control of transactions. Also called administrative control.

operational intelligence. intelligence required for planning and executing law enforcement and security operations.

Operation Identification. a crime-deterrent program in which homeowners mark their valuable items so that if stolen they may more readily be recovered by the police.

operative. a person who assumes a false identity for the purpose of obtaining information, usually concerning a criminal activity that cannot be discovered through conventional law enforcement methods.

opiates. a group of drugs, sometimes referred to as narcotics, used medically to relieve pain but which also have a high potential for abuse. Opiates derived from the Asian poppy include opium, morphine, heroin and codeine. Synthesized or manufactured opiates include meperidine and pethidine which are sold as Demerol and Mepergan.

opiate withdrawal. a body condition that usually begins within 4-6 hours after the last dose. Symptoms include uneasiness, diarrhea, abdominal cramps, chills, sweating, nausea, and runny eyes and nose. The intensity of symptoms depends on how much of the opiate substance was taken, how often, and for how long. Symptoms are generally strongest 24-72 hours after they begin and subside within 7-10 days.

opinion evidence. evidence of what the witness believes or infers in regard to facts in dispute, as distinguished from personal knowledge of facts. An expert witness might give opinion evidence. As a general rule, a witness can only testify to facts and not opinions or conclusions drawn from facts.

opinion of the court. a statement by which the court sets forth the factual and legal reasons for its decision.

opinion testimony. an exception to the general rule of evidence that prohibits a witness from testifying to anything other than facts of which he has direct knowledge. An opinion is a conclusion drawn by the witness and is admissible when no other description could be more accurate. As an example, witnesses are permitted to testify on such matters as distance, time, speed, size, weight, direction, form, identity, drunkenness, and similar matters, all of which require the witness to state his opinion. It is not essential for the witness to be an expert when he is giving testimony as to evidential facts such as these.

opioid. a substance that combines the actions of an analgesic, a hypnotic and a euphoriant.

opium. a narcotic substance appearing as dark brown chunks or as a powder and is usually smoked or eaten. Opium is found in Dover's Powder, Parapectolin and paregoric. It is used medically as an analgesic and antidiarrheal. Opium produces high physical and psychological dependence, and has a potential for abuse.

oppression. a wrongful act committed upon a person by a public officer under color of office; an act of cruelty, severity or unlawful exaction.

optical card. a type of access card containing rows of spots of varying transparency. The relative passage of light through the pattern of spots forms a readable code.

optical character recognition. the scanning of input data with an optical device that translates visual information into electronic impulses.

optical fiber. a glass fiber used to transmit light energy.

optimum service reliability. a desirable balance between service interruptions and the costs to improve service reliability.

optical scanner. an optical device used to translate visual information into electronic impulses.

optical turnstile. a turnstile used in conjunction with a badge or card reader and a CCTV camera. The turnstile has two upright columns with a beam passing between them. After an authorized person has been cleared for entry by the reader, the person passes through the turnstile and breaks the beam. A signal activates the CCTV camera and alerts a guard at a central monitoring location.

oral plea. a plea made by word of mouth in a court proceeding. Many jurisdictions require defendants to make oral pleas.

ordinance. a law passed by the law-making body of a city or town.

ordinary care. that care that a prudent man would take under the circumstances of the particular case.

organic nonvolatile poison. a class of poison which includes alkaloids (such as heroin and cocaine), barbiturates, glycosides, synthetic drugs, botulinus toxin and snake venom.

organic volatile poison. a class of poison which includes ethyl alcohol, aniline, phenol, gasoline, benzene and chloral hydrate.

organizational vulnerability. the total of susceptibilities to specific attack and the opportunity available to a hostile entity to mount that attack.

organization man. a person within an organization who accepts the values of the organization and finds harmony in conforming to its policies.

organized crime. a complex pattern of activity which includes the commission of statutorily defined offenses, in particular the provision of illegal goods and services but also carefully planned and coordinated instances of offenses of the fraud, theft and extortion groups, and which is uniquely characterized by the planned use of both legitimate and criminal professional expertise, and the use for criminal purposes of organizational features of legitimate business, including availability of large capital resources, disciplined management, division of labor, and focus upon maximum profit.

Organized Crime Intelligence System File. a computerized file and card index maintained by the Department of Justice. It includes financial information, participation in illegal organizations, business connections, associations, habits and other data pertaining to persons believed to be involved in organized crime activities.

original classification. an initial determination that information requires, in the interest of national security, protection against unauthorized disclosure, together with a classification designation signifying the level of protection required.

original jurisdiction. the lawful authority of a court or an administrative agency to hear or act upon a case from its beginning and to pass judgment on it.

o-r release. own-recognizance release, a legal device for freeing responsible citizens from going to jail or posting bail bond pending a court hearing.

oscillator. an electrical circuit that produces an audio tone or a radio frequency carrier.

outage. loss of signal in a channel, usually the result of a drop-out or a hit. Also a quantity of oil that is lost while in storage or being transported.

output. in communications, the signal level at the output of an amplifier or other device.

outside issue. in polygraphy, a circumstance unrelated to the primary issue being tested which poses a greater threat to the immediate well-being of the examinee than does the primary issue.

outside perimeter. a line of protection surrounding but not immediately adjacent to the structure or area under protection. A fence is a type of outside perimeter.

outside super-dampening concept. a concept in polygraphy which holds that an examinee may be so concerned over a matter not related to the polygraph examination that he is unable to form a psychological set on either the relevant or the control questions.

over-and-under gun. a double-barrelled gun whose barrels are stacked one above the other. Some over-and-under guns combine rifle and shotgun barrels.

overcharging. a police and prosecutor practice of charging or citing an offender with a more serious crime than actually committed or to charge a separate offense for every violation connected with the main offense. An objective of the practice is to strengthen the prosecutor's position in plea bargaining.

overcriminalization. enactment of legislation making marginal acts criminal and creating more criminal laws than can be enforced or are necessary.

overindictment. the inclusion in an indictment of charges that are more serious or more numerous than are warranted by the crime. This procedure is sometimes used as a negotiating tactic in plea bargaining.

overload. an excess of current passing through an electrical device.

overlook. in a numbers operation, a winning bet that was misplaced or overlooked in the daily tally.

overrecommend. to recommend a more severe sentence than would normally be imposed for a given offense so as to gain an advantage during any subsequent plea bargaining.

overt act. in criminal law, an open act which shows the intention of a person to commit a crime.

overt intelligence. information collected openly from public or open sources.

P

packy. a sneak thief who specializes in interrupting the flow of merchandise being unloaded from a truck and stealing some part of the cargo without being caught in the act.

padded book. a numbers book padded with many numbers placed after post time with the connivance of persons inside the numbers operation.

padding question. in polygraphy, a question inserted at the beginning and end of a probing peak of tension test. The padding questions are not relevant to the issue being evaluated. Also called an enveloping question.

padlock. a detachable and portable lock with a hinged or sliding shackle or bolt, normally used with a hasp and eye or staple system.

palmar print. an impression made by the under surface of the hand.

palm geometry reader. an access control device that optically scans the geometry of the hand.

palming. in shoplifting, the practice of holding in the palm of the hand a small item just prior to concealment. A shoplifter with a palmed item will frequently hold coupons or money in the same hand, reach into a purse or pocket and drop the palmed item inside.

pamphlet bomb. an explosive device designed to scatter leaflets or pamphlets over crowds of people.

panic alarm. a sensor or other device which reports a panic or emergency situation. In commercial applications, a panic alarm is usually called a hold-up alarm.

panic hardware. an exterior door locking mechanism which is always operable from inside the building by pressure on a crash bar or lever.

panoramic display. a device that displays all signals present in a given frequency band as vertical pulses on a horizontal trace.

pan/tilt. a motor device upon which a CCTV camera is mounted to allow the camera to move on two axes.

papaver bracteatum. a species of poppy from which an alkaloid called thebaine is derived. Thebaine is the source of many medically important compounds.

papaver somniferum. the Latin term for the poppy plant from which opium is produced.

paperhanging. forging checks; passing bad checks.

parabolic microphone. a microphone with a large disk-like attachment used for listening to audio from great distances.

parabolic mirror. a concave mirror with the curvature of a parabola. It is used in passive infrared detectors to define coverage zones.

paracentric key lock. a type of key lock having a spring-loaded core. When engaged, the core is in the retracted position. When not engaged, the core is in the extended position. This type of lock is commonly installed in file cabinets.

paraffin lift technique. a technique for collecting gunpowder residue from the skin of a suspect. Heated paraffin brushed onto the skin captures the residue for laboratory analysis.

paraldehyde. a drug classified as a schedule IV controlled substance.

parallel circuit. a circuit wired in parallel rather than in series; circuit interconnection in which all components share a common positive and common negative connection. Normally open devices are connected in parallel.

parallel tap. a wiretap in which a miniature transmitter and a microphone are wired into and draw power from the telephone line.

paramedic. an emergency medical technician trained and authorized to provide advanced life support.

paranoia. a personality disorder characterized by slowly developing, logical and well-systematized delusions of persecution and/or grandeur.

paraquat. a crop-destroying chemical sprayed from aircraft to destroy marijuana crops.

parasite tap. any type of wiretap device that draws its power from the telephone line.

parasympathetic nervous system. the division of the autonomic nervous system that dominates in relaxed situations. It performs routine "housekeeping" functions, such as digestion and maintenance of body temperature. The parasympathetic nervous system is significant in respect to the theory of polygraphy.

paregoric. a generic medicine containing opium. Used medically as an analgesic and antidiarrheal. Produces high physical and psychological dependence, and has a potential for abuse.

parens patriae. a duty assumed by the government to care for children who are neglected, delinquent, or without competent parents. In the United States, this duty is carried out at the state level of government.

parepectolin. a derivative of opium and a commonly abused narcotic drug. It is regulated by the Controlled Substances Act.

Parest. a trade name for the controlled ingredient methaqualone, a synthetic sedative. It is regulated under the Controlled Substances Act as a Schedule I depressant.

pari delicto. the fault or blame is shared equally.

Parkinson's Law. a concept which holds that work expands to fill the available time.

parlay. in a numbers operation, a bet on any combination of two of the three digits. Also called a bolita, bleeder, or double action.

parole. a release on certain conditions of a prisoner serving a sentence prior to the expiration of the sentence.

parol evidence rule. a rule which states that a written instrument or contract cannot be modified by an oral agreement. The rule is based on the concept that written contracts should contain all of the facts and agreements between parties and, therefore, should not be allowed to be altered orally at some future date.

parricide. the killing of one's mother, father, or other close relative.

particulars. the details of a claim or the separate items of an account. When stated in a proper form for the information of a defendant, such details are called a bill of particulars.

partnership. a legal relationship created by the voluntary association of two or more persons to carry on as co-owners of a business for profit; a type of business organization in which two or more persons agree on the amount of their contributions (capital and effort) and on the distribution of profits, if any.

Part I offenses. in Uniform Crime Reports, the group of offenses called "major offenses" consisting of criminal homicide, forcible rape, robbery, aggravated assault, burglary, larceny-theft, motor vehicle theft and arson.

Part II offenses. in Uniform Crime Reports, a set of offense categories concerning arrests for less than "major offenses" such as simple assault, drug abuse, and gambling.

party-dominated process. an aspect of the adversary system that gives to the judge the passive role of umpire and allows the prosecution and defense to be the major forces in a trial.

passing off. selling an imitation article by claiming it to be genuine.

passive acoustic monitoring. the use of microphones and ancillary equipment to provide surveillance by monitoring the sounds in a protected premise.

passive bridge. a method of communicating between a subscriber and a central station that uses regenerating circuitry to process and amplify signals.

passive filter. a noise suppressor or attenuator which covers that band of frequencies to which the filter is tuned.

passive imaging. forming a visual picture or image on a screen of a low light content without the aid of illumination.

passive infrared sensor. any sensor designed to detect rapid thermal (heat) changes. Passive sensors only receive and do not transmit energy.

passive microwave reflector. a metallic planar reflector that extends microwave span sensor coverage to areas having tight spaces or uneven terrain. It is also used for joining adjacent microwave sectors.

passive partner. the person who receives the physical attention during sexual activity. In homosexuality, the person whose genitals are being stimulated by the active partner.

passive reflector. a metallic cylinder which reflects rf energy at a particular frequency.

passive sensor. a sensor that does not generate or transmit signals.

passive ultrasonic detector. a detector that reacts to sound frequencies within a specified range, usually those associated with breaking glass or similar sounds suggestive of intrusion. Detectors are tunable to eliminate frequencies that are sources of false alarm input.

password. a unique word, usually up to eight characters in length, assigned to an authorized computer system user and typically linked to a user ID. Frequently, display of the password is suppressed when it is keyed in during the logon routine.

password authenticator. a pocket-sized unit which contains a pre-filed user PIN and a cryptographic algorithm for calculating a required reply number. In use, a computer network user logs on from a local terminal, utilizing the system's logon routine. At that point an authentication server attached to the host computer displays a challenge number. The user enters the challenge number into the password authenticator which generates a reply number. The user enters the reply number through the terminal. If the reply number is accepted, access is granted.

password protected document. a document in computer memory which cannot be edited, printed, filed or retrieved without the correct password.

pasted counterfeit. a small denomination bill that has been raised to a higher denomination bill by first thinning the original corners on one side and then pasting on new corners of a higher denomination. The new corners have usually been torn, one or two at a time, from other bills that are redeemed at full value.

past posting. in a numbers operation, betting

after post time when the winning number is known. The use of a padded book is usually involved.

patch panel. a panel that joins or terminates many different circuits. It features jacks, plug-ins, or simple terminal blocks.

patent ambiguity. an uncertainty in a written instrument that is obvious upon reading.

pathological liar. a person whose lying is compulsive; one who lies for no profit or gain.

pathology. the science or doctrine of diseases; that part of medicine which explains the nature, causes and symptoms of diseases.

patio-type sliding door. a sliding door that is essentially a single, large transparent panel in a frame (a type commonly used to give access to patios or yards of private dwellings). Single doors have one fixed and one movable panel. Double doors have two movable panels.

patricide. the killing of one's father.

pattern locator. a visual indicator on a volumetric-type sensor that allows the user to determine the boundaries of the sensor's protection pattern.

patterned gunshot bruise. a bruise around an entrance wound caused by contact between muzzle and skin. The pattern can sometimes be associated with the weapon used.

pavement princess. a prostitute, especially one who plies her trade at truckstops.

pawn shop detail. a team of law enforcement officers assigned to periodically visit pawn shops in search of reported stolen property.

Paxipam. the trade name of halazepam, a member of the benzodiazepine family of depressants. It is regulated under the Controlled Substances Act.

pay and switch. a theft by deception technique in which the thief purchases an item, switches the tag with a tag from a similar but more expensive item, and returns the item to the store to exchange it for the higher priced item of a different size or color.

payback. a method used to determine the relative attractiveness of investment proposals by determining the time frame required to recover initial investment.

payroll burden. a payroll cost, usually expressed as a percentage, which covers the cost of paid vacations, holidays, excused absences and disability benefits.

PCP. the most commonly used street name for phencyclidine, a hallucinogen that can produce in the user a sense of detachment, distance, and estrangement from surroundings. Numbness, slurred or blocked speech, and a loss of coordination may be accompanied by a sense of strength and invulnerability. PCP is unique among popular drugs of abuse in its power to produce psychoses indistinguishable from schizophrenia. It is frequently added to leafy material and smoked. PCP is sold on the street in a variety of pill forms, capsules, dust (usually white), amorphous clumps, and occasionally as a liquid. PCP is known by a variety of names which include angel dust, dust, crystal, crystal joints, hog, CJ, KJ, peace, peaceweed, supergrass, superweed, elephant tranquilizer, tranks, sheets, surfer, snorts, snuffles, cadillac, cyclosen, soma, mist, goon, TIC, TAC, T, killerweed, embalming fluid, and rocket fuel. The Controlled Substances Act lists it as a Schedule II drug.

peak of tension test. in polygraphy, a test designed to elicit in a guilty subject an emotional response to one specific question related to the crime. All other questions in the test are irrelevant or neutral. The tension in a guilty subject will build as the irrelevant questions are asked, and then peak on the relevant question.

peak-to-peak. a value based on the difference between the maximum positive and maximum negative points of a waveform.

pecking order. a term that describes the comparative ranks that humans hold in their business and social organizations.

peculation. embezzlement, or any wrongful act or illegal appropriation of money or property assigned to one's care.

pecuniary offense. a minor infraction of the law, such as a parking ticket.

pederasty. the unnatural carnal copulation of male with male, particularly of a man with a boy.

peel job. a method of safecracking in which a hole is drilled in one corner, a crowbar is inserted, and the exterior surface is ripped off or peeled back. Also called a rip job.

peeping tom. a person who trespasses for the purpose of observing persons inside a dwelling.

penal bond. a bond given by an accused, or by another person in his behalf, for the payment of money if the accused fails to appear in court on a certain day.

penal code. the criminal code of a jurisdiction. It defines criminal conduct and defenses thereto, and determines the punishments to be imposed.

penal sanction. the punishment authorized by law for committing a specific crime within a jurisdiction.

pen and ink counterfeit. a small denomination bill that has been raised to a higher denomination bill by removing the original denomination markings, usually with abrasives, and drawing in the design markings of a higher denomination.

pendant sprinkler head. a fire sprinkler head

suspended vertically from piping that runs close to and parallel with a ceiling. The piping is frequently concealed above a false ceiling with the pendant protruding through the ceiling.

pendente lite. a legal phrase which means "during the period while the action is pending."

penetrating gunshot wound. a wound caused when the bullet enters the body or an organ and does not exit.

penetration. as used in criminal law with respect to the offense of rape, the insertion of the penis into the parts of the female, no matter how slight.

penitentiary. a prison originally intended to keep the inmates in isolation both from society and one another, so that they could meditate on their evil past and be penitent. In current usage, the term is synonymous with prison.

pennyweighter. a shoplifter who specializes in stealing jewelry.

penology. the scientific study of corrections, including the justifications, rationalizations, theories, and aims of punishments, types of punishments, and their effectiveness.

pen register. an instrument that records telephone dial pulses as inked dashes on paper tape.

pentazocine. a narcotic agonist-antagonist used as a specific antidote for narcotic poisoning. It is sold under the trade name Talwin, and because of its morphine-like effects it is regulated under the Controlled Substances Act as a Schedule IV drug. On the street, pentazocine is frequently used in combination with tripelannamine. This combination is commonly referred to as "T's and B's" or "T's and Blues" with "T" referring to Talwin and "B" referring to the blue-colored tripelannamine tablet.

pentobarbital. the generic name of a barbiturate sold under the trade name Nembutal. It is regulated under the Controlled Substances Act as a Schedule II depressant.

Pentothal. the trade name of the controlled ingredient thiopental. It is an ultrashort-acting barbiturate which produces anesthesia within one minute after intravenous administration.

percent supervision. the rate of change in current or resistance to normal operating current or resistance in a supervised line required to produce an alarm signal. So called because the rate of change is expressed as a percentage.

perceptual barrier. a structure or object that discourages criminal attack by giving the appearance that an attack will be unsuccessful.

Percocet. the trade name of a product combining the controlled ingredient oxycodone, a semi-synthetic narcotic, and acetaminophen. It is listed as a Schedule II drug in the Controlled Substances Act.

Percodan. the trade name of a product containing the controlled ingredient oxycodone, a semi-synthetic narcotic. Addicts take Percodan orally or dissolve it in water, filter out the insoluble material, and "mainline" it. It is a commonly abused drug and is regulated under the Controlled Substances Act as a Schedule II narcotic.

per contra. in opposition.

per curiam. by the court. The term is frequently used to distinguish an opinion of the whole court from an opinion written by one judge.

percussion bomb. an exploding device that detonates upon impact or when struck.

peremptory challenge. a challenge to remove a person from consideration as a juror without assigning a reason or cause. In a trial, both sides have an equal number of peremptory challenges.

peremptory day. a day assigned for trial or hearing in court without further opportunity for postponement.

perforating gunshot wound. a wound caused when the bullet passes completely through the body, leaving both entrance and exit perforations.

performance bond. a bond that guarantees completion of an endeavor in accordance with a contract.

performance criteria. standards for determining effectiveness or efficiency. They frequently describe steps or products in the work process, and are so stated that workers know at any point what they have achieved, what remains to be achieved, and how their performance will be evaluated.

peripheral nervous system. that portion of the human body's nervous system lying outside the central nervous system. The physiological reactions recorded by the polygraph instrument originate in the peripheral nervous system.

perimeter barrier. a physical barrier used on the outside of a protected area to prevent, deter or delay unauthorized entry.

periodic imprisonment. a form of incarceration which allows a prisoner freedom except for certain periods, e.g., weekends.

peripheral device. a unit, distinct from a central processing unit and physical memory, that can provide a computer system with input or accept output from it. Terminals, line printers and disks are peripheral devices.

perjurer. one who knowingly makes, under oath, a false statement about an issue before a court, legislature, grand jury, or an executive branch of government.

perjury. a lie or false statement made intentionally under oath in a trial.

permanent circuit. circuitry capable of alarm transmission regardless of the alarm system control unit's operational mode. Examples of permanent circuits are telephone-line supervision and tamper alarms.

persistence display. a CRT that retains or stores an image after the electrical input signal is gone.

personal distance. the distance from about one and a half to four feet that is considered appropriate spacing for close friends and for conversations that concern personal matters. It is a principle of importance in conducting interrogations.

personal identification number. a number entered into and recognized by an automatic teller machine (ATM) or similar device when making a transaction. Also called PIN.

personality disorder. a disorder involving inflexible and maladaptive personality traits that impair functioning.

personal protective services. measures that increase the personal protection of a dignitary or important person who may be the target of a criminal or terrorist act.

personal recognition. a system of controlling the movement of people through personal recognition of them.

personal recognizance. a legal device which allows a person to be released from jail pending trial without being under bond. It is based on the promise of the individual to appear as demanded.

personal space. the area that humans actively maintain around themselves, into which others cannot intrude without arousing discomfort. The concept has application to interrogations.

person in need of supervision. one who is remanded to a juvenile facility, mental institution, or other custodial care without having been found guilty of a crime, because a court has determined that without such custodial supervision the individual may be a danger to himself and to others. The term refers primarily to youths. Also called child in need of supervision or juvenile in need of supervision.

Personnel Reliability Program (PRP). a Department of Defense program that seeks to enhance the selection, screening and continuous evaluation of persons assigned to various nuclear-related duties.

Personnel Security Investigation. any investigation required for the purpose of determining the eligibility of Department of Defense military and civilian personnel, contractor employees, consultants, and others affiliated with the DOD, for access to classified information, acceptance or retention in the US Armed Forces, assignment or retention in sensitive duties, or other designated duties requiring such investigation. A Personnel Security Investigation includes investigations of affiliations with subversive organizations, suitability information, or hostage situations.

perspective drawing. the representation of an object on a plane surface as it appears to the eye. It affords a better pictorial effect than other types of drawings.

perspective grid photography. a photographic technique for obtaining accurate measurements of a crime scene. Exact measurements are made of any rectangular object that will appear in the picture, or a template whose exact dimensions are known is placed in the field of view. Distances between objects that appear in the photograph can be calculated. The technique can also use discs instead of templates, and for small object photography coins can be used to establish scale.

PERT. an acronym for Program Evaluation and Review Technique, a planning and control process that requires identifying the accomplishments of programs and the time and resources needed to go from one accomplishment to the next.

pertinent question. in polygraphy, a question which when posed to a guilty subject will cause a response recordable by the polygraph instrument. Also called a relevant or crucial question.

perturbation. in spectroscopy, an irregularity in the spacing of the lines of band spectrum; a deviation of the values of terms in a spectral series.

petechial eye hemorrhages. in homicide investigations, tiny bleeding areas in the eyeball which correlate with traumatic asphyxia or choking.

Peter Principle. a principle which holds that in a hierarchy every employee tends to rise to his level of incompetence. Corollaries of the principle hold that in time every position tends to be occupied by an employee who is incompetent to carry out its duties, and that productive work is accomplished by those employees who have not yet reached their levels of incompetence.

pethidine. a synthetic narcotic chemically dissimilar to morphine but resembling morphine's effects. It is probably the most widely used drug for the relief of moderate to severe pain. Available in pure form as well as in products containing other medicinal ingredients, it is administered either orally or by injection, the latter method being the most widely abused. Tolerance and dependence develop with chronic use, and large doses can result in convulsions or death. It is also known as meperidine and is a Schedule II controlled substance.

petition. a formal request to an executive or judicial officer to perform some act within his power or authority, as to pardon, commute, reprieve, or adjudicate as delinquent.

PETN. a type of booster explosive.

petrichloral. a drug classified as a Schedule IV controlled substance.

pettifogger. an attorney of low character and integrity.

peyote. a cactus plant used by Indians in northern Mexico as a part of traditional religious rites. The fleshy parts or buttons of the peyote cactus yield mescaline, a hallucinogen. Peyote is regulated under the Controlled Substances Act as a Schedule I drug. An exemption has been granted, however, to the Native American Church which uses peyote in its religious ceremonies.

peyote button. the fleshy part of the peyote cactus from which mescaline, a hallucinogen, is derived.

phantom signal. an unexplained alarm signal.

Phase 1 Fire. the early (incipient) stage of fire which may last for several minutes or several days. Thermal decomposition in this stage produces airborne particles susceptible to detection. A fire is most controllable in phase 1.

Phase 2 Fire. the middle (visible flame) stage of fire which signals that human life is in danger.

Phase 3 Fire. the concluding (high heat) stage of fire in which combustibles burst into flame, superheated gases are generated, oxygen is rapidly depleted, and the fire spreads quickly.

phase measurement. in communications, the measurement of a fraction of a single cycle.

phenadoxone. an opiate classified as a Schedule I controlled substance.

phenanthrene alkaloids. one of two general categories of alkaloids extracted from opium. This category is represented by morphine and codeine. The other general category is the isoquinoline alkaloids.

phenapromide. an opiate classified as a Schedule I controlled substance.

phenazocine. an opiate classified as a Schedule II controlled substance.

phencyclidine. a widely abused hallucinogen. Originally developed for possible use as a human anesthetic, it was discontinued because of its side effects of confusion and delirium. It was later approved for use in treating animals, but the manufacturer discontinued production. Phencyclidine and a variety of chemically related analogs with similar psychic effects are illegally made in clandestine laboratories. More commonly known as PCP, it is called at least fifty other names that reflect the range of its bizarre and volatile effects. In its pure form, PCP is a white crystalline powder that readily dissolves in water. In less pure form, its color and consistency will range from tan to brown and from powder to a gummy mass. PCP is frequently added to leafy materials and smoked. Extreme psychic reactions are usually associated with repeated use of the drug, with intermittent recurrences long after the drug has left the body. Among all of the commonly abused drugs, PCP is regarded as posing the greatest risks to the user. The Controlled Substances Act lists it as a Schedule II hallucinogen.

phendimetrazine. the generic name of a stimulant drug sold legally as Statobex-D. It is a Schedule III controlled substance.

phenmetrazine. a controlled ingredient medically used only as an appetite suppressant. It is sold as Preludin and is widely abused. A common practice of addicts is to dissolve the tablets in water and inject the solution. Complications arising from such use are common since the tablets contain insoluble materials which upon injection block small blood vessels and cause serious damage, especially in the lungs and retina of the eye. Phenmetrazine is regulated under the Controlled Substances Act as a Schedule II stimulant.

phenobarbital. a commonly abused barbiturate sold as Luminal and Phenobarbital. It is usually taken orally or injected and is called barb, downer, blue, yellow jacket and sleeping pill. Phenobarbital is regulated by the Controlled Substances Act as a Schedule IV depressant.

phenomorphan. an opiate classified as a Schedule I controlled substance.

phenoperidine. an opiate classified as a Schedule I controlled substance.

phentermine. an anorectic (appetite-suppressing) drug with effects similar to those of the amphetamines. It is sold as Ionamin, Adipex-P, and by other names. Phentermine appears in the Controlled Substances Act as a Schedule IV stimulant.

pholcodine. an opium derivative classified as a Schedule I controlled substance.

phone business. number bets that are taken by telephone from persons who are not serviced by a pickup man.

phone freak. a person who makes long distance calls at someone else's expense.

photoelectric alarm. a system that uses a light beam transmitted from a light source to a receiving cell. Any object or person passing through the beam sets off the alarm.

photoelectric-beam smoke detector. a smoke detector that senses smoke particles using light scatter-sensing circuitry. The detector contains a sensing chamber which houses a light source and a photoelectric receiving cell. The cell is mounted so that it cannot receive light from the light source when the chamber is free of smoke particles. When particles enter the chamber they scatter light and cause the receiver to detect a change, resulting in an alarm.

photoelectric fuse. a bomb fuse sensitive to minute variations in light. The fuse functions when an influence from the target is exerted on a sensitive detecting device within the fuse itself.

Photo Electric Intoximeter. a breath testing device used by the police to determine alcohol concentrations in the blood of drivers suspected of being under the influence of alcohol.

photogrammetry. the process of determining measurements from photographs. Its application to security work is in recording crime and accident scenes. It requires the use of two cameras to produce photographs from slightly different but known vantage points. Precise measurements can be made from an analysis of the photographs.

photovoltaic power source. an array of solar power cells used as an electric generator and battery charge controller.

physical barrier. a barrier, either natural or structural, that provides protection to an area. For example, a natural barrier would be a river and a structural barrier would be a fence.

physical dependence. as relates to narcotic abuse, an alteration of the normal functions of the body necessitating the continued presence of a drug in order to prevent the withdrawal or abstinence syndrome, which is characteristic of each class of addictive drugs. The intensity of physical symptoms experienced during the withdrawal period is related directly to the amount of narcotic used each day. Deprivation of an addictive drug causes increased excitability of those same bodily functions that have been depressed by its habitual use.

physical security. that part of security concerned with physical measures designed to safeguard people, to prevent unauthorized access to equipment, facilities, material and documents, and to safeguard them against damage and loss.

physical security inspection. an on-site evaluation of a facility or part of a facility.

physical security plan. a plan that accounts for effective and economic utilization of a facility's full resources in meeting anticipated security threats.

physical security survey. an on-site evaluation of an entire facility for the purpose of discovering hazards or weaknesses. It is somewhat synonymous with physical security inspection.

Physicians Desk Reference. a book containing pictures and descriptions of commercial drug products. It is helpful to an investigator when making field (i.e., preliminary and tentative) examinations of suspected controlled substances.

physiological dependence. a physical craving of the body for a drug. If the drug is withdrawn, the body will react with predictable symptoms. The nature and severity of the symptoms depend on the drug and the dosage level attained.

piano hinge. a hinge designed to be the same length as the edge of the moving part to which it is applied. Also called a continuous hinge.

pick destructive. a term relating to any lock-picking technique which results in damage to the lock.

pick detectable. a term relating to any lock-picking technique which leaves traces of the picking.

pickpocketing. stealthily removing something of value from the pocket of another person, with intent to keep it. Because of the risk of bodily harm which it entails, this type of stealing carries a more severe penalty than ordinary stealing.

pickup man. in a numbers operation, a person who picks up numbers from writers or at drops and delivers them to persons higher up in the operation.

pieced note. a counterfeit bill created by piecing together a different section cut from each of a number of genuine bills of the same type and denomination. The counterfeiter will cut no more than two-fifths from each genuine bill to ensure they meet the requirements of redemption at full value.

piezoelectric detector. a detector that contains a piezoelectric element designed to respond to a specific frequency or frequency range; a detector that converts mechanical vibrations into electrical signals. A piezoelectric detector is used to sense noises associated with breaking glass.

pigeon drop. a bunco scheme committed by a team of con artists in which a wallet or purse containing money is placed so as to be found in the presence of the mark (intended victim) and one of the con artists. The mark is induced to agree to share the found money but to first place it and a sum of his own money as collateral with a third party (a member of the team) while an effort is made to locate the owner of the found money. The team separates from the mark, depriving him of his money.

piggyback. to slip through an electronically controlled access door by following closely behind a person that the system has allowed to enter. Also called tailgating.

piggyback entry. unauthorized interception and alteration of electronic communication between a computer and its user.

piminodine. an opiate classified as a Schedule II controlled substance.

ping ponging. in health care fraud, providing for unnecessary treatments at the same time needed services are performed.

pinhole lens. a special compressed optical lens used for covert observation. It is typically mounted in a wall so that a person on the back side of the wall can conduct a visual surveillance.

pink. the street name for a barbiturate.

pin tumbler. one of the essential, distinguishing components of a pin tumbler lock cylinder, more precisely called a bottom pin, master pin or driver pin. The pin tumblers, used in varying lengths and arrangements, determine the combination of the cylinder.

pin tumbler lock. a lock consisting of a plug which rotates with the key to throw or withdraw a bolt. Surrounding the plug is the shell, a fixed assembly into which the plug fits. A series of pins fit into matching cylindrical holes in these two lock parts. With the key withdrawn, the pins extend through the surface between the plug and the shell so that the plug cannot turn. Insertion of the correct key lines up pins in such a way that the outer end of each one matches the surface separating the plug from the shell, so the plug can turn to withdraw the bolt.

pin tumbler lock cylinder. a lock cylinder employing metal pins (tumblers) to prevent the rotation of the core until the correct key is inserted into the keyway. Small coil compression springs hold the pins in the locked position until the key is inserted.

pip switch. a switch on a polygraph instrument that permits calibration of the galvanic skin response component.

pipe bomb. a short length of pipe capped at both ends and drilled at one end to accept a fuse, which is used to detonate an explosive contained inside the pipe.

pipeman. a messenger or a person who receives and passes on messages in support of a criminal activity.

piquer. a person who derives sexual satisfaction from stabbing his or her victims with sharp instruments.

piracy. the forcible seizure of a seagoing vessel in peacetime. In recent years, piracy has also come to describe the seizure of aircraft, as in skyjacking.

pirate factory. a place where counterfeit products, such as unauthorized reproductions of tapes, records and books, are manufactured in violation of owner rights.

piritramide. an opiate classified as a Schedule I controlled substance.

Piso's justice. a punishment that is legally and technically correct but not morally justifiable.

pivoted door. a door hung on pivots rather than hinges.

pivoted window. a window which opens by pivoting about a horizontal or vertical axis.

placebo effect. the effect of a neutral or irrelevant aspect of an experiment that is intended to produce the same reaction in a participant as an important or relevant aspect.

Placidyl. a trade name for the controlled ingredient ethchlorvynol. It is used clinically as a hypnotic. Placidyl is especially dangerous in overdose because it is fat soluble and resistive to excretion. This depressant is a Schedule IV substance.

plain arch. a fingerprint pattern in which ridges enter on one side of the impression and flow or tend to flow out the other side with a rise or wave in the center.

plain English. readily understandable written or spoken words as opposed to codes or symbols.

plain impressions. inked fingerprint impressions obtained by simultaneously pressing all of the fingers of the hand and then the thumb. Plain impressions are not rolled impressions.

plaintext. data that are intelligible until transformed by secret keys into unintelligible data. Also called cleartext.

plaintiff. in law, the person suing the defendant.

plain view doctrine. a rule of law that states it is not a search within the meaning of the 4th Amendment to observe that which is open to view, provided that the viewing officer has a lawful right to be there. No warrant is required to seize items in plain view.

plain view seizure. seizure by a police officer of contraband within plain view at a place where the officer is lawfully present.

plain whorl. a fingerprint pattern which has two deltas and at least one ridge making a complete circuit. An imaginary line drawn between the two deltas will touch or cross at least one of the recurving ridges. This pattern is slightly different from a central pocket loop.

plain wrapper. an unmarked police car.

plantar print. an impression made by the surface of the foot.

plastic explosive. a putty-like explosive substance that can be molded into various shapes to increase the efficiency of charges. Composition C-4, which is approved for military use only, is a type of plastic explosive.

plasticine. a substance used by a forger to remove graphite from writings on paper.

plastic money. credit cards.

plastic paper. a street name for counterfeit money.

plastic print. a fingerprint, tire print, foot print or similar outline visible in a soft surface such as dirt, wax, blood, grease and paint.

platter charge. a concave-shaped steel plate attached to an explosive charge, usually employed to penetrate armor plate. The platter is aimed at a target when the charge is detonated, delivering a force up to 18,000 fps.

plea. a defendant's answer in court to the charges brought against him in a complaint, information or indictment.

plea bargaining. a process of negotiation between a prosecutor and a defense attorney in which the accused voluntarily pleads guilty, usually in exchange for lower charges and sentences.

pleasure-pain principle. the utilitarian concept that people endeavor to maximize pleasure (profit) and minimize pain (loss). Making the anticipated penalty greater than the expected gain is believed to deter rational men from committing crimes.

plenary. absolute, full power regarding the authority or jurisdiction of a court.

plenary confession. a complete and comprehensive confession to a crime.

plenum. a space in a structure that serves as the distribution area for heating and cooling ducts, generally a gap above a false ceiling.

plenum cable. any of several varieties of single and multiconductor cables designed to withstand fire damage and intended to be installed in plenums.

plethysmograph component. a component on some types of polygraph instruments which electronically records changes in blood volume, pulse rate, and blood oxygen content.

plug-in card. a machine-readable entry card. It has a printed circuit and an electric contact at one end. When inserted into a reader, electrical contact is made. It is used mostly for access control.

plug retainer. that part often fixed to the rear of the core in a lock cylinder to retain or hold the core firmly in the cylinder.

plumbing. services performed in support of covert operations, such as conducting surveillances, operating safehouses, and providing unaccountable funds.

plunger switch. a mechanical intrusion detection sensor activated by movement of the surface upon which it is mounted. As the plunger leaves its sheath, due to an opening, an alarm is triggered. A plunger switch is usually recess-mounted on a door jamb or a window sill.

pneumatic-tube heat detector. a line-type rate-of-rise heat detector consisting of a continuous loop of tubing mounted in a ceiling or overhead area. Ambient heat expands air in the tube. The expanded tube causes an alarm.

pneumograph. a major component of a polygraph instrument. It records the inhalation and exhalation cycles of the examinee's breathing pattern.

point. in fingerprint science, a ridge formed by one of the three basic ridge characteristics, i.e., bifurcation, ridge ending or dot.

pointing bulb. in arson investigations, a light bulb distended by heat and pointing in the direction of the heat source, often the fire's point of origin.

point of law. that which is a precedent or an issue to be decided.

point of origin. in arson investigations, the place where a fire is believed to have started.

point protection. the use of sensors to detect activity at or immediately adjacent to a protected target or to place the target inside a hardened container such as a vault or safe.

point-to-point installation. a type of alarm installation in which each sensor is connected directly to a control center by a pair of wires.

poke. the item taken by a pickpocket, e.g., a wallet or change purse.

polar coordinates method. a method for mapping an object in a crime scene sketch by giving its distance from some selected point plus the direction angle taken by the distance line from an axis. For example, if a handgun is found some distance from a house, the closest wall of the house can serve as an axis reference. By measuring from a door or window on the wall, the handgun can be fixed by distance with a tape measure and fixed by angle with a compass aligned to the wall.

polarity. the direction of electron flow, from negative to positive, in direct current circuits.

polarity reversal circuit. a direct current alarm-signal circuit that reverses polarity upon the initiation of an alarm. The polarity reversal is detected and annunciated by an alarm-signal receiver.

polarized-light microscope. a microscope which employs the use of polarized light to determine optical properties such as refractive index.

police connect. an alarm reporting system that is directly wired or channeled to a police station.

police discretion. the power or authority conferred by law to act in certain situations in accordance with an official's or an official agency's own considered judgment and conscience. For example, a police officer is required to make spontaneous and difficult decisions in unforeseeable situations. Police discretion allows the officer certain defined latitudes in such situations.

police intelligence. processed information relating to criminal activities, law enforcement and security operations that describes law and order.

police power. the right of the state to enact laws and enforce them for the order, safety, health, morals and general welfare of the public.

police prosecution system. a system common in the United Kingdom and Ireland in which certain crimes are prosecuted by high-ranking police officials rather than by appointed or elected prosecutors.

police station receiver. an alarm receiver in operation at a police station to receive alarm signals from protected premises.

police sweep. a concentrated effort to clean up a crime-prone neighborhood by making mass arrests of criminals and suspects.

policy. any one of several widely played games in which players bet money on numbers. Policy is similar to a lottery and is sometimes called the numbers game. Policy is based on some method of choosing winning numbers such as the US Treasury daily balance or pari-mutuel totals from horse races. A straight bet is based on three digit numbers, 000 to 999; parlay bets on two digit numbers, 00 to 99; and single action bets on one digit, 0 to 9.

polling. electronic interrogation between a central processor and transmitters or transponders to ascertain current system or sensor status.

polling system. a central station transmitter and receiver.

polling the jury. a part of trial procedure which permits that each juror be asked if the non-unanimous verdict of the jury is his verdict.

polycarbonate glazing products. lightweight, tempered plastics approximately 30 times stronger than acrylics, with superior resistance to impact and shattering.

polygram. a moving chart of a polygraph instrument upon which the inked pens place tracings. A polygraphist's opinion is based upon an interpretation of tracings on one or more polygrams.

polygraph examination. an examination of a person by a polygraphist using a polygraph instrument. The procedure includes a pretest interview, a polygraph test, and a post-test interview.

polygraph instrument. an electronic instrument that continuously records on a moving chart physiological changes that occur in an examinee's body as questions are asked during a polygraph test. The changes recorded relate to blood pressure, pulse, respiration rate and volume, and galvanic skin resistance. Contemporary polygraph instruments have one or two respiration monitors, a skin resistance monitor, and one or two cardiovascular activity monitors which operate synchronously with a chart drive, graph paper and pen registers.

polygraph technique. a lie detection technique based on the assumption that when an individual experiences apprehension, fear or emotional excitement, his/her respiration rate, blood pressure and galvanic skin resistance will sharply increase. A polygraph instrument records these physiological responses as questions are asked by a trained examiner. The examiner interprets the recordings and renders an opinion as to the truthfulness of the person examined.

polygraph theory. a theory which holds that a conscious mental effort to deceive made by a normal, healthy person will cause certain physiological changes which are recordable by the polygraph instrument.

polygraphy. the science of lie detection or truth verification. It is used to screen job applicants and employees, and to identify possible suspects in criminal cases.

Ponzi scheme. a confidence scheme in which money is collected from investors and part of it is paid back with high profits to encourage the early investors and others to increase their investments. When the total amount becomes substantial, the swindlers abscond with the investments.

pop pills. to ingest drugs in pill form.

pornography. art, expression, implication, speech, suggestion or writing which appeals to the base or sensual desires of a person and is contrary to the established moral code of the society.

poroscopy. the examination of the pores on the palms and fingers of the hand as a means of identification in addition to fingerprint identification. Friction ridges are dotted by pores which differ in position, shape and size. It is possible to discern a pore pattern in a small area of the hand and to use the pattern as a basis for identifying a suspect. Pores are permanent and appear in an infinite variety of patterns, thereby giving to poroscopy a theoretical validity similar to that of fingerprint identification.

portable detector. a device that can be moved from place to place and which features capabilities for local and remote annunciation.

ported coax. a type of buried field-disturbance sensor. It consists of a coaxial transmit cable and one or two coaxial receive cables. All cables are buried parallel, 4 to 6 inches below the surface and several feet apart. The transmit cable has a special "leaky" or ported shield which radiates electrical energy. An intruder moving in the energy field produces frequencies that initiate an alarm. Also called a leaky coax.

portrait parle. a system that uses numerous physical characteristics, such as height, weight and hair color, to describe persons.

posed photograph. a photograph used in court to illustrate the statement of a witness. It may depict actors representing the accused, victim or witness and other aspects of a scene.

positive correlation. a relationship between two variables in which a high rank on one measure is accompanied by a high rank on the other.

positive non-interfering and successive system. an alarm system which prevents subsequent operated stations from interfering with the transmission from a station that is in operation, and which also permits any station to transmit, in turn, its assigned number of rounds of code signal once the previously actuated station has completed its code.

positive non-interfering system. an alarm system in which the alarm initiating devices are electrically arranged so that when one device is operated to transmit an alarm, no other device operated over the same electrical circuit can interfere with the transmission of a complete alarm.

positive sanctions. rewards for socially desired behavior.

positive pressure phase. that phase of a blast wave in which compressed air moves outward and is bounded by an extremely sharp pressure wave front less than 0.0001-inch thick in which the pressure increases abruptly far above normal. The pressure wave front moves outward with an initial velocity greater than the velocity of sound at sea level (1,110 fps). This front applies a sudden and considerable thrust or push against any obstacle in its path. In water or earth, the same effect takes place and is called water or earth shock.

positive reinforcement. the strengthening of a response by the presentation of a stimulus.

positive transfer. transfer of learning that is accelerated and strengthened because it is based on prior learning or experience.

Posse Comitatus Act. an act that forbids the use of military personnel to enforce civilian law. Either military or civilian personnel or both may violate the act. The user of any part of the Army or Air Force for the prohibited purpose is the offender.

possession. a condition of fact under which a person can exercise dominion and control over property. Possession may be actual or constructive.

possible maximum loss. the loss that would be sustained if a given criminal target was totally taken or destroyed. For example, the possible maximum loss for a retail store would be the loss of the entire inventory.

post-conviction remedies. proceedings that may be brought after conviction, such as appeal of the conviction or sentence, request for commutation, pardon, reprieve, or stay of execution.

post-dated check. a check delivered prior to its date, generally payable on sight or on presentation on or after its date. It differs from an ordinary check by carrying on its face implied notice that there is no money on deposit to cover the check prior to the date, but with assurance that money will be on deposit on and after the check's date.

post-dictive validity study. in employee screening, a study in which integrity test scores of ordinary persons are compared with scores of convicted criminals. The study is used to assess the validity of an integrity test.

post hoc error. the result of a faulty reasoning process that attributes the cause of a given event to another event that occurred earlier.

post indicator valve. a valve used to monitor the main water supply to the fire sprinkler systems. It is usually located outside the building proper. A sensor is frequently installed on the valve so as to detect tampering.

post mortem. after death; an autopsy or examination of a dead body to determine the cause of death.

post mortem rigidity. the stiffening of the body after death. Chemical changes within muscle tissue cause the muscles to contract. Also called rigor mortis.

post mortem spoon. a device used to roll individual fingerprints from deformed hands or cadavers. The curved surface of the device (similar in appearance to a shoe horn) allows the finger to remain stable as the spoon rolls across the skin surface.

post mortem wound. a wound inflicted after death.

post time. in a numbers operation, the deadline for getting numbers to the "office" or into the hands of a trusted employee.

Pot Air Line. a nickname for the fleet of airplanes engaged in smuggling marijuana into the United States.

potato hazer. a homemade weapon made from a potato. Razor blades or nail heads protrude from the surface. It is used for throwing at police and security officers in riot situations.

potentiometer. a control for varying the resistance in a circuit. A volume control is a type of potentiometer. Also called a POT or pot.

pothead. a frequent user of hashish or marijuana.

Powell vs. Alabama. a case in which the U.S. Supreme Court in 1932 ruled that the Constitution guarantees the right to counsel in a state court trial whenever the defendant's life is at stake.

power conditioner. a device that provides clean power to computers and computer-based systems. A power conditioner removes electrical noise from power input lines and regulates voltage to keep it within the correct specification range for the equipment being powered.

power elite. a closely connected group of the corporate rich, political leaders, and military commanders who are presumed by some to decide most key social and political issues.

power interruption. an electrical failure resulting in loss of power or a degradation of quality caused by voltage surges, drops or lightning.

power line monitor. a device that monitors, records and analyzes AC line power for the purpose of identifying the times, types and severity of power line disturbances.

power of attorney. a document authorizing one person to act as attorney for, or in the place of, the person signing the document.

power supply. a device or a source that supplies power to electronic equipment.

prairie fire. a fast burning fire, usually fed by a high wind, which moves quickly through tall, dried vegetation in open expanses.

prazepam. a controlled ingredient in the benzodiazepine family of depressants. It is sold as Centrax and is a Schedule IV drug in the Controlled Substances Act.

pre-action sprinkler system. a fire suppression system, typically used in computer facilities, in which the system charges (fills with water) and readies for discharge while a human response is in progress to verify the initial alarm. If the system is not aborted by human intervention within a prescribed number of seconds, the water is discharged.

pre-alarm. a feature of an alarm system in which a visual/audible signal reminds the user to disarm his system upon entry to the protected area.

preamplifier. a device used to boost a signal's strength to a level above any interfering noise on the line.

preassembled lock. a lock that has all the parts assembled into a unit at the factory and, when installed in a rectangular section cutout of the door at the lock edge, requires little or no assembly. Also called integral lock, mono lock and unit lock.

precedent. an adjudged case or decision of a court which serves as an example or authority for a later identical or similar case.

precipitin reaction. a crime laboratory technique used to determine if a blood substance is or contains human blood.

preconcentrator. a device used to collect vapors before they are exposed to analysis by a vapor detector.

preconditioner. in communications, a device that modifies a waveform to remove low frequency components prior to AC coupled communication or recording.

predatory crime. illegal activity in which the criminal preys upon, exploits, attacks, or in any violative way takes advantage of the victim, usually a person unable to defend against the activity.

predatory vandalism. vandalism committed for material gain. Breaking into an automobile to rifle the glove compartment would be an example.

predictive efficiency. a measure of accuracy of a test or other predictive device in terms of the proportion of its predictions that have been shown to be correct.

pre-employment screening. a process for determining whether a prospective employee is trustworthy or capable of performing the functions required by the job.

pre-hearing investigation. an investigation made by a probation officer before the adjudication of a minor in a juvenile court. Its aim is to inform the judge of the juvenile's background, apparent reasons for the delinquent behavior, and any other information that might be useful in the judicial procedure.

pre-ignition indicators. in arson investigations, the characteristics of smoke and odor that precede visible flame and which may or may not suggest arson.

preliminary crime. a crime which is preparatory in nature and part of a larger purpose. Solicitation or incitement, attempt and conspiracy are preliminary crimes.

preliminary detention. the holding of an accused in confinement pending arraignment. If the accused has been arraigned, the term refers to holding him in confinement pending trial because bail has been denied or cannot be met.

preliminary hearing. the proceeding before a judicial officer in which three matters must be decided: whether a crime was committed; whether the crime occurred within the territorial jurisdiction of the court; and whether there are reasonable grounds to believe that the defendant committed the crime.

Preludin. a trade name for the controlled ingredient phenmetrazine, a stimulant medically used only as an appetite suppressant. Preludin is widely abused and much sought after by addicts. While the use of Preludin involves both oral and intravenous use, most of the abuse involves the injection of tablets dissolved in water. Complications arising from this practice are common since the tablets contain insoluble materials which upon injection block small blood vessels and cause serious damage, especially in the lungs and retina of the eye. On the street, Preludin is called speed, upper, black beauty, crank, meth, bam, and pink.

premeditated design. the mental purpose or formed intent to commit a crime, particularly the crime of murder.

premeditation. in law, planning in advance to commit a crime.

preponderance of evidence. a term relating to the burden imposed upon a plaintiff in a civil case. The plaintiff, to win, must establish a preponderance of evidence in support of the claim. Also, evidence which is more credible and convincing and which, when fairly considered, produces an impression stronger than opposing evidence.

pre-release orientation. the re-entry training or orientation given to an inmate immediately prior to release from prison. Its purpose is to reduce the difficulties of transition.

present cost. the amount of money one must set aside now to make one or more future payments.

present cost of a security measure. the immediate cost to purchase or develop the security measure plus the present cost of future maintenance and operating costs, less the present value of any future scrap value the security measure may have.

presentence report. a statement drawn up by a probation officer that gives the background information on an offender, including prior criminal record, social and personal history, results of interviews, and recommendations to the judge as to the sentence to be imposed.

presentment. written notice of an offense taken by a grand jury from their own knowledge or observation; or any of several presentations of alleged facts and charges to a court or grand jury by a prosecutor.

present value. the amount of money presently on hand which is equivalent to the receipt of one or more future payments.

present value of a security measure. the present value of the reduction in future losses which the security measure is expected to achieve.

pre-set questioning. an interviewing technique in which all questions have been determined prior to the interview and are the only questions asked.

pre-signal system. a system in which an automatic detector announces only through selected annunciators for the purpose of notifying certain key persons, such as security officers. After the alarm conditions have been investigated, a general alarm may be sounded or the alarm system restored to normal detecting conditions.

pressed padlock. a padlock whose outer case is pressed into shape from sheet metal and then riveted together.

pressure alarm. a device that signals the presence of an intruder when a pre-set amount of weight is placed on a surface, usually a mat.

pressure fuse. a bomb fuse sensitive to minute changes in external pressure. The fuse functions when an influence from the target is exerted on a sensitive detecting device within the fuse itself.

pressure-locked grating. a grating in which the cross bars are mechanically locked to the bearing bars at their intersections by deforming the metal.

pressure mat. a thin rubber or vinyl mat containing metallic strips. It is usually concealed under carpets and triggers an alarm when an intruder steps on it.

pressure release bomb. an explosive device designed to detonate when pressure on the bomb's container or outer structure has been released or relaxed, as in the case of a bomb having a detonator that will activate when subjected to a change in air pressure; also a bomb that will detonate when mechanical pressure on a spring-loaded trigger is released.

pressure sensitive bomb. an explosive device designed to detonate when subjected to pressure or contact on its exterior surfaces.

pressure sensor. a sensor used to protect an enclosed area that is airtight. The enclosed area is pressurized with air or gas to a given level. If the pressure drops (caused, for example, by the opening of a door) an alarm is triggered.

pressure switch. a supervisory sensor for monitoring the pressure drop in a fire sprinkler system.

presumption. an inference or belief as to the truth or falsity of a matter in the absence of any direct evidence to the contrary; a well-known deduction which may be made from certain facts which the law will allow.

presumption from possession. an inference that a person is guilty of theft when found to be in possession of the stolen property shortly after it was stolen.

presumption of fact. a logical inference which the trier of the facts is authorized, but not required, to draw from the evidence in a case.

presumption of innocence. a conclusion drawn by law in favor of a criminal defendant which requires acquittal unless guilt is established by sufficient evidence.

presumption of law. a rule which requires that a particular inference must be drawn from an ascertained state of facts.

presumptive evidence. evidence which must be received and treated as true until rebutted by other evidence. A statute might provide that certain facts are presumptive evidence of guilt.

pretrial conference. a meeting of the opposing parties in a case with the judicial officer prior to trial, for the purposes of stipulating those things which are agreed upon and thus narrowing the trial to the things that are in dispute, disclosing the required information about witnesses and evidence, making motions, and generally organizing the presentation of motions, witnesses and evidence.

pretrial detention. detention until trial is over of one who is ineligible for bail, or is unable to raise or post bail; a statutory program authorizing detention of an offender prior to trial where specific findings are made at a public hearing regarding the nature of the charged offense and the prior criminal history of the alleged offender.

pretrial discovery. in criminal proceedings, disclosure by the prosecution or the defense prior to trial of evidence or other information which is intended to be used in the trial.

pretrial identification proceeding. any proceeding prior to trial at which witnesses are called to identify the accused. Examples are lineups, confrontations, and photographic displays.

pretrial motion. a request made to the court before trial. It may cover such issues as change of venue, admissibility of a confession into evidence, and privileged communication.

pretrial procedure. a procedure established in many courts to speed up the disposition of cases by encouraging and assisting settlements before trial.

pretrial publicity. information disseminated concerning a crime, a defendant, or a forthcoming trial that is sometimes claimed by the defense to be prejudicial. It is often used by the defense in its request that the place of trial be moved.

preventive detention. holding of a person in custody without bail before trial on the ground that such custody keeps the offender from committing further crimes while the charges are pending.

preventive maintenance. a system of conducting regular checks and tests of equipment to permit replacement or repair of weakened or faulty parts before equipment failure results.

preventive patrol. a form of patrol that emphasizes deterrence of crime as opposed to reaction.

pre-wound station. a fire alarm station which when operated will annunciate a pre-determined number (usually four) of coded signals.

Primacord. a brand name for detonating cord, a product used in blasting.

prima facie. a Latin term meaning "at first view." It refers to evidence which is, according to law, sufficient to establish or prove a point, unless successfully rebutted by other evidence. For example, the placement of a corporate seal on an instrument is prima facie evidence that the instrument was executed by authority of the corporation.

prima facie proof. the proof which the plaintiff must show at trial before the defendant will be required to prove his defense to the action.

primary deviance. deviant behavior that is invisible to others, is short-lived, or is unimportant.

primary explosive. a small quantity of explosive material detonated by a firing device and which in turn detonates a booster explosive. The primary explosive is the second element in the basic firing chain typical of most explosions. The common primary explosive materials are mercury fulminate, lead azide, dinoly and lead styphenate.

primary password. in computer usage, a type of user password that is the first user password requested from the user. Systems may optionally require a secondary password.

primer residues. residues deposited on the thumb, forefinger and web area of the hand when the hand is used to discharge a weapon. Deposits are also made on the face and neck area when a rifle or shotgun is fired. The residues frequently contain antimony and barium which are components of most primer mixtures. Also called gunshot residue.

principal. a person for whom personal protective services are provided. Also, a chief actor in a crime, or an aider and abettor who actually or constructively participates in the commission of a crime, as distinguished from an accessory.

principal agent. an agent or spy who controls and pays others engaged in espionage or undercover investigations.

principal in the first degree. the actual offender; the person who committed the criminal act. There may be more than one principal in the first degree for a single crime, and a principal in the first degree does not have to be present at the crime or personally commit the act (as would be the case in a "murder for hire" situation).

principal in the second degree. one who with knowledge afoot, aids and abets the principal in the first degree at the very time the crime is being committed. A driver of a getaway car or a lookout would be a principal in the second degree.

principle of application. a principle which holds that the more an idea is applied and put to use, the more it is understood and remembered.

principle of emotional appeal. a principle which holds that appeals to emotion are communicated more readily than appeals to reason.

principle of line loss. a principle which holds that as the number of people involved in passing a message increases, there is an increase in distortion and delay of the message.

printed-circuit board. circuitry for computers and electronic devices. A board consists of nonconductive fiberboard or epoxy-glass base with a copper foil facing on one or both sides. Electrically conductive traces are etched into the copper surface and electronic components are soldered to the trace pattern to create the circuitry.

priority interrupt system. an alarm system in which interruptions to the system are processed on a priority basis.

prior restraint. a court or other government order forbidding or censoring printed matter before publication.

Prisoner Rehabilitation Act of 1965. a federal statute that permits selected federal prisoners to work in the community while still in an inmate status.

prisoner's rights. any rights to which convicts are entitled by law, usually as interpreted by the courts, such as freedom from cruel and unusual punishment, the right to receive visitors, or the right to prepare legal briefs.

prisonization. the process of learning about and adhering to the inmate subculture.

Privacy Act of 1974. a federal statute that reasserts the fundamental right to privacy as derived from the Constitution and provides basic safeguards for the individual to prevent the misuse of personal information by the federal government. The act provides for making known to the public the existence and characteristics of all personal information systems kept by every federal agency. It permits an individual to have access to records containing personal information and allows the individual to control the transfer of that information. Virtually all agencies of the federal government have issued regulations implementing the act. Civil remedies are provided when the requirements of the act are contravened.

privacy lock. a lock, usually for an interior door, secured by a button or thumbturn device, and not designed for key operation.

privacy transformation. the process of transforming intelligible data (plaintext) into unintelligible data (ciphertext). Also called encryption or encipherment.

private box. a fire alarm box used on private property belonging to and being maintained by a private party.

private law. that portion of the total body of laws dealing with those relations between individuals with which the government is not directly concerned. Private law can be divided into several branches such as contract law, property law, law of domestic relations, trust law and the law of torts.

private police. a general descriptor for security officers.

private prosecution. a system prevailing in England and some Continental countries that allows the victim of a crime to initiate criminal proceedings. In practice, unsuccessful private prosecution frequently leads to civil action against the complainant.

private radio carrier. a radio carrier owned and controlled by the central station organization.

private rehabilitation agency. a private organization providing care and treatment services, which may include housing, to convicted persons, juvenile offenders, or persons subject to judicial proceedings.

private sector. a general term meaning the non-government community; individuals and organizations of private industry.

private security agency. an independent or proprietary commercial organization whose activities include employee clearance investigations, maintaining the security of persons or property and/or performing the functions of detection and investigation of crime and criminals, and apprehension of offenders.

privileged communication. a legal principle based on a confidential relationship between two persons which may be invoked to exclude one from testifying against the other. In some relationships the exercise of the privilege is vested in the defendant. In others it is vested in the witness. The following relationships are generally recognized: husband and wife; attorney and client; physician and patient; and law enforcement officer and informant.

privileges. in computer usage, a means of protecting the use of certain system functions that can affect system resources and/or integrity. System managers grant privileges according to user needs, and deny privileges as a means of controlling access to functions of the system.

probable cause. a combination of facts and circumstances which would warrant a person of reasonable caution and prudence to believe that a crime has been or is being committed and that the person to be arrested is guilty of such crime. In the context of search and seizure, probable cause is a combination of facts and circumstances derived from credible sources which would warrant a person of reasonable caution and prudence to believe that crime-related evidence may be found in the premises to be searched.

probable cause hearing. a proceeding before a judicial officer in which arguments, witnesses or evidence are presented and in which it is determined whether there is sufficient cause to hold the accused for trial or dismiss the case.

probable maximum loss. the amount of loss a target of criminal attack would likely sustain in a single successful attack.

probation. a system meant to encourage good behavior in a person convicted of a crime by releasing him or her before confinement on certain conditions, one of which is that for a stated period of time he or she lead an orderly life.

probative fact. a fact which tends to substantiate another fact or issue.

procedural law. a subdivision of criminal law that provides the means and methods by which the rights and obligations created by the criminal law are to be vindicated and enforced. It defines the rules in which criminal cases are prosecuted. The laws of arrest and of evidence are examples of procedural law. Also called adjective law.

procedural rights. various protections that all citizens have against arbitrary actions by public officials.

procedural security. a combination of measures intended in their application to deter, delay, detect or deny intrusion by restricting access to a protected area.

process monitoring. the use of alarm equipment to detect and annunciate events associated with industrial machinery, such as temperature limits and overload switches.

processor. a device that processes data; a pro-

gram that carries out data processing functions.

PROCHECK. an FBI-maintained file containing information on prolific bad check passers. The file consists of information culled from existing investigative records and is accessible only to FBI personnel.

pro confesso. as confessed.

product. finished intelligence reports disseminated to users.

Professional Class I Burglar. a burglar who is able to successfully attack most alarm systems and pick locks. His targets usually are high risk commodities such as safes and vaults, cash, jewelry, furs, televisions, stereos, and appliances.

Professional Class II Burglar. a burglar who is able to circumvent alarm systems but is not sufficiently skilled to successfully attack them. He will usually go around an alarm, i.e., gain entry through the roof, floor or a wall. His targets usually are high and medium risk commodities.

Professional Class III Burglar. a relatively unskilled burglar who will avoid alarm systems completely. His targets are usually medium risk commodities.

profit. the excess of selling price over all costs and expenses incurred in making a sale. Also, the reward to an entrepreneur for the risks assumed by him in the development of a given enterprise.

profit center. an element or unit within a business organization where expenses and revenue are recorded and the net difference calculated as profit or loss. A profit center is typically a large segment of the organization and may comprise a cluster of operating activities.

pro forma. as a matter of form.

pro forma statement. a statement of income and expenses in a prescribed format; a projection or estimate of what may result in the future from actions in the present. For example, a pro forma statement might be designed to project future business operations if certain assumptions are realized.

program board. a card reader's circuit board. It contains the facility code for the reader. A board may be changed for the purpose of voiding all access cards previously issued. Also called a matrix board.

program evaluation and review technique. a planning and control process that requires identifying the accomplishments of programs and the time and resources needed to go from one accomplishment to the next. Also called PERT.

programmable cards. access cards that may be programmed at any time after manufacture. The magnetic-stripe card is an example.

programmable stand-alone card reader. a card reader that contains its own intelligence and has the capability for changing access codes and other functions.

progressive surveillance. a technique in which a subject is followed during a particular phase of his/her daily routine or during a specific period of time in one day. The surveillance is resumed on a later occasion at a phase or time when the previous surveillance was broken off.

proheptazine. an opiate classified as a Schedule I controlled substance.

projection. an ego defense mechanism in which an individual places the blame for personal problems upon others, or attributes to others his or her own unethical desires and impulses.

projection sketch. a drawing of a crime scene in which the walls of a room or building appear folded out.

prompt. a message or indication that appears on a CRT display or printer which instructs the operator to take action.

proof beyond a reasonable doubt. proof which precludes every reasonable hypothesis except that which tends to support and which is wholly consistent with a defendant's guilt and inconsistent with any other rational conclusion.

propagation. the travel of an electromagnetic radio wave through space.

properidine. an opiate classified as a Schedule I controlled substance.

Property Insurance Loss Register. a computerized register maintained by the American Insurance Association for the purpose of detecting false and duplicate claims, detecting fraudulent schemes involving fires, and identifying persons involved in arson-for-profit schemes.

property room. a place in a police department where evidence, lost and stolen property, and other accountable items are safeguarded pending use at trial, return to owners, destruction or other method of lawful disposition.

propoxyphene. a synthetic narcotic closely related to methadone. It is a Schedule II drug, and commercial preparations containing it are in Schedule IV. Darvon contains propoxyphene.

proprietaries. ostensibly private commercial entities established and controlled by intelligence services to conceal government affiliation or sponsorship of certain activities.

proprietary information. information owned by a company or entrusted to it which has not been disclosed publicly and has value.

proprietary interest. an interest applied where the Federal government has acquired some right or title to an area in a state, but has not obtained any measure of the state's authority over the area. Where the Federal Government has no legislative jurisdiction over its land, it holds such land in a proprietary interest and has the same rights in the land as does any other landowner.

proprietary system. a privately operated multiplex system, such as that used by businesses, schools and apartment buildings. It is typically situated on the premises being protected and is operated by technically competent persons trained in the use of the system's equipment and response procedures.

pro se. acting as one's own defense attorney in criminal proceedings; representing oneself.

prosecutor. an attorney employed to initiate and maintain criminal proceedings on behalf of the government (people) against persons accused of committing criminal offenses.

prostitution. offering or agreeing to engage in, or engaging in, a sex act with another in return for a fee.

protected area. an area continuously protected by physical security safeguards and access controls.

protected executive. a key member of senior management who is personally protected in some fashion by the organization's security function. A protected executive may be a target for assassination, kidnap, or extortion, and therefore a subject for protection in crisis management planning.

protected executive data form. a form containing personal information concerning a key executive who is protected by the organization's crisis management plan. The nature of data on the form is such that it would be helpful in situations involving kidnap, extortion and similar acts directed against the executive and/or immediate family. Typically attached to the form are photographs and handprinting/handwriting examples.

protective circuit. that element of an alarm system's control function which provides the means of conveying information from the various sensors to a common point.

protective custody. detention of an individual not amounting to an arrest. A practice sometimes used to protect persons from reprisal by criminals.

protective security service. in the DoD Industrial Security Program, a service which provides constant protection of a shipment at all times by one or more carrier custodians between receipt from the consignor and delivery to the consignee.

protective services. measures that increase the personal protection of a dignitary or important person who may be the target of a criminal or terrorist act.

protector. a telephone company terminal used to ground lightning strikes and to interface customer-owned wiring to the incoming telephone transmission line.

protocol function. a control function of a data transmitting and receiving system. The protocol function determines timing and format criteria that govern information interchange.

proton microscope. an optical apparatus capable of magnification of 600,000 or more, and thus six times as powerful as the strongest electron microscope.

prover tank. a small, mobile tank used to check the accuracy of meters; a calibration tank.

provisional exit. an authorized temporary exit from prison for appearance in court, work furlough, hospital treatment, appeal proceedings, or other purposes that require departure from prison but with expectation of return.

proxemics. the study of the interpersonal distances humans use in structuring transactions. The distances are: intimate, used where a close relationship exists; personal, which is not defensive but also not close; social, used in small groups and social situations; and public, used when interacting with larger groups. Proxemics has relevance to "personal space" in the context of interrogation.

proximate cause. the effective cause of loss or injury; the cause that sets other causes in operation; a responsible cause of an injury; an unbroken chain of cause and effect between the occurrence of an act and the damage it leads to. For example, improper training of a security officer can be the proximate cause of the officer's illegal actions.

proximity alarm. a device that generates an energy field around a metal or electrically conductive object when connected to the object. Touching the object or disturbing the energy field around it will trigger an alarm.

proximity card. an identity card containing a microcircuit. When placed in close proximity to a reader, the card will activate the reader's system, which might be an access control system, an automatic teller machine, or a point-of-sale transaction system.

proximity effect. the phenomenon of nonuniform current distribution over the cross-section of a conductor caused by the variation of the current in a neighboring conductor.

proximity fuse. a fuse designed to activate by radio signals. Also, a bomb fuse designed to detonate at a given range from the target without requiring any physical contact with the target to initiate the firing action.

proximity test. a test used in firearms identification to determine the distance between muzzle and point of bullet contact. It is based on the proposition that a particular weapon, using particular ammunition, will disperse gunpowder residue in a particular pattern. The pattern produced in a proximity test can be compared against a pattern observed in a shooting incident under investigation.

pseudoperforating gunshot wound. a wound in which the bullet does not exit the body and an exit wound is created by a bone fragment.

psilocybin. an active ingredient of the psilocybe mushroom which is used in traditional Indian rites. When eaten, these "sacred" or "magic" mushrooms affect mood and perception in a manner similar to mescaline and LSD. Another active ingredient of this mushroom is psilocyn, and both can be synthesized chemically. They are listed in the Controlled Substances Act as Schedule I hallucinogens.

psilocyn. an hallucinogen derived from the psilocybe mushroom. It is chemically related to LSD, and is classified as a Schedule I controlled substance.

psychedelia. a collective term for the world of mind-altering drugs and drug takers as well as drug paraphernalia.

psychedelic experiences. heightened and often inappropriate emotional reactions, mood changes of an extreme character, tactile and visual distortions, and vivid hallucinations.

psychobabble. indiscriminate use of psychological concepts and terms as an affected style of speech.

psychogalvanic skin reflex. a physiological phenomenon not yet completely understood. It is measurable with the polygraph instrument by: connecting an examinee's hand or fingers to small electrodes charged with a slight electrical current; the circuit is relayed through a galvanometer which balances the examinee's skin resistance against a fixed resistor; and minute changes in skin resistance are recorded. The polygraphist interprets the recording in forming an opinion.

psychograph. a profile of the human abilities required in the performance of a particular job.

psychological autopsy. an investigative technique used in suspected or apparent suicide cases. The technique attempts to determine whether death resulted from suicide, and if so, the motive. Information obtained from friends, relatives, and records is gathered, collated and analyzed. The technique provides a systematic means to examine social, personal, and physical events leading to the act.

psychological dependence. with regard to drugs, a compelling desire to use repeatedly a particular drug, accompanied by anxiety, irritability or depression when the drug usage is stopped. Also known as psychic dependence.

psychological profile. a description of the personality and characteristics of an individual based on an analysis of acts committed by the individual. The description might include age, race, sex, socioeconomic and marital status, educational level, arrest history, location of residence relative to the scene of the act, and certain personality traits. A profile is based on characteristic patterns of uniqueness that distinguish certain individuals from the general population. Regarding criminal acts, patterns are deduced from a thoughtful analysis of wounds, weapon used, cause of death, position of the body, and similar conditions.

psychological stress analyzer. a lie detector that can be used without the subject knowing he/she is being tested. By analyzing the stress in the subject's voice it purports to determine whether or not the truth is being told. Also called a psychological stress evaluator.

psychological set. in polygraphy, a concept which holds that a person's fears, anxieties and apprehensions will be directed toward the situation which presents the greatest immediate threat to self-preservation or well-being, generally to the exclusion of all other less threatening circumstances.

psychological test. a general term for any effort (usually a standardized test) that is designed to measure the abilities or personality traits of individuals or groups.

psychopath. a person suffering from mental aberrations and disorders, especially one who perceives reality clearly except for his or her own social or moral obligations and seeks instant gratification in criminal or otherwise abnormal behavior.

psychopathology. the science and study of mental abnormalities.

psychopharmacology. the study of the psychological and social effects of drugs.

psychotic disorder. a disorder characterized by a generalized failure of functioning in all areas of a person's life.

psychotomimetic drug. any drug that induces symptoms of psychosis.

public defender. an attorney employed by a government agency whose official duty is to represent defendants unable to hire private counsel.

public disclosure. the passing of sensitive information or materials to any member of the public.

public distance. the zone from 12 to 25 feet between individuals. Individuals interacting at this range are considered to be not personally involved.

public key cryptography. a method of data transmission that features an algorithm having one key for encryption and one key for decryption. The encryption key is public, while the decryption key is secret.

public law. that portion of the total body of laws which deals with the government either by itself or in its relations with individuals. Public law can be divided into several branches such as constitutional law, administrative law, public health law, vehicle/traffic law, and criminal law.

public officer. a person vested with a governmental power who performs a function for the benefit of the public.

pugilistic attitude. the posture of a person killed by burning. In this condition, the fists and arms are drawn up similar to a boxer's stance.

puller. a device which when inserted into the keyway of a lock or when attached to the spindle of a combination lock will allow the lock to be forcibly withdrawn.

pullout device. a device used on mechanical power presses and similar machines to pull the operator's hands away from the closing dies should they inadvertently be within the point of operation. The device consists of mitts worn by the operator and connected by cables to the ram of the machine.

pull station. a fire alarm initiating device that transmits an alarm signal when manually operated. Also called a pull box or manual station.

pull trap. a device with a mechanical triggering mechanism typically installed on infrequently used doors or windows. The pull trap's plunger is connected by wire or string to a screw eye on the jamb. When an opening occurs, the pull trap sends an alarm signal.

pulse count. a feature of an intrusion detection system in which an alarm is triggered only after there has been a series of detections in a short period of time. A pulse count is used in difficult environments where false alarms are a problem.

pulse count sensor. a motion detector, usually passive infrared, which requires several activations within a pre-set time period before triggering an alarm.

pulse extender. a device that increases a short duration signal to help insure that an alarm is triggered. Also called a pulse stretcher.

pulverizer. a machine that pulverizes documents beyond recognition. It is usually used to destroy heavy, bulky documents such as ledgers and log books.

punch coded card. an access control card having a specific pattern of punched holes. A compatible card reader uses optical or mechanical means to interpret the card's code. The technique is based on the Hollerith principle.

punch job. a safecracking technique in which the dial is forcibly removed. The exposed combination lock spindle is then punched into the safe's compartment with a heavy mallet.

puncture wound. a wound made by the insertion into the body of a sharply pointed instrument.

punitive damages. damages awarded over and above compensatory damages which serve to make an example of, or punish, the wrongdoer. Also called exemplary damages.

pure risk. a situation which carries only a possibility for cost or loss.

purge. the removal of arrest, criminal or juvenile record information from a records system.

purse snatching. grabbing a person's purse with intent to steal it or its contents. Because of the personal danger involved, it is usually punishable more severely than simple larceny or theft. Moreover, if the taker encounters physical resistance and forcibly overcomes it, the offense escalates to the more serious one of robbery.

push button lock. a type of mechanical lock that is opened by pressing numbered or lettered push buttons. The buttons may be pressed in sequence or in unison.

push key. a key which operates the Ace type of lock.

push knife. a thin, flexible blade that can be inserted in the space between a door and jamb to release a spring-loaded bolt.

PVC conduit. a tubing or hollow shield composed of polyvinyl chloride. It is used for protection of electrical wiring and alarm data lines in high-moisture environments.

PVC laminate. the compositional materials of many varieties of access cards.

pyramid scheme. a form of investment fraud in which the victim is offered a distributorship or franchise to market a particular product. The contract also authorizes the victim to sell additional franchises. The promoter represents that the marketing of the product will result in profits, but that the selling of the franchises will result in quicker return on investment. The victim consequently expends greater energies on selling franchises than on sale of products. Finally, a point is reached where the number of investors is exhausted, leading to the collapse of the pyramid. The product itself is often overpriced, and no real effort is made by the promoter to sell the product.

pyroelectric infrared sensor. a sensor that detects the temperature of a distant object without actually being in physical contact with it.

pyrolagnia. sexual pleasure derived from setting fires. Some arsonists have been found to be afflicted with pyrolagnia.

pyrolitic condition. a condition in wood caused by its exposure to low temperature heat over a long period. The condition appears as charring or carbonization, and in this state the wood has a much lower ignition point. Spontaneous combustion will not result, but the pyrolitic condition increases the fire hazard.

pyromania. a compulsion or mania to set things on fire.

Q

Q access authorization. an access authorization granted by the Nuclear Regulatory Commission based on a full field investigation conducted by the Office of Personnel Management, the Federal Bureau of Investigation, or other US Government agency which conducts personnel security investigations.

Q factor. a rating applied to coils, capacitors and resonant circuits.

Quaalude. the trade name of a widely abused synthetic sedative chemically unrelated to the barbiturates. A large dose can cause convulsions and coma; chronic use can lead to dependence; usually taken orally or injected. Also called lude and 714. Quaalude is no longer legally manufactured.

quad selector. a device that allows simultaneous viewing of pictures from four separate cameras on one CCTV monitor.

qualified endorsement. an endorsement that qualifies or limits the liability of the endorser. If an endorser endorses an instrument "without recourse," he does not assume liability in the event the maker fails to pay the instrument when due.

quality circles. a technique used by management to involve workers in the planning process. The method typically uses committees that spend part of their time suggesting solutions to problems.

quantity/distance. a term relating to safety standards or directives that control the amounts and kinds of explosives that may be stored and the proximity of such storage to buildings, highways, railways and other facilities.

quantum meruit. a legal term which means the "amount deserved." It is the relief in money awarded to a plaintiff in an action based on a contract implied by law.

quartzoid bulb. a fire detection device that operates on a thermostatic principle. When air temperature around the bulb reaches a rated point the bulb will break, causing an alarm.

quash. to make void and without effect.

quasi-contract. a legal doctrine applied to situations in which there is no specifically drawn contract. It prevents unjust enrichment or injustice by treating the situation as if a contract actually had been in effect.

quasi-crime. an offense not classified as a crime but is in the nature of a wrong against the public, and which is frequently punished by a fine, forfeiture or similar penalty.

questioned document. a document whose genuineness is questioned, normally because of origin, authenticity, age or the circumstances under which the document was written.

question spacing. in polygraphy, the elapsed time between an answer given by an examinee and the following question asked by the polygraphist during a test. The elapsed time is usually not less than 15 seconds.

queue. a lineup of operations or input signals in a system. For example, images from CCTV cameras may be queued to appear on a single monitor on a sequential and priority basis.

quick assets. assets that are quickly convertible into cash.

quick entry. no-knock entry made by law-enforcement officers.

quickie strike. a spontaneous or unannounced strike of short duration.

quick match. cord impregnated with black powder and used as a fast-burning fuse.

quick plant. an audio bugging transmitter that is easily installed or dropped in the target area.

quickpoint. a type of gun sight designed to eliminate the need to sight down the barrel. The shooter's eye is able to pick up a pink dot which when centered on the target provides an accurate sight picture.

quid pro quo. something for something.

quiet air. airwaves undisturbed by radio transmissions. Quiet air is the opposite of busy air.

quill. a folded matchbook cover used for holding, smoking or sniffing drugs.

quinine. a substance commonly used to dilute or cut heroin but which also has legitimate uses.

quorum. the number of people which must be present at a meeting before the business of the meeting can be properly transacted.

rabbeted jamb. a door jamb in which the projecting portion of the jamb which forms the door stop is either part of the same piece as the rest of the jamb or securely set into a deep groove in the jamb.

racemethorphan. an opiate classified as a Schedule II controlled substance.

racemoramide. an opiate classified as a Schedule I controlled substance.

racemorphan. an opiate classified as a Schedule II controlled substance.

raceway. a protective shield installed over surface wiring for safety and physical protection of the wires.

Racketeer Influenced and Corrupt Organizations Act (RICO). a section of the U.S. Code that makes it a crime to be engaged in a pattern of racketeering activities. RICO also allows triple damages to any injured party. It is found in 18 USC, Section 1962.

racketeering. obtaining money or other valuables by fraud, illegal use of political advantage, or threat of violence. The term is most often associated with activities of organized crime.

rack mount. a term referring to equipment designed for mounting within a standard enclosure.

rad. a measure of the dose of any ionizing radiation to body tissues in terms of the energy absorbed per unit mass of the tissue. One rad is the dose corresponding to the absorption of 100 ergs per gram of tissue.

radar sensor. a sensor that uses a radar principle to detect motion in a protected area.

radiac. a term used to designate various types of radiological measuring instruments or equipment. It is derived from the words "radioactivity detection indication and computation," and is normally used as an adjective.

radial cracks. a spider-web pattern of cracks in glass plate from which a determination can be made as to the direction of force and impact point.

radial loop. a fingerprint pattern in which a loop flows in the direction of the radius bone of the forearm.

radiation detector. an intrusion sensor that emits radiation waves and annunciates when the pattern of normal waves is disturbed.

radiation dose. in nuclear security, the quantity of radiation absorbed, per unit of mass, by the body or by any portion of the body.

radiation fuse. a bomb fuse sensitive to minute detection of nuclear radiation. The actual functioning of the fuse is caused by an influence from the target being exerted on a sensitive detecting device within the fuse itself.

radioactive delay. the gradual diminishing of the quantity of a radioactive substance due to the spontaneous disintegration of nuclei by emission.

radioactive emanation. a gaseous product of the spontaneous disintegration of a radioactive substance. The most important radioactive emanations are actinon, radon and thoron.

radioactive isotope. by common usage, any radioactive nuclide produced in a reactor or in a particle accelerator.

radio frequency. electromagnetic waves used in radio communications to carry information. Also known as rf.

radio frequency alarm. a system that operates by setting up a pattern of radio signals between two antennas. Movement in the protected area causes an imbalance, resulting in an alarm signal.

radiograph. a shadow picture produced by passing x-rays or gamma-rays through an object and recording the variations in the intensity of the emergent rays on a suitable photographic or sensitized film.

radio interference. the inhibition or prevention of clear reception of a broadcast signal.

radiological control area. an area encompassing all known or suspected radiological contamination at a nuclear weapon accident site.

radiological sabotage. in government nuclear security, a deliberate act directed against a nuclear plant or transport.

radio noise. in radio astronomy, the emission of electrical energy with a spectrum that is essentially a continuous one, in contradistinction to the discrete frequencies of radio signals.

radio spectrum. the entire range of frequencies in which useful radio waves can be produced. It extends from approximately 15 kilohertz to 30,000 megahertz.

radio telemetry system. a system that uses radio frequency transmitters and receivers for sending and receiving alarm and supervisory signals over long distances. An advantage of this system is that it does not require wire runs, which can be expensive and difficult to install.

radome. a protective housing for a microwave transmitter or receiver. It is usually made of a glass-fiber or plastic material.

rail. a horizontal framing member of a door or window sash which extends the full width between the stiles.

raising. in forgery, altering a check to increase the amount payable.

random access. access of computer data in a random fashion, without having to consider all irrelevant data on the device, or in file, that precede the needed data.

random interlace. in CCTV, a technique for scanning that does not define a strict relationship between adjacent scan lines in sequential fields. Random interlacing produces an image that is less refined than broadcast-quality interlaced scanning.

random sample. a sample of units drawn from a larger population in such a way that every unit has a known and equal chance of being selected.

rape. unlawful sexual intercourse, by force or without legal or factual consent.

rape kit. any of several types of kits, some of which are available commercially and others made from commonly available materials. A kit typically consists of paper bags to collect the victim's clothing and bedsheets, sterile envelopes, vials, microscope slides, and swabs for collecting debris (hairs, fibers, soil, grass, etc.) and body fluids (blood, seminal fluid, saliva, fecal matter, etc.), and a sterile comb for obtaining pubic hair samples.

rape without force or with consent. sexual intercourse with a female legally of the age of consent, but who is unconscious, or whose ability to judge or control her conduct is inherently impaired by mental defect, or impaired by intoxicating substances.

rap sheet. a file or document containing such data as a subject's arrest record, charges preferred and case dispositions. Also called an information sheet or criminal history sheet.

raster. in CCTV, the area of the picture tube scanned by the electronic beam.

raster burn. a defect in the target of a television-image pickup tube. It appears as an aberration on the video picture. Also called burn-in.

rate compensation heat detector. a heat detector that compensates for thermal lag. In operation, the unit alarms at the rated operating temperature regardless of whether the heat increases rapidly or gradually. The sensing element consists of a pair of expansion struts and electrical contacts housed in an expandable outer shell. Ambient heat expands the outer shell and relieves pressure on the struts. This operates electrical contacts that trigger an alarm.

rated capacity. the discharge capacity in ampere hours specified for a battery.

rated operating temperature. the minimum temperature at which a heat detector will consistently initiate an alarm.

rate of rise. a principle of fire detection in which sensors measure the rate of temperature increase in a protected area over a given period of time. If the temperature of the surrounding air rises faster than a predetermined rate, an alarm is produced. The rate of rise detector is regarded as being superior to the fixed-temperature detector on the grounds it is more sensitive and not subject to thermal lag.

RDX. a type of booster explosive.

reactance. the opposition to the flow of alternating current caused by inductance or capacitance of a component or circuit.

reaction distance. the distance a moving vehicle travels between the time the driver observes an obstacle and the time the brakes are applied or a maneuvering action initiated.

reaction formation. an ego defense mechanism which prevents dangerous desires and impulses from being carried out by fostering opposed types of behavior and attitudes.

read and execute access right. a security feature of a computer system in which an authorized user is allowed to read and execute files, but not modify them.

read-out. a means for displaying an electronically transmitted message in a form meaningful to human intelligence.

real cost. a measure in dollars of costs pertaining to the replacement of lost assets plus all related costs.

real evidence. evidence furnished by the things themselves as distinguished from a description of them; tangible items of evidence such as a gun, a bullet slug, or a controlled substance.

real image. an optical counterpart of an object, produced on the surface at which light rays converge after passing through a lens. The real image of an object-point is the point at which light originating in the object-point is finally converged after traversing the optical system.

real-time process. in computer usage, a process that responds to events in related or controlled processes as they occur, rather than when the computer is ready to respond to them.

reasonable care. the care that prudent persons would exercise under the same circumstances.

reasonable cause. a combination of facts and circumstances which would warrant a person of reasonable intelligence and prudence to believe that an offense has been or is being committed. Also called probable cause.

reasonable doubt. any uncertainty in the minds of jurors which would cause them to find a defendant not guilty of a crime. In order to convict, the government must prove that the accused is guilty beyond any reasonable doubt.

reasonable force. the least amount of force that will permit an officer to subdue or arrest a subject while still maintaining a level of safety for himself and the public.

reason to suspect. a combination of facts and circumstances not amounting to probable cause.

rebuttable presumption. a presumption that is open to rebuttal by evidence; a presumption which stands until disproved.

rebuttal. the proof presented at a trial by the plaintiff intended to overcome the evidence introduced by the defendant.

recapture rate. the rate of interest necessary to provide for the return of the initial investment. Recapture rate is different than interest rate, which is the rate of return on an investment.

Receipt of Stolen Property. a section of the U.S. Code that prohibits the receipt, concealment, sale or disposal of goods, wares or merchandise of value of $5,000 or more which have moved in interstate or foreign commerce with the knowledge that the goods had been stolen or unlawfully converted. The law is found in 18 USC, Section 2315.

receive modem. a device for taking data from a telephone line.

receiver. any device capable of receiving a message.

recess mounted switch. a mechanical or magnetic sensor mounted on an interior surface of a protected area in such a way that it is not easily seen.

recidivism. the repetition of criminal behavior; habitual criminality.

reconnaissance. a mission undertaken to obtain, by observation or other detection methods, information about the activities of persons or groups.

recording pens. the hollow, stainless steel styli seated in individual cradles atop a polygraph instrument. They are counterbalanced by adjustable nuts, and serve the function of marking the polygraph chart.

record prints. inked finger, palm or sole impressions obtained for identification purposes.

rectangular coordinates method. a method for mapping an object in a crime scene sketch by giving its distance from two mutually perpendicular lines. For example, if the crime scene is a room and the object to be mapped is a knife on the floor, two mutually perpendicular walls can be used as reference points. A measurement is made from the knife to one wall (north or south) and a measurement is made from the knife to an-

other wall (east or west). The knife is then fixed or located, and can be shown in a sketch as lying in a particular spot.

reduced phenolphthalein test. a test to determine the presence of blood in a stain or substance of unknown origin. Like the benzidine test, it is preliminary in nature, i.e., not entirely conclusive.

redundant design. a design of machinery or equipment involving two or more components so arranged that failure of one calls one or more of the others into service.

reed switch. a type of magnetic contact switch with metallic reeds sealed in a glass tube.

reefer. a marihuana cigarette.

reformatory. a correctional facility that was originally conceived of as a place where offenders would reform or change their criminal behavior, attitudes and values. In modern usage, it is a place where juvenile offenders are kept in custody.

refresh the memory. the use of notes or memoranda to stimulate or revive a testifying witness' recollection. Such notes or memoranda can be taken as evidence.

regenerative feedback. a squeal caused by the output of an amplifier feeding back to its own input.

register. a device that makes a permanent record of alarms.

regrade. a determination that classified information requires a different degree of protection against unauthorized disclosure than currently provided, together with a change of classification designation that reflects such different degree of protection.

regression analysis. a method for describing the nature of the relationship between two variables, so that the value of one can be predicted if the value of the other is known.

regulated power supply. a power supply that provides a constant output regardless of input voltage variations.

Regulation Z. a term describing rules issued by the Board of Governors of the Federal Reserve System as regards implementation of the Truth-in-Lending Act.

regulatory crime. a crime that violates an order of a federal or state regulatory agency; for example, the Food and Drug Administration or the Securities and Exchange Commission.

rehabilitation. the change of an offender's behavior, mental attitude, and values in such a way that he ceases committing criminal acts.

re-key. the process of changing a keylock or a card reader to accommodate a new key set or entry code.

relative amplitude spectrum. one of several

criteria used in measuring speech for access control purposes.

relative frequency. in frequency distributions, the frequency of a specific class mark divided by the total number of figures in the data.

relative impact measure. a dimensionless measure of the relative impact of a violation to computer system integrity. It is expressed as a function of the characteristics of perpetrators, characteristics of the perpetrators' targets, and the characteristics of the flaws in the security measures that operate to protect the computer system.

relay. an electrically operated switch that opens/closes contacts when voltage is applied or removed.

release. conditional, temporary, or permanent discharge from custody.

relevant evidence. evidence having a tendency to make the existence of a fact more probable or less probable than it would be without the evidence; evidence which is directly related to the offense and tends to prove or disprove any fact at issue.

relevant question. in polygraphy, a question pertaining directly to the issue being tested. In theory, a relevant question will produce in the guilty subject a response recordable by the polygraph instrument. Also called a crucial, pertinent or material question.

relock switch. a switch on an electric lock that retains the bolt in the retracted position until the door is closed.

remand. to recommit, as when a prisoner's habeas corpus application is dismissed and he is remanded to prison.

remedial law. law concerned with the procedure involved in carrying out substantive law, i.e., the laws of arrest, trial, bail, etc.

remote keypad. a keypad mounted away from the alarm system's control panel and used to arm/disarm an alarm system and/or shunt circuits.

remote reset. restoration of a tripped alarm from a remote location.

remote station fire alarm system. a system of electrically supervised devices employing a direct circuit connection between alarm initiating devices or a control unit in protected premises and signal-indicating equipment in a remote station, such as a fire or police station.

remote station system. a system where the alarm signal is transmitted to a remote location operated by an independent party.

remote terminal. a device for communicating with a computer system from a location that is apart from the central computer facility.

removable core lock. a lock from which the entire core can be removed as a unit and replaced.

removable mullion. a mullion separating two adjacent door openings which is required for the normal operation of the doors but is designed to permit its temporary removal.

render safe. to employ particular procedures or modes of action to recover, neutralize and finally dispose of explosive ordnance or other hazardous materials.

render safe procedures. that portion of explosive ordnance procedures which provides for the interruption of functions or separation of essential components to prevent a detonation or function.

rendition. the surrender or delivery of a person by the senior executive of the state or area to which the person has fled.

rent-a-cop. a term describing a company that hires out security officers.

repeater facility. a location that uses radio equipment to relay radio signals between a central station, satellite station and/or protected premises.

replevin. a court action to recover possession of property unlawfully taken or detained. Title to the property must be in the person bringing the action. Thus, if title passes to the buyer and the seller refuses to deliver the goods, the buyer may bring an action in replevin to get possession of the goods. Or the seller, under a conditional sale contract by which he retains title to the goods until payment is made, may recover the goods by an action in replevin if the buyer does not make the payments called for by the contract.

reply. the document submitted by the plaintiff to a lawsuit in answering the counterclaims of the defendant.

reporting line. an electrically supervised wire circuit used for the transmission of alarm signals from a protected area to a central receiving point.

reprieve. a stay or delay in the execution of a sentence.

request standards. examples of comparison materials, such as handwriting samples, which are requested from a source related to the investigation.

res adjudicata. a legal doctrine which holds that a controversy once having been decided or adjudged upon its merits is forever settled so far as the particular parties involved are concerned. Its purpose is to avoid vexatious lawsuits.

reserved keyway lock. a high-security lock with a special keyway unique to a single or limited number of users. Key blanks are usually registered to control unauthorized copying.

reset. to restore an alarm to a normal condition.

res gestae. things done; transactions.

residential treatment center. a residence in which offenders are temporarily living, under conditions less confining than in a jail or prison, and where the major emphasis is on therapy.

residual air. in polygraphy, air remaining in the lungs even after the deepest possible expiration.

residual contamination. radiation contamination that remains after available technology has been applied to remove it.

residual data. processable information remaining from prior use of fixed or movable electronic data processing media. Classified residual data in storage, on volumes, and on magnetic media are usually erased or overwritten by the application program if erasure is not supported by the system softwear and cannot be done manually.

residual risk. that portion of risk which remains after security measures have been applied.

res ipsa loquitur. a theory of recovery for personal injury which presumes that under certain conditions the injury would not have occurred if the defendant had been careful.

resistance. the electrical equivalent of friction. It is a function of the materials used in the components or in the conductive circuit path. Resistance is measured in ohms.

resistance-bridge smoke detector. a smoke detector that contains a resistance-bridge whose resistance will drop in the presence of smoke particles, thereby producing an alarm.

resisting an officer. resisting or obstructing a law enforcement officer in the performance of an official duty.

resistivity. the electrical resistance offered to the passage of current; the opposite of conductivity.

resistor. an electronic component that provides a specific amount of resistance in a supervised protective circuit.

res judicata. the legal defense that the issue presented has previously been adjudicated between the same parties.

resonance. the condition of an electrical circuit when it responds with maximum effect or amplitude to an applied frequency causing a maximum flow of current or voltage level.

resonance control. a control on a polygraph instrument that permits the polygraphist to narrow an excessively wide cardiographic tracing.

resonant cavity. a hollow metal cylinder the dimensions of which are chosen to make it strongly reflect a radio signal of predetermined frequency. Also called a passive reflector.

respondeat superior. Latin words that mean the master is liable for the acts of his agent;

the principle in law which transfers liability to a principal for the negligent acts of his agent.

respondent. the person who formally answers the allegations stated in a petition which has been filed in a court; in criminal proceedings, the one who contends against an appeal.

response overload. stimuli so excessive or demanding that the system they are acting upon is unable to respond.

response time. the time elapsed between an alarm annunciation and reaction on the part of designated response personnel.

restitution. the act of giving back money or property that was stolen. This may be done voluntarily, perhaps in hopes of obtaining a more lenient sentence, or it may be ordered by a court as part of a sentence or as a condition of probation. Restitution does not necessarily relieve an accused of the necessity of standing trial and facing criminal sanctions, but it often does so in practice, or it acts to placate a complainant and to reduce the severity of the sentence.

restraint of trade. illegal action taken to prevent the free flow of goods in a market economy. Restraint of trade may take such forms as the holding back of improved products, the monopolistic control of raw materials, or agreement among corporations to fix prices and to not compete against each other.

restricted area. a general term describing an area which requires controlled access due to sensitive or classified materials kept therein.

Restricted Data. as used in the DoD Industrial Security Program, information concerning the design, manufacture or utilization of atomic weapons, the production of special nuclear material, and the use of special nuclear material in the production of energy.

restricted keyway. a special keyway and key blank for high security locks, with a configuration which is not freely available and which must be specifically requested from the manufacturer.

restrictive covenant. a provision in an agreement limiting or restricting the action of one of the parties to the agreement. Thus, a seller of a business may agree not to engage in the same business within a certain number of years. Or a deed may contain a covenant restricting the type of building that may be placed upon the property.

restrictive indorsement. an indorsement used in negotiating a negotiable instrument to a person for a specific task such as "for collection only."

retained image. in CCTV, an image retained on the target of the image-pickup tube. It is a "burn-in" of short duration and appears on the monitor screen as a bright flare-like glow. Exposure of a nonfiltered image-pickup tube to an extremely bright source over an extended period of time can result in a permanent burn-in.

retarding transmitter. an alarm transmitter that delays transmission of an alarm signal for a predetermined time, usually seconds.

retentionist. one who favors the retention or reinstitution of capital punishment.

retribution. the just-deserts theory of punishment which holds that an offender should suffer to the extent deserved by the seriousness of the crime so that justice may be served.

retro target sensor. a sensor that is a transceiver and uses a reflecting target to return the transmitted beam back towards the receive portion of the sensor.

retro zoom lens. a CCTV lens fitting that reduces the collective focal lengths of a zoom lens. A gain is made in wide angle coverage, but there is a proportional loss in telephoto power.

return. the endorsement made by an officer upon a warrant, stating that he or she has done what was required by the warrant.

return call verification. a technique for restricting access to a computer's dial-up ports. A person wishing access to a computer by phone dials a designated number and gives an identification code. If the code is correctly given, the call is transferred to a line that provides access. Also known as dial-up/call back or handshake verification.

revenge. a motive imputed to a defendant; a motive for punishment; retaliation.

revenue center. an element or unit within a business organization where income is accumulated and identified with a specific project or organizational entity. Also called income center.

reverse polarity transmission alarm. an alarm caused when the flow of current in a transmission line is reversed. The current reversal, or absence of voltage, is interpreted as a trouble condition.

reversible error. an error sufficient to warrant a reversal of judgment by an appellate court; substantial error claimed as prejudicial to the complaining party's case.

reversible lock. a lock which may be used for either hand of a door.

reversible transformations. coded data so designed that plaintext is uniquely recoverable from ciphertext. Reversible transformations preserve the data that has been operated on so as to allow a reversal of the process. Also called encrypting transformations.

revolving-door justice. a term critical of the manner in which the criminal justice system repeatedly releases dangerous defendants.

rhodamine B. a tracing powder used to mark objects likely to be touched by a culprit. The powder is converted to a cherry-colored dye by the skin's natural moisture.

ribbon cable. a flat electrical cable containing several individually insulated conductors. Ribbon cable may have each conductor identified by a different color, or it may have a common color for all.

rice-paper edition. self-incriminating information printed on rice paper so it can be chewed and swallowed if its owner is in imminent danger of being caught, as in a raid on a numbers racket.

ridge count. in fingerprint classification, the number of fingerprint ridges between the core and the delta.

RIF. an acronym for reduction in force, a phrase the federal government uses when it eliminates specific job categories in specific organizations.

rifling characteristics. in firearms identification, the number, dimensions and direction of twist in the barrel of a weapon, plus its caliber. These general features help an examiner match a particular firearm with particular bullets

right to counsel. a provision of the Sixth Amendment to the US Constitution which requires that in all prosecutions the accused shall enjoy the right to have the assistance of counsel for his defense. The Supreme Court has held that where incarceration may be a consequence of the prosecution, the defendant is entitled to appointed counsel in the event he cannot afford one.

rigor mortis. a stiffening of the body's muscles after death in a generally predictable pattern and time frame. It first appears in the face and jaws, before proceeding downward through the neck to the arms, chest and abdomen and finally to the legs and the feet. Rigor mortis of the entire body occurs within eight to twelve hours after death, but eighteen more hours may pass before the body is completely enveloped. Rigor mortis is an indicator of time of death.

rim cylinder. a pin or disc tumbler cylinder used with a rim lock.

rim hardware. hardware designed to be installed on the surface of a door or window.

rim latch. a latch installed on the surface of a door.

rim lock. a lock designed to be mounted on the surface of a door.

ringback. an acknowledgment from a central station to a subscriber that a signal has been received.

ringer. a telephone bell and the electrical circuit that makes it work.

riot. the coming together of a group of persons who engage in violent and tumultuous conduct, thereby causing or creating a serious, imminent risk of causing injury to persons or property, or public alarm.

rip job. a method of safecracking in which a hole is drilled in one corner, a crowbar is inserted, and the exterior surface is ripped off or peeled back. Also called a peel job.

ripple. amplitude variations in the output voltage of a power supply caused by insufficient filtering.

risk. the loss potential that can be estimated by an analysis of threat and vulnerability. Reducing either the threat or the vulnerability reduces the risk.

risk acceptance. a willingness to accept the maximum probable loss associated with a successful criminal attack.

risk-adverse. a willingness to accept a higher probability of a small dollar loss in return for a lower probability of a large dollar loss. The opposite of risk-preferring.

risk analysis. an analytical tool used to minimize risk by applying security measures commensurate with the relative threats, vulnerabilities, and values of the assets to be protected.

risk assessment. a detailed study of the vulnerabilities, threats, likelihood, loss or impact, and theoretical effectiveness of security measures. Security administrators use the results of a risk assessment to develop security requirements and specifications.

risk avoidance. the practice of removing or placing a crime target outside the effective reach of criminals.

risk management. a business discipline consisting of three major functions: loss prevention, loss control and loss indemnification.

risk-preferring. a willingness to accept a higher probability of a large dollar loss in return for a lower probability of a small dollar loss. The opposite of risk-adverse.

risk reduction. the practice of reducing criminal opportunity by reducing the exposure of an asset to the possibility of criminal attack.

risk spreading. the practice of using security equipment and procedures to discourage, deter and deny criminal attack.

risk transfer. the practice of purchasing insurance to reduce the extent of loss associated with a successful criminal attack.

ritalin. a commonly abused amphetamine. Also known as speed, upper, black beauty, crank, meth, bam, pink.

rival hypothesis. an explanation that competes with the original hypothesis in a study.

RJ31X jack. a special telephone line jack that must be installed to connect digital communicators and tape dialers to the telephone line.

roach. the butt of a marijuana cigarette, so called because after it has been smoked and/or shared it resembles a wet cockroach.

roach clip. a device for holding a hashish or marijuana cigarette so it may be smoked to the very end.

robbery. the unlawful taking or attempted taking of property that is in the immediate possession of another, by force or threat of force.

roentgen. a unit of exposure of gamma (X-ray) radiation in the field of dosimetry. One roentgen is essentially equal to one rad.

roentgen equivalent man/mammal (REM). one REM is the quantity of ionizing radiation of any type which, when absorbed by man or other mammals, produces a physiological effect equivalent to that produced by the absorption of one roentgen of gamma radiation.

role conflict. a situation in which two or more social roles make imcompatible demands on a person.

role expectations. commonly shared norms about how a person is supposed to behave in a particular role.

roll. in CCTV, a loss of vertical synchronization that causes the CRT's picture to move up or down.

rolled impressions. inked fingerprint impressions obtained by rolling the fingers from one side to the other. This technique captures maximum ridge detail.

roller strike. a strike for latch bolts. It has a roller mounted on the lip to reduce friction.

roper. a pimp; a member of a con artist team who spots and brings a victim into contact with other team members.

roping. undercover work in which the investigator assumes a different identity in order to obtain information.

rose. the part of a lock which functions as an ornament or bearing surface for a knob, and is normally placed against the surface of the door.

rotary interlocking dead bolt lock. a type of a rim lock in which the extended dead bolt is rotated to engage with the strike.

rotary switch. a switch that has several contact points around a rotating shaft. The switch may make or break several different circuits depending on the position of the rotating shaft.

rounder. that member of a shoplifting team who distracts the sales clerk by moving the clerk around and away from the merchandise targeted for theft.

rubber gas grenade. a tear gas grenade covered with rubber or soft plastic so as to minimize the possibility of injury when the grenade is fired into a rioting mob.

rubber lifter. a material used for lifting latent fingerprints. The material comes in sheet form or as a tape. A removable plastic cover protects the adhesive side of the lifter. The adhesive side is applied to a powdered print and peeled back, capturing the print. Rubber lifters work well on curved surfaces.

rule of strict construction. the requirement that a statute be interpreted literally in accordance with its terms, rather than its spirit. The rule is often applied to criminal statutes.

runaway. a juvenile who has been adjudicated by a judicial officer of a juvenile court, as having committed the status offense of leaving the custody and home of his or her parents, guardians or custodians without permission and failing to return within a reasonable length of time.

runaway grand jury. a grand jury that asserts its independence of the prosecutor and, often assisted by a special prosecutor, presses investigations over and beyond the desires of the regular prosecutor.

rundown burn pattern. in arson investigations, charring seen on floor joists and other under-floor surfaces which suggests that burning liquid on the floor's surface flowed downward.

runner. an employee of a central station responsible for restoring an alarm at a subscriber's location and assisting the police or fire department who have responded to the alarm; an employee of a numbers or lottery operation who carries messages.

run the trapline. in criminal investigations, to check all sources of information for leads in a particular case.

rush. a slang word that describes the effect of drugs in the body shortly after being taken.

Russian Time Cube. a sophisticated, yet easy to operate, electronic time delay device used in the construction of terrorist bombs.

sabotage. the willful and malicious disruption of the normal processes and functions of an organization.

safe cover. a magnetized cover placed over the entry controls to a safe or vault. If the safe cover is removed without first disarming a sensor, an alarm is triggered.

Safeguards Information. in nuclear security, information not otherwise classified as National Security Information or Restricted Data which specifically identifies a licensee's or applicant's detailed security measures for physical protection of special nuclear material or security measures for physical protection and location of certain plant equipment vital to the safety of production or utilization facilities.

safe house. a secure, unbugged meeting place.

sag. a short-term decrease in line voltage, usually resulting from a short-circuit or a sudden increase in electrical load on the line. Also called line dip or voltage dip.

sail switch. an airflow sensor used in fire and environmental control systems. The switch has a flat piece of material positioned in a defined airspace. When a given amount of air moves against it, a set of contacts is closed and an alarm triggered.

salami technique. a fraudulent technique in which small amounts of money are debited/credited to a large number of separate accounts, usually with the help of a computer. A large accumulation of money can be diverted when small amounts are stolen from many accounts.

saliva. a clear, odorless, tasteless fluid produced by certain glands in the body to keep the mouth moist. The presence of saliva can be tested for in a crime laboratory. In secretors, saliva contains large amounts of the blood group substances (A, B, or H). Saliva also contains an enzyme called amylase which may be detected separately in persons who are non-secretors.

salvage value. the estimated worth of an item after it is fully depreciated.

sampling smoke detector. a type of smoke detector that draws air from one or more protected areas and analyzes the sample at a central point.

sash operator. a mechanical device which is used to move or pivot and to adjust the position of a movable sash within the window frame. The sash operator, in some assemblies, may also act as a locking device in lieu of, or in addition to, a sash lock.

saucer pattern. a cone shaped pattern that appears in glass plate fractured by a penetrating force. In a cross sectional view, the tip of the cone is on the entering side of the glass with the large end of the cone on the exiting side.

sandwiching. a shoplifter's practice of holding an item to be shoplifted against the outside of a purse or pocket just prior to concealment.

sanitize. the deletion or revision of a report or document so as to prevent identification of the sources and methods that contributed to or are dealt with in the report.

satellite station. a remote or unattended station linked by communication channels to a central station.

satisfaction of judgment. a document which states that a recorded judgment has been paid and satisfied.

Saturday-night special. an inexpensive handgun, so called because of its use in robberies (on Saturday nights).

sawed-off shotgun. a shotgun having one or more shortened barrels, usually less than 18 inches in length.

saw job. a safecracking method in which a high-speed power saw with a diamond or carborundum blade is used to saw a hole into the safe.

scab. an employee who continues to work for an organization while it is being struck by co-workers.

scam. a crime, particularly a crime involving trickery. Also, an undercover police operation in which criminals are tricked into revealing their involvement in criminal activities.

scanner. a motorized CCTV camera mounting that moves from side to side to survey a large area.

scatter diagram. a display of the relationship between variables using dots on a graph.

scene analyzer. a video motion detector that calls operator attention to the disturbed portion of a scene. It is intended to assist the operator in assessing an alarm condition.

Schedule A. a category used by the Office of Personnel Management for those excepted federal positions for which it is not practicable to hold any examinations and which are not of a confidential or policy-determining nature.

Schedule B. a category used by the Office of Personnel Management for those excepted federal positions for which competitive examinations are impracticable, but for which the person must pass a noncompetitive examination. Included here are positions assigned to Navy or Air Force communications intelligence activities and national bank examiners in the Treasury Department.

Schedule C. a category used by the Office of Personnel Management for those excepted federal positions which are policy-determining or which involve a close personal relationship between the incumbent and the agency head or his/her key officials.

Schedule I Controlled Substance. a substance which has a high potential for abuse, has no currently accepted medical use, and for which there is a lack of accepted safety for use under medical supervision.

Schedule II Controlled Substance. a substance which has a high potential for abuse, has a currently accepted medical use or a currently accepted medical use with severe restrictions, and which may lead an abuser to severe psychological or physical dependence.

Schedule III Controlled Substance. a substance which has a potential for abuse, is less than the substances in Schedules I and II, has a currently accepted medical use, and which may lead to moderate or low physical dependence or high physiological dependence.

Schedule IV Controlled Substance. a substance which has a low potential for abuse relative to the substances in Schedule III, has a currently accepted medical use, and which may lead an abuser to limited physical dependence or psychological dependence relative to the substances in Schedule III.

Schedule V. a substance which has a low potential for abuse relative to the substances in Schedule IV, has a currently accepted medical use, and which may lead an abuser to limited physical dependence or psychological dependence relative to the substance in Schedule IV.

schizophrenia. a group of disorders characterized by thought disturbance that may be accompanied by delusions, hallucinations, attention deficits, and bizarre motor activity.

scientific and technical intelligence. information concerning foreign progress in basic and applied scientific or technical research and development, including engineering R&D, new technology and weapons systems.

score. to purchase illegal drugs.

Scotch verdict. a verdict in which the charges against the defendant are declared not proved, and which permits the defendant to be charged and tried again if new evidence is found. So called because of its use in Scotland.

Scotland Yard. the popular name for the headquarters of the London Metropolitan Police. The office took its name from the original building's back premises, Scotland Yard, through which the public entered.

scrambled signature identification. an identification procedure in which the genuine signature of an authorized person is scrambled into many parts and placed on file. A descrambling lens optically reassembles the filed signature for comparison with a signed document presented for cash or other purpose.

scrambler. a device that disguises information so as to make it unintelligible to those who should not obtain it.

screamer. in electronic countermeasures, an rf field strength and audio amplifier combination that causes feedback when positioned near a concealed transmitter.

screening interview. an initial interview for a job that serves to determine which applicants are to be given further consideration.

scrimmage wound. a stabbing wound that has been enlarged by movement of the weapon or the victim. A notch along the side of the puncture is a characteristic of a scrimmage wound.

sealed lead-acid battery. a battery similar in construction to an automobile battery, but used to power alarms and serve as a backup to lighting and alarm systems. A sealed lead-acid battery is rechargeable, has relatively good temperature characteristics, but has a low energy density.

sealed source. any special nuclear material or byproduct material encased in a capsule designed to prevent leakage or escape of that nuclear material.

search. the examination or inspection of a location, vehicle, or person by a law enforcement officer or other person authorized to do so, for the purpose of locating objects relating to or believed to relate to criminal activities, or wanted persons.

search warrant. an order issued by a judicial officer which directs a law enforcement officer to conduct a search for specified property or persons at a specific location, to seize the property or persons, if found, and to account for the results of the search to the issuing judicial officer.

seasonally adjusted annual rate. a calculation of economic activity in which the actual activity in a month is adjusted to remove seasonal influences. Seasonal adjustment attempts to account for month-to-month variations resulting from normal changes in the number of working days.

secobarbital. a commonly abused barbiturate, usually taken orally or injected. Also called barb, downer, blue, yellow jacket and sleeping pill.

secondary code. a supplemental code used to activate keypad functions. It is often used as a temporary code assignment in order to maintain the integrity of the primary code. Also called an auxiliary code.

secondary evidence. evidence inferior to primary evidence. For example, an original document pertinent to an issue cannot be found. Secondary evidence of the existence of the document could be made by oral testimony and/or a copy of the original document. Also called next best evidence.

secondary missile wound. a wound caused by a flying fragment created when a bullet or other projectile strikes an object in the environment nearby the victim.

secondary password. in computer usage, a user password that may be required at login time, immediately after the primary password has been correctly submitted. Primary and secondary passwords can be known by separate users, to ensure that more than one user is present at the login.

second degree murder. killing committed during the course of a quarrel and in the heat of passion.

Secret. as used in the DoD Industrial Security Program, a designation applied to information or materials the unauthorized disclosure of which reasonably could be expected to cause serious damage to the national security. Examples of serious damage include disruption of foreign relations significantly affecting the national security, significant impairment of a program or policy directly related to national security, revelation of a significant military intelligence operation, compromise of significant military plans or intelligence operations, and compromise of significant scientific or technological developments relating to national security.

Secret Controlled Shipment. as used in the DoD Industrial Security Program, a shipment of Secret material through a commercial transportation mode using protective security services (PSS).

secret interest. interest hidden or concealed from third party knowledge.

secretor. a person whose body fluids contain a water soluble form of the antigens of the A, B, O blood group found in his or her red blood cells. Approximately 80% of the population are secretors; the other 20% are called nonsecretors. Human saliva and semen are the two body fluids that contain the largest amounts of these substances.

secret writing. writing which is concealed by including it within the text of other writing or by the use of chemicals.

Section 1983 suit. a civil suit brought under Section 1983 of Title 42, USC, called "Civil Action for Deprivation of Civil Rights." It is the primary vehicle used by litigants who seek damages and/or injunctive relief from the police (and other public officials) when there is an allegation that one's constitu-

tional or federally protected rights have been violated.

secure access multiport. a black box device that operates outside the host computer to screen incoming calls. If the caller enters a valid code (via a touch tone telephone or encoder) the SAM disconnects the line, matches the code to a preprogrammed telephone number in the call-back directory, and returns the call to the authorized location.

secure access unit. a black box device that operates outside the host computer to screen incoming calls. If the caller enters a valid code (via a touch tone telephone or encoder) the SAU disconnects the line, matches the code to a preprogrammed telephone number in the call-back directory, and returns the call to the authorized location. A more complex and flexible variation of SAU is SAM, a secure access multiport.

secure telephone system. a telephone system that uses scramblers and/or line supervision circuitry to enhance security of communications.

security and privacy standards. a set of principles and procedures developed to insure the security and confidentiality of criminal or juvenile record information in order to protect the privacy of the persons identified in such records.

security erase. a feature of a computer system which upon command will erase sensitive documents in memory by writing over them.

Security File. the name of a file maintained by the US Civil Service Commission. It lists persons who might be ineligible for government clearance because of questioned loyalty or subversive activities. The file is developed from published hearings of federal and state legislative committees, public investigative bodies, reports of investigation, publications of subversive organizations, and various newspapers and periodicals. The file is used by investigative and intelligence officials of federal agencies.

security film. a polyester film applied to the interior surface of glass plate. Security film can significantly increase a glass plate's resistance to impact and reduce the flying glass hazard. It has practical use in environments where bombings and "smash and grab" threats exist.

security glazing. special glass designed to provide physical protection. It is usually laminated, and different varieties are rated according to degree of resistance.

security in depth. the use of a series of barriers in a protection design.

Security Investigations Index. a card file maintained by the US Civil Service Commission.

It lists persons investigated by the Commission and other agencies since 1939. Information from the index is available to security investigators having a bona fide employment or investigative interest in a listed person.

security loop. an electrically supervised wire circuit used for the transmission of alarm signals from a protected area to a central receiving point.

security management. persons, not necessarily uniformed or armed, who direct the activities of a security operation or organization.

security operator terminal. in computer usage, a class of terminal enabled to receive messages sent to a security officer or other person charged with generating responses to emergency conditions.

security utility. a computer program designed to protect computer system resources against unauthorized use or tampering. At the system level, a user ID/password routine restricts logon access. At the file level, users are granted access rights on a right and need to know basis. Within files, user rights are further defined as to read, execute and modify privileges.

security vulnerability assessment. a risk management methodology for examining and assessing security risks, threats and vulnerabilities that exist within an operating entity.

sedition. an attempt, short of treason, to excite hostility against a sovereign government among its own citizens.

seismic sensor. an intrusion detection sensor installed underground and designed to detect surface vibrations and/or pressure. These include electrical stress cable, piezoelectric sensors, geophones, and balanced pressure sensors. A seismic sensor converts ground movement or vibration into electrical impulses that are received by a processor. Comparator circuitry eliminates impulses that are not characteristic of an intruder, such as human footsteps and digging actions. The geophone sensor allows a human operator to listen to vibrations and judge their meanings. Seismic sensors can also be used in an earthquake detection system, particularly systems that are installed at high-rise buildings. Excessive seismic vibration might, for example, cause an elevator to stop at the next available floor.

seizable items. items for which a search warrant may be issued. Examples of seizable items are instruments of a crime to include private papers, stolen or embezzled property, a kidnapped person, a human fetus or corpse, contraband, and other tangible evidence of the commission of a crime.

seizure. the taking into custody of law, by a law enforcement officer or other person authorized to do so, of objects relating to or believed to relate to criminal activity.

selective coded system. a system that utilizes fire alarm initiating devices, each of which is capable of transmitting its own individual code.

selective incapacitation. a sentencing strategy in which individual sentences are based on factors that predict future criminality, and which are used to identify and confine, for an extended period, those offenders who represent the most serious risk to the community.

selective protection of assets. selective application of protective measures to identified assets, supplemental to normal business controls, safety practices, and general physical security.

self-contained card reader. a card reader that has its own built-in intelligence and is not dependent on an external device to make entry/exit decisions. Also called a stand-alone reader or an off-line reader.

self-defense. the protection of oneself or one's property from unlawful injury or the immediate risk of unlawful injury; the justification for an act which would otherwise constitute an offense on the ground that the person who committed it reasonably believed that the act was necessary to protect self or property from immediate danger.

self-destructing badge. a paper identification badge that reacts to electrically produced light by turning a dark color over an approximate 8 hour period. If exposed to direct sunlight the badge will immediately darken. The darkening effect cancels the badge as an acceptable identification document. It is typically used as a visitor badge at indoor environments.

self-destructing seal. a seal which once in place cannot be removed without destroying it.

self-incrimination. a testimonial or verbal communication from an individual or his performance of some physical act which requires his conscious mental cooperation, which utterance or act implicates him as being a perpetrator of criminal activity.

self-report study. an investigation by means of a questionnaire or similar device in which the respondent is asked to indicate the nature, extent, and frequency of personal illegal and deviant behavior.

selvage. the border of a chain link fence formed by twisting adjacent pairs of wire ends together.

semaphore arm. a type of gate arm which opens in an upward arc.

semen. the fluid expelled by the male at sexual climax and which may be detected by a crime laboratory. Semen consists of two parts: spermatazoa and seminal fluid.

Semiconductor Chip Protection Act of 1984. an act which confers protected status on registered chips.

seminal fluid. the liquid portion of semen (male ejaculate) which is present even in men with no detectable spermatazoa. It contains chemicals such as acid phosphatase, spermine, and choline, the A, B, and H blood group substances in secretions, and other proteins and enzymes which may be tested for in a crime laboratory.

sensitive compartmented information. as used in the DoD Industrial Security Program, information and materials that require special controls for restricted handling within compartmented intelligence systems and for which compartmentation is established.

Sensitive DP Program. a computer application program whose unauthorized modification for fraudulent purposes could result in serious misappropriation or loss of physical or financial assets, other than data. The objective of sensitive program control is prevention and detection of unauthorized program modification, substitution, or execution.

sensor. a device designed to produce a signal or other indication in response to an event or stimulus within its detection area. Also called a detector.

sentence. a judgment in a criminal proceeding.

sentencing council. a group of judges who meet on a more or less regular basis to discuss sentencing decisions in pending cases in order to render non-binding recommendations to the trial judges, who are usually members of the council.

sentencing disparity. an unwarranted, inappropriate, and unjust variation of punishment from one offender to another. A disparity can be identified by comparing the sentencing practices of judges and jurisdictions, and by applying particular statistical analyzing techniques to offender characteristics.

sentencing hearing. in criminal proceedings, a hearing during which the court or jury considers relevant information, such as evidence concerning aggravating or mitigating circumstances, for the purpose of determining a sentencing disposition for a convicted person.

sequencer. an electronic component that selects in sequence the various data for each of the functions at a terminal.

sequential access memory. a term referring to a storage medium or device that allows access to stored data only in a predetermined pattern of retrieval. For example, if needed data is located in the middle of a magnetic tape, the device must wind the tape until the storage point of the needed data is reached.

sequential card reader. a card reader that requires the use of a card plus the input of a sequential code at a keypad.

sequential switcher. a CCTV switcher that displays camera views in a predetermined order. Camera sequencing and dwell time may be programmed for automatic operation and have a manual override feature.

sequester. to keep a jury in custodial supervision during a trial so as to prevent contact with the public or press; to separate prospective witnesses so that they cannot influence one another's testimony.

series circuit. a single current path created by connecting devices end-to-end in a normally closed loop.

series connection. the simplest possible connection of an electrical circuit, as in the connection of a battery and lamp bulb in a flashlight.

series radio tap. in electronic countermeasures, a radio transmitter which obtains power from the telephone line to which it is attached and is installed in series or in line with one wire.

serious misdemeanor. a class of misdemeanor having more severe penalties than other misdemeanors, or procedurally distinct; sometimes a statutory name for a type of misdemeanor having a maximum penalty much greater than the customary maximum one year incarceration.

service life. the length of time a product will meet or exceed the performance criteria for which it was designed.

service loop. a deliberate surplus of wire looped at one or more points in the wire run for future system modifications or servicing.

service of process. delivering a summons, subpoena or citation upon a person in a legal proceeding.

service reliability. a measure of the composite of all causes of service interruptions.

severance. the act of separating the trials of two or more defendants or of two or more charges against a single defendant, rather than holding one trial at which the defendants or charges are tried together.

sex offenses. the name of a broad category of varying content, usually consisting of all offenses having a sexual element except forcible rape and commercial sex offenses.

sex psychopath. a catchall name for persons who repeatedly and compulsively violate sex laws. The term is generally regarded as a stigmatizing label with little precise or scientifically reliable and valid predictive implications.

sex pyro. a person who derives sexual pleasure from starting or watching fires.

sexual assault. touching the body of another with a sexual intent and without the consent of the person being touched.

sexual harassment. the use of the power in one's job to gain sexual favors or punish the refusal of such favors.

shackle. the hinged or sliding part of a padlock that does the fastening.

shaped charge. an explosive charge shaped so as to enable the concentration of the explosive action to have a greater effect in penetrating resistant materials such as steel and concrete.

shaped dice. gambling dice having cut or shaped corners that alter the odds.

sharp. a cheat; swindler; con artist; bunco artist.

shaving. reducing the score in a sporting event, usually a basketball game, so as to illegally profit from betting.

shear line. the joint between the shell and the core of a lock cylinder; the line at which the pins or discs of a lock cylinder must be aligned in order to permit rotation of the core.

shell. a lock cylinder, exclusive of the core. Also called a housing.

shell company. a corporation without assets such as those established by white-collar criminals in bond swindles, money-laundering operations and mutual-fund schemes.

shell marks. in firearms identification, the marks observed on a fired shell. These marks, which can be made by the weapon's extractor, ejector, firing pin and other parts, are revealing as to the particular weapon that fired the shell.

shelter. a place providing temporary care or custody for juveniles, battered wives, rape victims, and others. Shelters may also be used for persons in need of supervision, persons charged with minor offenses, or persons held pending adjudication of their cases.

Shepard's cane. an earth-resistivity meter used to measure the resistance of soil to the passage of electrical current.

sheriff. usually the chief law enforcement officer in a county and generally charged with keeping the peace, making arrests, executing process of the courts, keeping the jail, opening the sessions of the courts, maintaining order in the courts and performing other duties prescribed by law.

sheriff's deed. a deed executed by a sheriff pursuant to a court order in connection with the sale of property to satisfy a judgment.

shield dial. a type of safe dial constructed with a shield designed to prevent finger smudges that can aid a safecracker in composing test combinations.

shielded line. a type of transmission line whose elements restrict or prevent the escape of propagated radio waves. This characteristic prevents radiation of unwanted radio interference from the line, and also protects the line from outside interference.

shim. a thin, flexible piece of metal or plastic (such as a credit card) which when inserted between the bolt and the strike will defeat the spring bolt lock.

shiv. a knife, razor or other sharp instrument used as a weapon.

schizoid personality. a personality characterized by unsociability, seclusiveness, serious mindedness and eccentric behavior.

shock front. that phase of a blast wave which occurs immediately after detonation of a bomb. This front travels with a velocity approximately equal to the speed of sound. The leading edge of the front is expressed in terms of pounds per square inch (psi) above atmospheric pressure. It is the magnitude of this peak pressure which largely determines the degree of damage produced by the blast. Following the peak pressure at the shock front, the pressure gradually drops off to atmospheric, then to a pressure below atmospheric, and finally returns to atmospheric pressure. The blast wave travels outward from the detonation point. As it gets further away, the magnitude of the wave decreases, therefore decreasing the destructive effect.

shoe. a false passport.

shoe fetishist. a man who derives sexual pleasure from the sight, smell, feel and taste of a female's shoes or feet.

shoemaker. a forger of false passports.

shooting gallery. a place where narcotics users congregate to inject drugs.

short-barreled rifle. a rifle having one or more barrels less than 16 inches in length whether made by design or modification.

short ringup. ringing up sales on a cash register for less than the full amount of a purchase and thereafter pocketing the difference. For example, the cash sale of a $10 shirt is rung up on the cash register as a $1 sale to cover the subsequent theft from the cash drawer of $9.

short throw deadbolt lock. a lock having a deadbolt five-eighths of an inch long or less. It is susceptible to forced entry attack.

short weighing. a practice which involves the packaging stages of production. A producer, for example, might fill containers 90% of their capacity and charge retailers for the entire amount.

shotgun microphone. a highly directional microphone with a tube-like appearance.

shoulders. in fingerprinting science, the points at which the recurring ridge of a loop pattern turns inward or curves.

shredder. a machine that cuts paper documents into small pieces so as to render unreadable any information contained in them.

shrinkage. a decrease in inventory; loss of volume or bulk. Shrinkage is usually applied in the context of employee or customer pilferage.

shunt. a deliberate shorting-out of a portion of an electric circuit.

shunting. an interviewing technique intended to overcome digression by the interviewee and return to the original line of questioning. A shunt consists of a short question that appears to arise out of an interest in what the subject is saying, but is designed to bring the conversation back to an issue of interest to the investigator.

shunt switch. a switch, usually key operated, that shunts or bypasses a sensor or sensors for some temporary purpose, such as to allow entry through a controlled entry without use of the required access card.

shylocking. loan sharking; loaning cash at an extremely high rate of interest.

shyster. one who uses underhanded tricks; an unethical attorney.

siamese connection. a fire hydrant having a double connection from a single water source.

sight draft. an instrument of payment negotiated through banks. Negotiable documents are attached, such as an order bill of lading, thus ensuring payment by the consignee to the negotiating bank in exchange for the documents and prior to the delivery of the goods.

sight sensor. a sensor device that reacts to changes in light or electrical field patterns.

sigint. signal intelligence.

signal encoding device. a device that initiates the transmission of an alarm signal sent to a central station.

signal silencing switch. a manual switch which allows an audible alarm to be silenced after the emergency has been acknowledged.

signal to noise ratio. the ratio between useful signal and disturbing noise.

signature security service. a service designed to provide continuous responsibility for the custody of shipments in transit, so named because a signature and tally are required from each person handling the shipment at each stage of its transit from point of origin to destination.

signature verification system. a computer-aided system that digitizes and compares the dynamic characteristics of a handwritten signature against a known signature on file. The technique analyzes shapes and timing sequences intrinsic to formation of letters in the signature.

sign/countersign. code words used in certain operations, tests or emergencies.

Significant Derogatory Information. as used in the DOD Industrial Security Program, information that by itself will justify an adverse security clearance determination or prompt an adjudicator to seek additional investigation or clarification.

significant reaction. a strong deceptive pattern in the chart of a person tested by the polygraph technique.

silent alarm. a noiseless alarm transmitted from the scene of a hold-up, intrusion or other emergency for the purpose of summoning help.

silent room. in electronic countermeasures, an area shielded acoustically against eavesdropping. Also called an acoustic room.

silent treatment. a subtle form of intimidation in which an interviewer, by silence, suggests that the interviewee should make another answer.

silicon intensified target tube. a CCTV tube designed to operate effectively in a lighting range from daylight to quarter moon.

silicon tube. a television pickup tube which uses thousands of light-sensitive diodes to create the target image. It is 10 times more sensitive than the vidicon tube and can thereby function satisfactorily at lower light levels.

sill. the lowest horizontal member of the window frame.

silver nitrate. a solution used to develop latent fingerprint impressions. It will react to sodium chloride (salt) which is present in most latent impressions. Silver nitrate is also used in a powder or paste form to mark decoy objects which when placed into contact with the skin of the touching person will cause a color reaction to the skin.

silver oxide battery. a battery with a high energy density and which is regarded as being excellent for compact circuit applications. Two types of cells are manufactured: the monovalent cell and the more powerful divalent cell.

simple assault. unlawful intentional threatening, attempted inflicting, or inflicting of less than serious bodily injury, in the absence of a deadly weapon.

simplex. a multiplex system that can transmit in only one direction on a transmission line.

simulated camera. a genuine-appearing but nonfunctional camera intended as a crime deterrent. It is typically mounted out of reach in a conspicuous position in an area having a history of employee pilferage, shoplifting, misconduct, robbery, etc. Some models are stationary, some scan, and most are equipped with a red pilot lamp. Also called a dummy camera.

simulated deception responses. in polygraph, physical and mental efforts by the examinee to influence recordings of the polygraph instrument during a test. The examinee's purpose is to create false deception responses that cannot be differentiated from genuine deception responses. Examples of efforts include contraction of the anal sphincture muscle, controlled breathing, and mental concentration on issues other than those being tested.

simultaneous impressions. inked fingerprint impressions obtained by simultaneously pressing all of the fingers of the hand and then the thumb. Also called plain impressions.

simultaneous transmission. a full duplex system where transponders and receiver communicate with each other simultaneously.

sine qua non rule. a rule of law which holds that a defendant's conduct is not the cause of an event if the event would have occurred without it. Also called the "but for" rule.

single-acting door. a door mounted to swing to only one side of the plane of the frame.

single action man. a numbers writer who specializes in taking single-action bets on any one of the three numbers, and usually writes up to post time for each number.

single-circuit system. a system with sensors wired in series within a single alarm circuit. Only one electrical line passes through each sensor. Return is via a common lead or ground.

single entry system. an access control system that has anti-passback protection. A single entry system requires that a card used to enter an area be used to exit that area before it can be reused for entry. This prevents the "passing back" of an access card from an individual who has gained entry to one who has not.

single line service. a shipping service that moves freight from point of origin to destination over the lines of only one carrier.

single-point failure. a failure of one independent element of a system which creates an immediate exposure to a hazard and/or causes the entire system to fail.

single-pole double-throw switch. a switch that connects one wire to either of two other wires.

single stroke bell. an audible signalling device which uses a bell that gongs once when operating power is applied.

sinsemilla. a variety of marihuana derived from unpollenated, female cannabis.

Sir Francis Drake swindle. a type of mail fraud in which the victim is notified by letter that he is a descendant of Sir Francis Drake (or some other notable person) and is entitled to a share in the estate, but that a sum will be required for litigation.

situational management. any management style that recognizes that the application of theory to practice must necesssarily take into consideration, and be contingent upon, the given situation.

skin pop. to inject a drug into a muscle or beneath the skin.

slam hammer. a tool used by a car thief to physically pull out the cylinder of an ignition lock. It is similar in function to a dent puller which is used to pull dents out of an auto. Also called a slapper.

slam puller. a burglary device used to remove lock cylinders or key cores. It usually consists of a slender rod with a heavy sliding sleeve. One end of the rod has a screw or claw for insertion into the lock. The other end has a retaining knob. When the sleeve is jerked away from the lock, striking the retaining knob, the lock cylinder or key core is forcibly pulled out.

slander. false and defamatory statements about a person.

slave relay. a relay activated by a master relay or similar controlling device.

slide bolt. a simple lock which is operated directly by hand without using a key, a turnpiece, or other actuating mechanism. Slide bolts can normally only be operated from the inside.

slide-rule discipline. an approach to discipline that eliminates supervisory discretion and sets very specific quantitative standards as the consequences of specific violations. For example, an employee who is late for work more than four times in a 30-day period would be automatically suspended for three days.

sliding metal gate. an assembly of metal bars, jointed so that it can be moved to and locked in position across a window or other opening, in order to prevent unauthorized entry through the opening.

slip-knifing. a burglary attack method in which a thin, flat, flexible object such as a stiff piece of plastic is inserted between the strike and the latch bolt to depress the latch bolt and release it from the strike. The slip-knifing of windows is accomplished by inserting a thin stiff object between the meeting rails or stiles to move the latch to the open position, or by inserting a thin stiff wire through openings between the stile or rail and the frame to manipulate the sash operator of pivoting windows.

slow plea. a very short trial on stipulated evidence following the defendant's plea of not guilty. The procedure is sometimes used to preserve appeal issues which would be forfeited by a guilty plea.

smack. heroin.

smart card. a plastic identification card embedded with an integrated circuit chip. The card has both a coded memory and microprocessor intelligence. It can record card transactions and store data. Also called a chip-in card.

smart modem. a modem controlled by a microprocessor.

smart tag. a tag or label that identifies the product to which it is attached.

smash and grab. a criminal method for stealing valuables from a glass enclosed display area, e.g., the glass is smashed, the valuables are grabbed and the criminal flees before a response can be made.

smoke detector. a device that detects airborne particles associated with smoke. It differs from a heat detector and is considered superior to it because smoke is usually detectable in advance of heat. There are two types of smoke detectors: photoelectric and ionization. The photoelectric detector operates in a beam-break or light-scattering principle. Particles that enter a chamber interrupt a beam or scatter light, causing an alarm. The ionization detector senses electrically charged ion particles associated with smoke generated at the incipient or early stage of a fire. When both types are combined in a single unit, it is called a combination smoke detector.

smuggling. unlawful movement of goods across a national frontier or state boundary, or into or out of a correctional facility.

snatch squad. in riot control operations, a police/security team used to capture ring leaders.

sneeze machine. a device used in riot control operations. It is mounted in the cargo carrying area of a small truck and disperses an irritant powder for the purpose of forcing people to leave.

sniffer. an instrument used to measure the concentration of combustible gases in the air; a dog trained to detect odors characteristic of certain substances, such as drugs and explosives; a tuning device used to determine possible sources of ultrasonic frequencies within a protected area that may cause an ultrasonic detector to initiate a false alarm.

snorting. the usual means of abusing cocaine. The drug is sniffed into the nose where it is absorbed by the nasal membranes.

snow. random spurts of electrical energy or interference that disrupts the pattern of a televised picture.

snuff spoon. a tobacco snuff spoon, used also as a cocaine sniffing spoon; also called a coke spoon.

social control. a deterring effect on criminal activity resulting from the presence of people.

social distance. the space that extends from four to twelve feet around an individual, in which most business contacts take place.

social-impact theory. a theory which holds that when social forces affect a situation, the pressure on any one member of a group is lessened because the impact of the social forces is spread over the entire group. As the group increases in size, the pressure on separate members decreases.

social observation. the simple presence of people which has a deterring effect on criminal activity. Also called social control.

sociogram. a diagram showing the interactions between members of a group.

sociopathic personality. antisocial character disorder marked by moral deviation and often total involvement in crime.

sodium vapor lamp. a lamp that emits a golden yellow glow caused by an electric current passing through a tube of conducting illuminous gas. It is more efficient than the mercury vapor and incandescent lamps, and generally used where the color is acceptable, such as on bridges and roadways.

sodomy. unlawful physical contact between the genitals of one person and the mouth or anus of another person, or with the mouth, anus or genitals of an animal.

soft drug. a psychologically but not physically addictive drug such as hashish, marijuana and related hemp plants and products.

software. a program or programs that direct computer operating systems. Software encompasses the various computer languages and the operating programs written in those languages.

soft x-ray examination. a crime laboratory technique in which objects are examined using x-rays ranging from 4 to 25 kilovolts. Radiographs produced with soft x-rays can reveal characteristics not observable through other techniques. Soft x-ray examination is used to evaluate paintings, fabrics, papers, inks, gunshot residues, and jewelry. Hard x-rays (25 to 140 kilovolts) are used to examine gross, metal objects.

solar battery. a battery that charges through a photovoltaic cell. It can be used to power sensors in outdoor applications.

sole proprietorship. a type of business organization in which one individual owns the business. Legally, the owner is the business and personal assets are typically exposed to liabilities of the business.

solicitation. commanding, encouraging or requesting another person to commit a crime.

solid state. a term referring to electronic components that are "semiconductor" in construction and which do not utilize tubes or mechanical parts. The vast majority of electronic security systems is based on solid state technology.

solved case (or offense). a founded criminal offense in which the police have identified the perpetrator. A "solved" determination does not necessarily result from a judicial decision.

somatic nervous system. the division of the parasympathetic nervous system related to the external world and generally under voluntary control.

sonic motion detection. a system that uses audible sound waves to detect the presence of an intruder in a protected area.

soporific substance. a generic term for all compounds or drugs used for inducing sleep.

sound discriminator. a type of detector that responds to specific sounds or sound frequencies such as the sound of breaking glass.

sound sensor. a sensor that uses microphone circuitry to detect and initiate an alarm when sounds of a given volume or of particular characteristics are received.

sound spectrograph. an instrument that electronically produces pictorial patterns of speech and other sounds. The spectrograms of a known voice can be compared against the spectrograms of an unknown voice for the purpose of identifying or eliminating suspects. A sound spectrograph is not a lie detection instrument.

source. a person, thing or activity which provides information.

source material. uranium or thorium, or any combination thereof, in any physical or chemical form, or ores which contain by weight one-twentieth of one percent or more of uranium, thorium or any combination thereof.

space protection. the use of sensor devices to detect an intruder in an enclosed space. Ultrasonic and microwave sensors are frequently used in space protection.

spalling effect. in bomb incident investigations, the spalling, scabbing or flaking condition on a steel or concrete surface created by an explosive charge striking the reverse side of the surface.

spall marks. in arson investigations, cracks and loosened concrete seen on the remaining concrete structure of a burned building. They indicate that the fire was enhanced by an accelerant.

span sensor. a type of sensor used to protect straight and narrow spaces between two points.

Spanish Prisoner. a type of mail fraud in which the victim receives a letter from someone claiming to be falsely imprisoned and who offers to share a hidden treasure if the victim will send money to secure the prisoner's release.

spark gap protection. the use of a spark gap to dissipate unwanted buildup of high-voltage electrical energy.

Special Access Program. a Department of Defense program imposing "need to know" or access controls beyond those normally provided for access to Confidential, Secret, or Top Secret information. Such a program includes special clearance, adjudication, or investigative requirements, special designation of officials authorized to determine "need-to-know," or special lists of persons determined to have a "need-to-know."

special activity. an activity, or functions in support of such activity, conducted in support of national foreign policy objectives abroad that is planned and executed so that the role of the US Government is not apparent.

Special Background Investigation. a Department of Defense personnel security investigation consisting of all of the components of a Background Investigation plus certain additional investigative requirements.

special bet. in a numbers operation, a bet made with an agreement that if the player wins the payoff will be at odds higher than normal. Such bets are accepted from only the best customers, and are usually restricted to a dollar minimum.

special deterrence concept. a concept which holds that future crimes by a specific offender can be prevented by imposing a penalty so severe it outweighs the pleasure or profit derived from the crime and convinces the offender to not pursue further criminality.

special endorsement. the designation of a certain person to whom the instrument is payable. Thus, if an instrument is endorsed "Pay to the order of John Jones," followed by the endorser's signature, no one but John Jones can receive payment for the instrument or transfer it.

Special Investigative Inquiry. a Department of Defense supplemental personnel security investigation of limited scope conducted to update or assure completeness of a prior investigation or to prove/disprove relevant allegations that have arisen concerning a person about whom a personnel security determination has been previously made and who, at the time of the allegations, holds a security clearance or sensitive position.

special nuclear material access authorization. an administrative determination that an individual who is employed by or is an applicant for employment with an affected Nuclear Regulatory Commission contractor licensee of the NRC may work at a job which affords access to or control over special nuclear material and that permitting the individual to work at that job would not be inimical to security.

special operating procedures. written instructions which pertain to a specific post or patrol.

specific characteristics. in observation and description, the detailed characteristics of a person, e.g., color of hair and eyes, shape of head and face, mannerisms, marks and scars.

specific criminal intent. an intent of the criminal to act with voluntariness, foresight of the consequences, and with a further ulterior purpose in mind. A general criminal intent is present when a person takes another's property voluntarily and with foresight. Specific criminal intent is present when the criminal takes further action to permanently deprive the owner of his property.

spectrographic analysis. the qualitative and quantitative analysis of a substance, its composition and properties on the basis of its study with the spectrograph.

spectrophotometer. an apparatus for studying and measuring the distribution and relative intensities of the components of different frequencies in the spectrum of light source.

spectrum analysis. the study and interpretation of spectra and the investigation and qualitative analysis of substances and bodies through their spectra and spectral lines.

spectrum analyzer. an electronics countermeasure device that detects the presence of radio frequency transmissions characteristic of covertly installed transmitters.

speedball. a mixture of cocaine and heroin.

speed loader. a device which holds rounds in a pattern aligned with the cylinder of a revolver. All rounds (usually 5 or 6) are inserted simultaneously into the cylinder, thereby speeding the loading process.

speedy trial. the right of a defendant to have a prompt trial. It is guaranteed by the Sixth Amendment to the Constitution of the United States and is intended to protect an accused from long pretrial detention or from an interminable period of living under the shadow of charges not adjudicated.

Speedy Trial Act of 1974. a statutory scheme that provides time periods within which federal trials must begin. Subject to certain narrow exceptions, a federal trial must commence within 60 days of arraignment.

spent fuel. in nuclear security, irradiated nuclear fuel that has undergone at least one year's decay since being used as a source of energy in a power reactor. Spent fuel includes the special nuclear material, byproduct material, source material, and other radioactive materials associated with fuel assemblies.

spermatazoa. the male reproductive cell, the presence of which may be tested for in evidence analyzed by a crime laboratory.

spermine. a chemical found in seminal fluid which is tested for by means of a crystal test called the Barberios test.

spike. the needle used to inject illegal drugs; an undesirable momentary surge in electrical current or signal that can cause equipment malfunction.

spike microphone. in electronic countermeasures, a contact type microphone with a long, needle-like extension used for listening through walls.

spill light. the lumens emitted from a fixture which are outside of the beam spread.

spiral search. a type of search conducted at an outdoor crime scene. The area to be searched is delineated by markers into one large circle. Two or three searchers proceed at the same pace within fingertip distance along adjacent paths that spiral in toward the center of the circle. When a piece of evidence is found, all searchers halt until it is processed. At a given signal, the search resumes until the center is reached.

split image lens. a special lens that permits the viewing of two different fields. Two scenes can be photographed by a single camera. It is useful for comparing two different fields, or when an insufficiency of space will allow only one camera where two are needed.

split notes. counterfeit bills created by splitting the paper of higher denomination and lower denomination notes. The halves are pasted together so that each note consists of a high denomination on one side and a low denomination on the other side. The counterfeiter passes all the bills at the higher values.

split sentence. a term in jail or prison with weekend furloughs to be spent with family, or weekday furloughs so that the offender can continue to work at his regular job. The time spent outside of confinement does not count as time served.

spontaneous combustion. ignition of fire in an object by internal development of heat without the action of an external agent.

spontaneous exclamation. an utterance concerning an event made by an individual in a state of surprise and which is not the product of deliberation or design. It is an exception to the hearsay rule and is admissible as evidence. Also called spontaneous declaration.

spook. slang term for a spy.

spoon. a small quantity of a narcotic, usually heroin; also any spoon-like device used to heat and liquefy illegal drugs for injection.

spot. in a numbers operation, a store, apartment, hallway or other fixed location where a writer locates himself to accept bets.

spot analysis technique. in polygraphy, a technique of chart interpretation in which recorded responses to relevant questions are closely analyzed. These spots or locations on the charts are considered extremely important to the polygraphist's opinion.

spotlighting. a security lighting technique in which high-intensity light is directed at an already detected intruder so as to track and hinder his progress.

spot protection. protection afforded individual objects or very small areas by one or more detectors.

spot smoke detector. a type of smoke detector that sets up a short beam of light between a sender and a receiver inside the detector. When smoke interrupts the beam, an alarm is activated.

spotter. a person, sometimes an employee, who watches for theft opportunities and sells the information to criminals; a lookout; a person hired by a retail store to watch for and report shoplifters; a person employed by a numbers operator to report the presence of strange persons or police officers nearby the number location or a drop; a person who frequents court buildings and areas near police stations to become familiar with police officers, detectives and undercover officers and to spot informants; that member of a car theft ring who looks for and determines the location of automobiles to be stolen; that member of a hijack team who first locates and points out the targeted truck and, following the hijack, trails the truck as a lookout until it arrives at its planned place of concealment.

spread eagle. a standing or prone position assumed by a person being searched for weapons.

spreading. a technique of forced entry through a door by spreading the door frame apart until the bolt disengages from the strike.

spring bolt. a spring mechanism in a lock that moves the bolt into the strike and holds it in place.

spring contact sensor. a switch-type sensor that uses a spring to detect an opening of a door or window.

spring-loaded bar. a bar placed inside a window's jamb and kept in position by the spring's tension. One end of the bar rests on a pressure pad. Opening the window or attempting to reach through a broken pane to remove the bar will release pressure on the pad, triggering an alarm.

spurious alarm. a false alarm caused by an equipment defect.

stall. that member of a pickpocket team who distracts the victim while the pickpocketing act is performed.

stand-alone card access system. a system in which the card reader mechanism is attached to a set of control electronics. All required components are contained in one box and there is no reliance on an external computer.

stand-alone computer system. a computer system not connected to a data processing facility and designed to be operated by one person at a time. A personal computer is a type of stand-alone computer.

standard acrylic glazing products. lightweight, tempered plastics having an impact resistance about 17 times greater than glass of equivalent thickness.

standard ammunition file. a collection of standard ammunition samples used by a firearms examiner to compare against questioned samples.

standard consolidated statistical area. the area formed by two or more standard metropolitan statistical areas that run together.

standard deviation. in the study of variability or dispersion of a set of observations, the measure of the average of the amounts that the individual numbers deviate from the mean of all the observations. A low standard deviation indicates a tendency of values to cluster about the mean. A high standard deviation indicates a wide variation in values.

standard document. in criminal investigations, a document recognized as proven, genuine or acknowledged that has been obtained from a known and reliable source, such as official records, and is known to be the product of a particular person or machine.

standard federal regions. geographic subdivisions of the US established to achieve more uniformity in the location and geographic jurisdiction of federal field offices as a basis for promoting more systematic coordination among agencies and among federal-state-local governments and for securing management improvements and economies through greater interagency and intergovernmental cooperation.

standard metropolitan statistical area. a county or group of counties including at least one city with a population of 50,000 or more. In the New England states, SMSAs consist of towns and cities instead of counties.

standard plate glass. basic window plate glass not suitable for security applications.

standards. in criminal investigations, specimens of handwriting produced in the normal course of events.

standards of comparison. known specimens against which questioned evidence is compared. The character of the articles or materials to be collected as known specimens is determined by the circumstances of the investigation. Known specimens might be handwriting samples obtained from a suspected forger or pubic hair samples obtained from a suspected rapist.

standards of conduct. an organization's formal guidelines for ethical behavior.

standards of performance. statements that tell an employee how well he or she must perform a task to be considered a satisfactory employee. Standards can cover how much, how accurately, in what time period, or in what manner, the various job tasks are to be performed.

standard steel door. a door consisting of a steel grid frame around which is wrapped sheet steel in varying thicknesses. It provides good protection against forced entry.

standing waves. a pattern of radio energy in space which varies in intensity from point to point caused by reflections of radio signals.

Star Chamber. a former English administrative court with criminal jurisdiction. In modern usage, the term describes court proceedings held without access by public or press and without a publicly available transcript or record.

stare decisis. a Latin term which means "stand by the decision." The term conveys the idea that the law should adhere to decided cases. The doctrine holds that when a court has laid down a principle of law applicable to a certain set of facts, the court will apply the principle in all future cases where the facts are substantially the same.

stash. a hidden cache of illegal drugs.

State Department Lookout File. a computerized file maintained by the Passport Office of the U.S. Department of State. It lists defectors, expatriates, repatriates, criminals, wanted persons, subversives, deserters and other persons whose activities or background justify inquiry. The principal use of the Lookout File is to identify those passport applications which require other than routine adjudication in determining eligibility.

state's evidence. testimony given by an accomplice which incriminates other principals, usually given under an actual or implied promise of immunity.

State vs. Bryant. a case in which the Minnesota Supreme Court held that a closed door toilet stall in a department store washroom was a privately protected area, so that the police observations and the pictures taken through a ceiling ventilator could not be used as evidence in the prosecution of an offender.

static discharge. the sudden release of accumulated static. Static discharge can cause damage to relatively delicate components such as integrated circuits.

statistical inference. use of information, observed in a sample, to make predictions about a larger population.

statistical significance. a measure of the likelihood that a change observed in an experiment was due to chance and not to some systematic effect or treatment.

status. the condition of a system, zone, circuit or sensor at a particular time.

status offense. an act declared by statute to be an offense when committed by a juvenile but not when committed by an adult. Examples are truancy, running away from home, curfew violation, and drinking of alcoholic beverages.

statute law. law derived from enactments of legislatures. Statute law is a source of criminal law.

statute of frauds. a statute, enacted with variations in all the States, providing that certain contracts cannot be enforced unless they are in writing signed by the party against whom the contract is sought to be enforced. The writing need not be a formal document signed by both parties. A written note or memorandum of the transaction signed by the party to be bound by the agreement is sufficient.

statute of limitations. a state statute that limits the time within which legal action may be brought, either upon a contract or tort. State and federal statutes also limit the time within which certain crimes can be prosecuted. The purpose of the time limitation is to make it impossible to bring suit many years after a cause of action originates, during which time witnesses may have died or important evidence may have been lost.

statutory law. rules formulated into law by legislative action. The Constitution of the United States and the constitutions of the various states are the fundamental written law. All other law must be in harmony with the constitutions, which define and limit the powers of government. State constitutions must be in harmony with the Constitution of the United States. Congress, cities and towns, and other governmental units find in the constitutions their authority, either express or implied, to enact certain laws. These legislative enactments are called statutes and constitute the greater part of the written or statutory law. Statutory law supplements and supersedes common law.

statutory rape. consensual sexual intercourse between a male and a female who is under the age of consent. In some jurisdictions, the term also applies to consensual sexual intercourse between a custodian and a patient or a custodian and an inmate.

stay of execution. an order to delay the execution of a sentence.

steel-jacketed bullet. a lead bullet encased in a steel jacket for the purpose of increasing its penetrating capacity.

stellar light tube. a CCTV tube designed to operate effectively in a lighting range from daylight to starlight.

stellate gunshot wound. an entrance wound having a star-shaped appearance. It is caused when the muzzle at time of discharge is against a hard bony surface, such as the forehead. The explosive force of gases produced by the discharge create ragged skin tears that radiate from the bullet hole.

step regulator. a device that provides voltage regulation by selective switching among taps in response to input voltage. A step regulator will shield the AC line load from electric noise and rapid voltage fluctuations. Also called an electronic tap changer.

stereobinocular microscope. a relatively low-powered microscope used for making crime laboratory examinations.

sterilize. to remove from material to be used in covert operations any marks which can identify it as originating with the sponsoring organization.

stick. a marihuana cigarette.

stile. a vertical framing member of a sash. A meeting stile is one which mates with a stile of another sash, or a vertical framing member of the window frame when the sash is in the closed position.

stimulation test. in polygraphy, a test intended to stimulate interest on the part of the examinee by demonstrating the accuracy of the polygraph instrument. The test might require the examinee to reply "no" to all questions in a short series. All of the questions are truthfully answered with a "no" except for one. The polygraphist identifies the one untruthful answer, thereby demonstrating to the examinee the accuracy of the polygraph instrument. A stimulation test tends to heighten the anxiety of a guilty subject and ease the anxiety of an innocent subject.

sting operation. a covert operation in which members of the police pose as criminals in order to gather information, obtain evidence, and make arrests of persons engaged in criminal activities.

Stockholm syndrome. sympathy or compassion expressed by a hostage victim on behalf of the abductor, so called because of its appearance in hostages who were held inside a bank vault in Stockholm.

stockpiling. a shoplifter's practice of arranging merchandise in a shopping cart so as to make the theft convenient. A high-value concealable item placed under a purse in the top section of the cart is an example of stockpiling.

stop (of a lock). a button or other device that serves to lock and unlock a latch bolt against actuation by the outside knob or thumb piece.

stop and frisk. a procedure used by police on patrol to inquire into the activities of a person reasonably believed to be involved in a criminal act. The stop element is the asking of questions; the frisk element is a pat-down type search made when the person's answers, conduct or appearance lead the officer to think that the person may be armed. Also called a field inquiry or investigatory stop.

stop bet. in a numbers operation, a bet across the board on a particular number. The player would win if the selected number came out in any one of the three possible positions.

straight bomb. a bomb in which all of the component parts are visible to the naked eye. Also called an open bomb.

straight-line depreciation. an accounting term which shows the reduction of the cost or other basis of an asset, less estimated salvage value, in equal amounts over the estimated useful life of the asset.

strain gauge sensor. a sensor that detects the pressure of added weight or stress upon a surface. A strain gauge sensor placed under a floor can detect an intruder walking on the floor.

strangulation by ligature. suicidal or homicidal strangulation with the use of cord, nylon hose, necktie, belt or similar item.

strategic special nuclear material. uranium-235 (contained in uranium enriched to 20 percent or more in the U-235 isotope), uranium-233, or plutonium.

stratified sampling. a technique in which the population to be sampled is broken into subsets and then certain of the subsets are selected for sampling. For example, an auditor might place all invoices into ten subsets according to dollar values and then choose to examine three particular subsets according to his interest.

streaking. the flaring of objects along the horizontal axis on a CCTV monitor.

street callbox. a direct-line telephone callbox used by police officers on patrol.

street crime. a class of offenses, sometimes defined with some degree of formality as those which occur in public locations, are visible and assaultive, and thus constitute a group of crimes which are a special risk to the public and a special target of law enforcement preventive efforts and prosecutorial attention.

street dealer. a middleman in the chain of intermediaries between the importers and the pushers of dangerous drugs.

stress interview. an interview in which the questioner deliberately creates a stressful situation for the interviewee in order to elicit observable responses. Common tactics include challenging the veracity of the interviewee, frequently interrupting answers, and silence on the part of the questioner for an extended period.

stress sensitive cable. electrical cable that produces a varied signal as a function of stress on the cable. It is used as a sensor for walls and fences and is buried at perimeter locations.

stress sensor. a sensor that responds to load changes as a result of motion.

striations. marks on bullets produced by rifling in a barrel. As an expended bullet passes through a barrel it is grooved by the barrel's rifling pattern. Striations on a bullet obtained as evidence can be compared against striations on bullets fired from a suspect weapon, thereby making it possible to link a weapon with a crime.

strict construction. the requirement that a statute be interpreted literally in accordance with its terms, rather than its spirit. It is frequently applied to criminal statutes.

strict liability. the concept that one can be held responsible for some acts without the necessity of proving mens rea or blame, fault or negligence. For example, strict liability could be applied in the prosecution of a corporate executive whose employees carelessly adulterated company products.

strict liability statute. a statute which categorically forbids a certain act or omission without regard to the offender's state of mind (intent). Strict liability statutes are usually found in the regulatory area of public health, safety and welfare. The crimes created by such statutes are often called public torts. Examples are speeding and hunting without a license.

strike. a metal plate attached to or mortised into a door jamb to receive and hold a projected latch bolt and/or dead bolt in order to secure the door to the jamb.

strike reinforcement. a metal plate attached to a door or frame to receive a strike.

striker pistol. a non-lethal pistol powered by compressed air which fires pellets containing tear gases or indelible dyes. It is used to "take out" or mark ring leaders in riot situations.

strip method. a method of searching at an outdoor crime scene. The area to be searched is delineated by markers into one or more large rectangles. Two or three searchers proceed slowly at the same pace within fingertip distance along paths parallel to one side of a rectangle. When a piece of evidence is found, all searchers halt until it is processed. The search resumes at a given signal. When the searchers reach the end of the rectangle, they turn and proceed back along adjacent lanes, and continue the process until the entire rectangle has been covered.

strobe light. a type of bright flashing light which can be installed on the exterior of a protected premises. During a detected intrusion, the strobe light would activate and draw attention to the location of the intrusion.

stroboscopic lighting. a security lighting technique in which rapidly flickering illumination is activated in a protected area penetrated by an intruder.

strongarm robbery. a robbery in which the offender uses physical force or the threat of it. Also, a type of robbery in which the criminal uses stealth, speed and physical violence, as in a mugging.

strong room. a secure room or area designated as a storage repository for sensitive material of such size or nature that it cannot be stored in the standard security containers. A strong room will meet or exceed the security specifications for the containers it augments.

strung out. high on drugs.

subculture of violence. a way of life attributed to large sectors of the lower social classes. In it there is much dependence on force or the threat of force to establish identity and gain status. The subculture of violence may lead to criminality as a method of problem-solving.

subcutaneous injection. a method used by a drug abuser to administer a drug by inserting a hypodermic needle beneath the skin surface.

subliminal perception. the registration of sensory information that influences behavior without producing any conscious experience of the stimulus.

subordination. the substitution of one person in place of another with reference to a lawful claim, demand or right so that the substitute succeeds to the rights of the other in relation to the debt or claim, its rights, remedies or securities.

subornation of perjury. an offense in which a witness is induced secretly to provide false testimony.

subpoena. a written order issued by a judicial officer requiring a specified person to appear in a designated court at a specified time in order to serve as a witness in a case under the jurisdiction of that court, or to bring material to that court.

subpoena duces tecum. a process issued out of court requiring a witness to attend and to bring with him certain documents or records in his possession.

subrogation. the legal process by which one party endeavors to recover from a third party the amount paid to an insured under an insurance policy when such third party may have been responsible for causing the loss.

subscriber. an alarm company customer; an alarm system purchaser or lessee. Often used to describe a client who pays a fee to have his alarm system monitored.

subscriber account code. a number assigned to an alarm customer's digital communicator so it can be recognized by the alarm company's digital receiver.

substantive law. that part of the general body of laws which creates, defines and regulates rights. Adjective or remedial law prescribes methods of enforcing rights and obtaining redress for their invasion. It is a subdivision of criminal law which defines the types of conduct constituting crimes. It also provides for punishment of crimes, and lays down rules on such matters as the capacity of persons to commit crimes and the defenses that persons charged with crimes may legally employ.

subvoice grade line. a telephone or transmission line that has not been balanced for voice grade communications. A subvoice grade line is suitable for simple electrical transmissions such as direct wire or McCulloh loop.

suction effect. in bomb incident investigations, a wave of pressure toward the point of detonation which occurs after the blast wave. It is a consequence of a vacuum created when air is powerfully and instantaneously pushed outward by the blast.

suicidal cuts. in suicide investigations, parallel and overlapping incisions of varying length and depth. They represent a progression from hesitation to final resolve on the part of the victim.

sulfondiethylmethane. a depressant classified as a Schedule III controlled substance.

sulfonethylmethane. a depressant classified as a Schedule III controlled substance.

sulfonmethane. a depressant classified as a Schedule III controlled substance.

summary arrest. an arrest made of a suspect at or near the scene of the crime; an arrest without court process.

summons. a written order requiring a person accused of an offense to appear in a designated court at a specified time to answer the charge.

super dampening concept. in polygraph, a concept which holds that a person is likely to respond randomly, weakly or not at all to relevant questions of a polygraph test if he considers an outside, non-relevant issue to be a greater threat to his well-being than the main relevant issue being tested.

superficial perforating gunshot wound. a wound in which the skin is torn, giving a lacerated appearance. This type of wound can be mistaken for a wound made by a knife.

super high frequency. a band of the radio spectrum operating between 3000-30,000 megahertz.

superquick impact fuse. a bomb fuse designed to function immediately upon impact, before any penetration, thus giving maximum surface effect. It is normally utilized when the target is of light construction such as aircraft.

supervised closing. an action in which a signal is sent to a central station to inform that the subscriber is closing the business, i.e., is setting the alarm.

supervised directwire alarm. a leased pair of wires that are dedicated from the subscriber premises to the central office monitoring station. The pair of wires are supervised by a direct voltage delivered by the subscriber control to the alarm receiver. Since the pair is supervised, it offers a higher degree of security than tape dialers or digital dialers and the central station can distinguish an alarm signal from phone line trouble.

supervised line (or circuit). a cable or wire which if cut, broken, shorted or grounded will so indicate at a monitoring location.

supervised opening. an action in which a signal is sent to a central station to inform that the subscriber is opening the business, i.e., is turning off the alarm.

supervised system. an alarm reporting system that includes circuitry to annunciate abnormal circuit conditions, such as a power loss or drop, or a short.

suppression. in polygraphy, an indicator of deception which appears as an involuntary reduction in the respiratory amplitude of the pneumograph tracing in response to a stressful question. A trend of four respiratory cycles is commonly regarded as suppression.

suppression hearing. a hearing to determine whether or not the court will prohibit specified statements, documents, or objects from being introduced into evidence in a trial.

Supreme Court of the United States. the highest court in the United States. It consists of nine justices appointed for life, and has ultimate jurisdiction for deciding the constitutionality of state and federal laws and for interpreting the Constitution. Also called the court of last resort.

surface grazing. a security lighting technique in which high-intensity illumination is directed at the surface surrounding an already detected intruder to produce exaggerated shadows intended to confuse the intruder while tracking his progress.

surface mounted switch. a mechanical or magnetic sensor mounted on an interior surface of a protected area in such a way that it is visible.

surge suppressor. a device that clips or reduces the effect of a high-voltage transient, such as a lightning spike. A surge suppressor provides protection against the particular type of transient it is designed to clip. It will not regulate voltage to limit surges and sags.

surveillance. secretly observing the behavior of another, visually or electronically.

surveillance receiver. in electronics countermeasures, a radio receiver used to monitor radio transmitter bugs or beacons.

suspect. a person, adult or juvenile, considered by a criminal justice agency to be one who may have committed a specific criminal offense, but who has not been arrested or charged.

suspect document. any writing which may have been altered, fabricated or forged.

suspended sentence. a sentence imposed by a court but not put into execution.

suspense file. a file which calls attention to work actions required to be performed on certain dates.

suspicion. belief that a person has committed a criminal offense, based on facts and circumstances that are not sufficient to constitute probable cause.

sweatbox. an interrogation room.

sweep. to search for the presence of electronic eavesdropping devices in a given area with the use of special detection equipment.

swindle. intentional false representation to obtain money or any other thing of value, where deception is accomplished through the victim's belief in the validity of some statement or object presented by the offender.

swinger. a momentary circuit opening or closing which causes an alarm or trouble signal with no apparent reason for the activation.

swinging bolt. a bolt that is hinged to a lock front and is projected and retracted with a swinging rather than a sliding action. Also called a hinged or pivot bolt.

switch runner. a section of thin vinyl material containing electrically conductive strips that operate as normally open switches. A circuit is closed when weight is applied, causing an alarm. The runner is usually placed under carpeting, as in a hallway, to detect intrusion.

symbolic assembly language. a computer language that directly interacts with the hardware; also called a low-level language, as opposed to higher level languages such as COBOL and FORTRAN.

symbolic interactionism. an interpretive perspective which says that individuals learn meanings through interaction with others and then organize their lives around these socially created meanings.

sympathetic inks. any of several chemical solutions used to make invisible writings. A sympathetic ink is made visible by a reagent or special light.

sympathetic interrogating approach. a method of obtaining information from a suspect or hostile witness in which the interrogator rationalizes the offense, minimizes the moral implications, and generally portrays the suspect in a favorable light. This approach is often used with first offenders.

sympathetic nervous system. the division of the autonomic nervous system that dominates in emergencies or stressful situations.

symptomatic question. in polygraphy, a question designed to determine the existence of an outside issue which might interfere with the successful conduct of the test.

sync level. the level of the peaks of synchronizing signal.

sync signal. the signal employed for the synchronizing of scanning.

syndicate. an ongoing, coordinated conspiracy, characterized by hierarchy and division of labor, and involving a relatively large number of criminals. The syndicate or organized crime is in partial or total control of numerous illegal activities, such as usury, gambling, prostitution, pornography, drug traffic, extortion, and hijacking. It also controls many legal enterprises, such as restaurants and trucking firms, which are frequently used to conceal the sources of illegally obtained money and to accomplish other criminal purposes.

synergism. cooperative action or reaction by two or more substances whose total effect is greater than the sum of their separate effects. For example, a synergistic effect frequently results from the combined ingestion of drugs and alcohol.

synthetic drug. a chemically developed drug;

a drug not made from natural sources. Demerol, dolophine, and methadone are synthetic drugs.

system. an orderly arrangement of interrelated components operating as an integrated whole.

system architecture. a term referring to the scheme by which various types of equipment are interconnected to form a coherent system.

system card reader. an access control card reader that does not have its own built-in intelligence and relies on a central system controller to make entry/exit decisions. The central controller also provides the signal to activate the door strike. Also called an on-line card reader.

system code. a number or alphanumeric sequence printed on an access control card. The number is used for record keeping and card control purposes.

systemic poison. a poison that acts on the nervous system and organs of the body. The symptoms of systemic poisoning vary widely. The nature of impairment by systemic poison is related to the amount of poison consumed, the manner of consumption, and whether the victim's body has a built-in tolerance of the poison. Common types of systemic poisons are metal salts, organic poisons

and most of the poison gases such as phosgene, hydrogen sulphide and carbon monoxide.

system password. in computer usage, a password required by a terminal before login can be initiated at the terminal.

systems analysis. a methodologically rigorous collection, manipulation and evaluation of organizational data in order to determine the best way to improve the functioning of the organization (the system) and to aid a decision-maker in selecting a preferred choice among alternatives.

systems approach. a logical method for problem solving in which a comprehensive solution is developed in relation to a problem having several dimensions. A type of systems approach follows three general steps: assessment of vulnerability, implementation of countermeasures, and evaluation of effectiveness.

systems management. the application of systems theory to managing organizational systems or subsystems. It can refer to management of a particular function or to projects or programs within a larger organization.

system software. a program or programs that direct the operation of a computer system.

tactical intelligence. intelligence immediately useful to the enforcement forces of an agency.

tailgate. to enter through an access control point close behind an authorized person without satisfying the access identification routine.

tail piece. the unit on the core of a cylinder lock which actuates the bolt or latch.

tailpit worker. a pickpocket who steals from the side of his victim, e.g., from the side pockets of a jacket.

Takayama hemochromogen test. a microcrystal test which is specific for blood. When the Takayama chemical solution is added to dried blood, characteristic red crystals are formed which can be seen under the microscope.

take-off contact. a type of contact used on sliding glass doors to wire-connect foil tape and glass breakage detectors to the protective circuit.

take out. in riot control operations, to neutralize ring leaders by capture or the use of weapons.

"take the package". accept an employer's early retirement offer, usually with terms favorable to both the employer and the employee.

talbutal. the generic name of a depressant legally sold as Lotusate, and regulated under the Controlled Substances Act as a Schedule III drug.

talesman. one who is summoned to be added to a jury in order to compensate for a deficient number; any member of a panel from which a jury is to be chosen.

Talwin. the trade name of a narcotic known generically as pentazocine. It is a Schedule IV narcotic.

tamper-resistant hardware. builders' hardware with screws or nut-and-bolt connections that are hidden or cannot be removed with conventional tools.

tamper switch. a spring-loaded switch installed in such a manner that it is compressed by the object which it is protecting, such as a door, window or housing cover. If the protected object is interfered with, the spring will operate the switch and send an alarm.

tangential gunshot wound. a wound caused by a bullet which enters the body at an extreme angle, causing an abrasion and leaving a residue track on the skin.

tape dialer. an automatic dialing device that transmits prerecorded messages over telephone lines to predetermined parties.

tare. the weight of a truck, rail car or other conveyance when empty. The tare is deducted from the gross weight of the loaded conveyance when determining freight charges.

target market. the specific individuals, distinguished by socioeconomic, demographic and/or interest characteristics, who are the most likely potential customers for the goods and/or services of a business.

target of opportunity. an entity that becomes available by chance to an intelligence agency for the collection of needed information.

TASER. a non-lethal rifle used by the police to subdue violent persons. The rifle fires an electrically charged dart that temporarily immobilizes the offender. TASER is an acronym for Thomas A. Swift Electric Rifle.

task analysis. an analysis of a work process for the purpose of revealing specific tasks, task interrelationships, the work environment, work tools and equipment, work criticalities, time requirements, and the skills, knowledges, and abilities required of the workers.

task force. a temporary organizational unit charged with accomplishing a specific mission.

taste/smell sensor. a sensor device that reacts to changes in the chemical makeup of the substance or air surrounding it.

tattooed gunshot wound. a close-range wound characterized by gunpowder tattooing in and around the bullet hole. The tattooing consists of charring at the entry point, and powder grains and combustion products embedded in the skin.

taut wire detection. a system of intrusion detection that features a strong wire strung tautly along the top of a fence or wall. A change in the tension on the wire (caused, for example, by someone climbing the fence) sets off an alarm.

Tax Reduction Act Employee Stock Ownership Plan. a type of employee stock ownership plan which offers additional investment tax credit to the corporate sponsor.

technical listening devices. devices and items of equipment primarily used or designed for wiretap, investigative monitoring, or eavesdropping.

technical security. measures that prevent or detect the installation of bugs, taps, and other electronic eavesdropping devices.

technical services. specialized law-enforcement agency functions such as electronic eavesdropping, wiretapping, communications, identification, laboratory activities, record-keeping, and temporary detention.

technical surveillance. in electronic countermeasures, the bugging, wiretapping, televising or radio tracking of another's activities.

Teichmann Test. a laboratory test to determine the presence of blood in a stain or substance of unknown origin. If blood is present, hemin crystals form upon application of a reagent. It is a confirmatory test, i.e., it is used to confirm a test by a different procedure. It is also called a Hemin Crystal test.

telephone analyzer. a device that detects electronic eavesdropping equipment present in telephone sets and telephone transmission lines.

telephone boiler room. a room equipped with a bank of telephones used by swindlers to sell worthless bonds, real estate, or stock. Also known as a bucket shop.

telephone dialer. a device that dials the number of a central station and communicates alarm information. It includes tape dialers and digital communicators.

telephone entry system. an entry control system that has a telephone at the point of entry and a telephone at an operator's location inside the protected area. The person seeking entry dials a coded sequence that gives connection to the operator. The operator verifies the code and dials a coded sequence that activates an electric strike to open the entry door. This system is sometimes supplemented with CCTV.

telephone line monitor. an electronic device, installable in an alarm system control panel, that will trigger a local alarm if the telephone line is cut or ceases to function.

telephone scrambler. a device used at both the transmit and receive ends of a telephone line for the transmission of scrambled voice communications. Multiple codes are switch-selectable. Speech frequency inversion is a common method of scrambling telephone signals.

temazepam. the generic name of a depressant legally sold as Restoril, and regulated under the Controlled Substances Act as a Schedule IV drug.

tempered glass. a type of windowplate approximately six to seven times more resistive to breaking than standard glass. When fractured, tempered glass shatters into small, comparatively harmless pieces.

Tempest. a type of electronic espionage in which electromagnetic emissions or leakages from electronic equipment are analyzed. Also a set of standards for the manufacture and testing of equipment so as to eliminate compromising emanations.

template. a precise detailed pattern used as a guide in the mortising and drilling of a door or frame to receive hardware.

temporal pattern fire alarm signal. a distinctive audible signal having an output of two short tone bursts followed by one long tone burst. It typically announces an evacuation.

temporary insanity. insanity which existed only at the time of the act; a legal defense.

temporary operating procedures. written instructions issued for a short period of time to cover a situation of limited duration.

tension wrench. an instrument used in picking a lock. It is used to apply torsion to the cylinder core.

tented arch. a fingerprint pattern in which most of the ridges enter upon one side of the impression and flow or tend to flow out the other side.

terminal. a connection point for circuit or other wires.

terminal block. in electronic countermeasures, the point at which telephone instruments are connected to the interior phone lines of a building.

terminal box. in electronic countermeasures, the point at which telephone lines are spliced or connected to cables.

terminal strip. multiple connection points for wires.

terrain-following sensor. a sensor capable of adjusting the protection zone to varied terrain with the use of multiple antennas or reflecting devices.

territoriality. behavior displayed by an individual or group in connection with the ownership of a place or a geographic area.

terrorism. the unlawful use or threatened use of force or violence by a revolutionary organization against individuals or property for the purpose of coercing or intimidating governments or groups, often for political or ideological causes. Terrorism is distinguished from other criminal acts, psychopathic acts, or acts of warring states.

Terry vs. Ohio. a 1968 case in which the U.S. Supreme Court validated the police practice of stopping and making reasonable inquiries of a person reasonably suspected of criminal activity. Additionally, the court held that if under such circumstances the police officer reasonably concludes that the person he has stopped may be armed and dangerous, he is entitled for the protection of himself and others to conduct a carefully limited search of the outer clothing in an attempt to discover weapons which might be used to assault him.

testamentary capacity. the capacity of a person to understand the nature of his business and the value of his property, to know those persons who are natural objects of his bounty, and to comprehend the manner in which he has provided for the distribution of his property.

test graph markings. in polygraphy, the signs and symbols placed by the polygraphist on a moving chart while the examination is in progress. Test graph markings assist the polygraphist at a later time when the chart is interpreted.

testimony. the presentation of evidence by a witness under oath.

tetrahydrocannabinol. the psychotoxic ingredient of hashish and marijuana as well as all plants of the genus Cannabis. It is classified as a Schedule I controlled substance. The term is a shortened version of delta-9-tetrahydrocannabinol, one of the 61 unique chemicals found only in Cannabis. Also called THC.

tetryl. a type of booster explosive.

Thai stick. a short section of bamboo containing marihuana buds.

THC. tetrahydrocannabinol (or delta-9-tetrahydrocannabinol), the active ingredient of cannabis.

thebacon. an opium derivative classified as a Schedule I controlled substance.

theft. larceny, or in some legal classifications, the group of offenses including robbery, burglary, extortion, fraudulent offense, hijacking, and other offenses sharing the element of larceny.

Theft From Interstate Carrier. a law that prohibits embezzling and stealing of goods moving as part of interstate or foreign shipments. It is found in 18 USC, Section 659.

Theory of Territoriality. a theory which holds that proper physical design of housing encourages residents to extend their social control from their homes and apartments out into the surrounding common areas. In this way, the residents change what previously had been perceived as semi-public or public territory into private territory. Upgrading the common areas results in increased social control which has the effect of reducing crime. Also called defensible space.

Theory X. a management theory which assumes that the average employee inherently dislikes work, must be coerced to work toward the achievement of organizational objectives, has little ambition, and wants security above all.

Theory Y. a management theory which assumes that the average employee regards work as natural as play or rest, is self-directed, is committed to organizational objectives to the extent they satisfy personal needs, accepts and seeks responsibility, and is imaginative and creative in solving work problems. The theory also holds that under the conditions of contemporary industrial life the potentialities of the average employee are only partially utilized.

thermal fire detector. a heat-responsive device such as tubing, cable, or a thermostat.

thermal lance. a bar packed with aluminum and magnesium wire or rods, and connected through a regulator to an oxygen container. It burns like a high-powered sparkler and is consumed while being used. A thermal lance is capable of defeating most safes currently manufactured. Also called a burning bar.

thermal viewing device. a portable device that uses the infrared spectrum to detect heat emanations. It can be operated in total darkness and is used to detect heat given off by suspects in hiding, concealed equipment in operation, living disaster victims, and in some instances recently buried bodies.

thermistor circuit. a circuit used in ultrasonic sensors to prevent a detection range shift due to temperature variances in the sensor environment.

thermonuclear weapon. a weapon which produces a portion of its yield by the fusion of light nuclei such as those of deuterium and tritium.

thermostatic cable. a fire detection product consisting of two wires held separately by a heat-sensitive covering. The covering melts when a pre-set temperature is reached. The wires come into contact, triggering an alarm. The cable can be installed throughout a wide area.

third wire tap. in electronic countermeasures, the activating of a telephone microphone by adding a third wire to the circuit so that the telephone microphone is in the on mode while the hand set is in the "hung up" position.

threat. the declaration by words or action of an unlawful intent to do some injury to another, together with an apparent ability to do so.

threat. the means through which an ability or intent of a threat agent to adversely affect an asset is manifested. Threats can be classified as human intentional, human unintentional, environmental natural, and environmental fabricated.

threat agent. a method or object used to exploit a vulnerability. Threat agents might be fire, earthquake, and sabotage.

Threatcon Red. a terrorist threat condition declared by U.S. military forces in response to an imminent threat of terrorist acts against US military personnel or facilities in a general geographic area. This threat may be based on information that terrorist elements in an area have plans or preparations for terrorist attacks against specific persons or facilities.

Threatcon White. a terrorist threat condition declared by US military forces in response to a non-specific threat of terrorism against US military personnel or facilities in a general geographic area. This threat may be based on information that terrorist elements in an area have general plans concerning military facilities.

Threatcon Yellow. a terrorist threat condition declared by US military forces in response to a specific threat of terrorism against US military personnel or facilities in a particular geographic area. This threat may be based on information that terrorist elements are actively preparing for operations in a particular area.

three-point lock. a locking device required on "A-label" fire double doors to lock the active door at three points, i.e., the normal position plus top and bottom.

threshold circuit. a timing circuit that extends a sensor-originated alarm indication of very short duration. This allows an alarm signal of a few milliseconds to be increased to one second or more for assured transmission to, and reception by, an alarm annunciator.

threshold inquiry. a brief questioning of an individual, short of an arrest, which gives no right to search the person. Also, a situation in which a Miranda rights warning would not be required.

throughput. the middle step in data processing of a system's operation. It comes after input and before output. Also, the speed and capacity of a computer, measured by the time it takes to produce desired results.

throughput rate. the measurable rate at which persons, vehicles or units pass through an access point.

throughscan. a term referring to a method of intrusion detection that uses sensors consisting of separate transmit and receive units which create a point-to-point detection pattern.

thumb cuff. in polygraphy, a device placed on an examinee's thumb during testing. It consists of an inflatable cylindrical rubber bladder enclosed in a metal housing. The thumb cuff electronically enhances detected changes in the examinee's blood pressure and pulse rate.

thumbcuffs. a device for controlling and holding unruly persons who are in custody. They are a smaller version of handcuffs but are placed on the thumbs.

thumb piece. the small pivoted part above the grip of a door handle, which is pressed by the thumb to operate a latch bolt.

thumb turn. a unit which is gripped between the thumb and forefinger, and turned to project or retract a bolt.

tidal volume. in polygraphy, the volume of air moved in or out of the lungs with each respiratory cycle. Tidal volume is a factor associated with measurements made by the pneumograph component of the polygraph instrument.

tight hole. an oil well about which information is restricted and passed only to those authorized for security or competitive reasons.

tilt-switch sensor. an intrusion detector used in fencing systems. Movement of the switch housing to a sufficient degree will make or break a contact. Fencing systems usually require activation of more than one tilt-switch sensor within a given time for an alarm to be triggered.

time/date generator. a device in a CCTV system that displays the time and date in the monitor display. It is useful for logging and documentation.

time delay circuit. a circuit that creates a time delay. For example, a home alarm system might include a time delay for the home-owner to set the alarm and exit without triggering an annunciation.

time division multiplexing. a signaling method characterized by the sequential and noninterfering transmission of more than one signal in a communication channel. Signals from all terminal locations are distinguished from one another by each signal occupying a different position in time with reference to synchronizing signals.

time interval. in polygraphy, the elapsed time between questions asked during a test. The time interval during a specific test ranges between 15-25 seconds. During a screening test the interval is somewhat shorter.

time lapse imaging. an image-recording system that takes periodic sequential samples of a scene. A time lapse video camera, for example, might record a 1 second segment every 3 seconds.

time limit cutout. a feature of a fire alarm system in which the maximum duration of the alarm signal is limited to not less than 3 minutes and not more than 15 minutes.

time-mechanical initiator. a timing device used to initiate a bomb's detonator. An alarm clock and pocket watch are common types of time-mechanical initiators.

time served. the total period spent in confinement for a given offense or on a given charge, usually computed as time spent before and after sentencing. In some instances, when persons are held without bail pending trial, the sentence is to time already served, thus permitting immediate discharge.

time zone. a feature of an access control system which allows access only within established time frames.

tissue builder. an undertaker's supply item which when injected into the fingertips of a deceased person will round out wrinkled tips so that fingerprint impressions can be obtained.

TL-15. a term used by Underwriters' Laboratories to describe a combination-locked steel container offering 15 minute protection against an expert burglary attack using common hand tools.

TL-30. a term used by Underwriters' Laboratories to describe a combination-locked steel container offering 30 minute protection against an expert burglary attack using common hand tools.

toke pipe. a short-stemmed pipe used by marijuana smokers.

tolerance. with regard to drugs, a bodily condition that requires ever-increasing amounts of a drug in order to achieve the desired effect, or that a diminished effect results from regular use of the same dosage.

toolmark. an impression, cut, scratch, gouge, or abrasion made when a tool is brought into contact with an object. A toolmark may be classified as a negative impression, as an abrasion-type mark, or as a combination of the two.

toolmark examination. a crime laboratory examination which seeks to determine if a given toolmark was produced by a specific tool. In a broader sense, a toolmark examination includes the analysis of objects which forcibly contacted each other; were joined together under pressure for a period of time and then removed from contact; or were originally a single item before being broken or cut apart. A toolmark is generally considered the result of contact between an object (the tool) and a softer material.

top-down method. a method for organizing and planning in which objectives are set by a senior executive or board of directors in concert with a top management steering committee.

top guard. an overhang of barbed wire strands or barbed tape along the top of a fence or other perimeter barrier, usually facing outward and upward at a 45 degree angle.

Top Secret. as used in the DoD Industrial Security Program, a designation applied to information or materials the unauthorized disclosure of which reasonably could be expected to cause exceptionally grave damage to the national security. Examples of exceptionally grave damage include armed hostilities against the US or its allies, disruption of foreign relations vitally affecting the national security, the compromise of vital national defense plans or complex cryptologic and communications intelligence systems, the

revelation of sensitive intelligence operations, and the disclosure of scientific or technological developments vital to national security.

torch job. a safecracking method in which a cutting torch is used to burn a hole into the side of the container. The cutting tool is usually an oxyacetylene torch, a thermal lance or burning bar, or a thermite grenade. Also called a burn job.

tort. a civil wrong committed when a person's private right is interfered with; a wrongful act committed by one person against another person or his property. It is the breach of a legal duty imposed by law other than by contract. The word tort means "twisted" or "wrong."

tortfeasor. one who commits a tort.

total luminaire efficiency. the percentage of a fixture's lamp lumens in the total light output, taking into consideration beam lumens and spill light.

toucheur. a person who is irresistibly drawn to touch the body of another person. Male toucheurs are common in large crowds that present opportunities for disguised pinching and caressing.

toxic gas alarm. a system for detecting quantities of toxic substances in the surrounding atmosphere before they become threatening to human life. The system usually employs a continuous-action air sampler.

toxicology examination. an examination to determine the cause of death in a suspected poisoning case. The types of poisons typically looked for are volatile poisons (carbon monoxide, alcohols, cyanide, and solvents), heavy metals (arsenic, mercury, lead, and antimony), solvent soluble compounds (aspirin, nicotine, and drugs of abuse) and miscellaneous poisons (pesticides, inorganic compounds, plants, caustics, and insects).

TR-30. a term used by Underwriters' Laboratories to describe a combination-locked steel container offering 30 minute resistance against an expert burglary attempt utilizing a torch.

TR-60. a term used by Underwriters' Laboratories to describe a combination-locked steel container offering 60 minute resistance against an expert burglary attempt utilizing a torch.

trace. an amount of a substance too minute to be measured or present in a negligible concentration.

trace metal detection. an investigative technique in which a chemical solution (8-hydroxyquinoline in ethyl alcohol) is sprayed on the hands of a suspect believed to have recently handled a heavy metal object such as a gun. The hands are then examined under regular light and ultraviolet light. If the skin has been in recent contact with metal, a shaded discoloration will be apparent. It might also be possible to discern on the skin a pattern corresponding to the shape of the metal object.

trace restore switch. a switch on the polygraph instrument that causes the galvanic skin response pen to return to its base line.

trachea choke hold. a type of choke hold used by the police to subdue violent subjects. Pressure is applied to the windpipe (trachea) to reduce the subject's air intake. Because this hold is lethal, it is banned by policy or law in many jurisdictions.

trade secret. information that derives independent economic value from not being generally known to and not being readily ascertainable by other persons who can obtain economic value from its disclosure or use, and is the subject of efforts that are reasonable under the circumstances to maintain its secrecy. Examples would be formulas, patterns, compilations, programs, devices, methods, techniques, and processes.

traffic engineering. an engineering discipline that deals with the planning and geometric design of streets, highways and abutting lands, and with traffic operations thereon, to achieve the safe, convenient, and economic transportation of persons and goods.

trailer. a fuse-like arrangement of combustible materials extending from a fire's point of origin, placed by an arsonist for the purpose of spreading the fire.

training by objectives. a training method judged to be effective to the extent that the trainees achieve well-defined objectives based on job tasks.

transceiver. a transmitter and receiver mounted in a single housing.

transcript. a verbatim record of the proceedings of a trial or ancillary proceedings. It is required for purposes of possible appeal.

transducer. a device that converts one form of energy to another, e.g., sound energy to electrical energy.

transferred intent. intent that is legally transferred from one act to another. For example, if a defendant kills one person while intending to kill another, his intent to kill is transferred to the person killed.

transformer. an electric device which by electromagnetic induction transforms electric energy from one or more circuits to one or more circuits at the same frequency, usually with changed values of voltage and current.

transient. a brief power surge in an electrical line.

transmission. the sending of information from one location to another by radio, microwave, laser, or other nonconnective methods, as well as by cable, wire, or other connective media.

transmit modem. a device for sending data over a telephone line.

transmitter. a device that produces a radio frequency or other electrical signal for conveyance to a compatible receiver.

transmitter/receiver. a device capable of maintaining two-way communication between subscriber premises and a central station.

transnational crime. illegal activity involving more than one sovereign nation, or in which national borders are crossed, as in international terrorism, drug smuggling, and arms trafficking.

transom bar. the horizontal frame member which separates the door opening from the transom.

transom catch. a latch bolt fastener on a transom, having a ring by which the latch bolt is retracted.

transparent lifting tape. a material used to lift latent fingerprints. The adhesive side is rolled flat onto the powdered print and peeled back. The tape is mounted on a card having a background color in contrast to the color of the powder.

transponder. a device that gathers and converts alarm sensor data for transmission to a signal processor.

Transportation of Stolen Property. a Federal law that prohibits the transportation in interstate or foreign commerce of any goods, wares or merchandise of a value of $5,000 or more, with the knowledge that such materials were stolen, converted or taken by fraud. The law is found in 18 USC, Section 2314.

transporter. that member of an auto theft ring who delivers a stolen car to the buyer.

transverse noise. a form of electrical noise interference that is typically generated by switching power supplies, utility company switching, and the operation of heavy electrical equipment.

trapdoor entry. an entry point to a computer system which has been left unprotected due to lax security or oversight.

trap loop. a pattern of electrified wire installed in crawl spaces and similar areas. If the pattern is interrupted an alarm is triggered.

trap protection. the use of sensors to detect an intruder approaching the vicinity of a protected target with a view toward apprehending the intruder.

trap zone. an interior protected zone where an intruder is likely to enter; an area made to appear attractive to an intruder. Protection is deliberately concentrated in the zone so that the intruder will be caught.

Travel Act. a Federal law that prohibits travel in interstate or foreign commerce or the use of any facility in the interstate or foreign commerce with the intent to promote, carry on or facilitate any unlawful activity. The law is found in 18 USC, Section 1952.

trespass. entering upon the property of another without consent after receiving, immediately prior to entry, notice that entry is prohibited, or remaining upon the property after receiving notice to depart.

trial. the examination in a court of the issues of fact and law in a case, for the purpose of reaching a judgment.

trial by ordeal. proceedings held in ancient times at which the guilt or innocence of an accused was determined by his ability to withstand torture without confessing.

triangulation. in electronic countermeasures, a process used to locate a beacon by use of multiple direction-finding receivers.

triazolam. the generic name of a suppressant legally sold as Halcion, and regulated under the Controlled Substances Act as a Schedule IV drug.

tribadism. the derivation of sexual satisfaction by a female from rubbing against the body of another female. Tribadism is practiced by some female homosexuals.

tribal law. the rules of law, generally unwritten, in a tribe or tribe-like subculture of a nation. Tribal law will usually be granted official standing provided it does not conflict with the laws of the nation.

trickle charge. a continuous direct current, usually at very low current, applied to a battery to maintain it at peak charge or to recharge it after it has run down.

trier of fact. the individual or group with the obligation and authority to determine the facts, as distinct from the law, in a case. In a jury trial, the jury is the trier of fact and is charged with accepting the law as given to it by the judge.

trigger pull. the amount of pressure, usually expressed in pounds, necessary to fire a weapon by pulling the trigger.

trigger transmitter. in electronic countermeasures, a device used to turn on a remotely located bug on command through a switch receiver.

trimeperidine. an opiate classified as a Schedule I controlled substance.

trinitrotoluene (TNT). a highly explosive compound usually stable in its cast form. In color it is cream or yellow and is commonly produced in half pound and one pound blocks.

trip circuit. a circuit requiring a short (closure) to initiate an alarm.

Trojan Horse. instructions covertly inserted to a computer program that will allow surreptitious unauthorized access to data. The instructions operate through a pretext of serving one purpose when the real intent is devious and potentially damaging.

trouble condition. an abnormal condition of an alarm system or circuit.

trouble signal. a signal which indicates trouble occurring in the components or wiring of an alarm system.

TRTL-30. a term used by Underwriters' Laboratories to describe a combination-locked steel container offering 30 minute protection against an expert burglary attack utilizing common hand tools and cutting torches.

TRTL-60. a term used by Underwriters' Laboratories to describe a combination-locked steel container offering 60 minute protection against an expert burglary attack utilizing common hand tools and cutting torches.

true bill. an indictment issued by a grand jury.

trunk facility. that part of a communication channel connecting two or more leg facilities to a central or satellite station.

try key. a key blank milled to fit a particular keyway. Raking and turning the try key in the keyway may cause the lock to open. Also called a jingle key.

tryout keys. a set of keys which includes many commonly used bittings. They are used one at a time in an attempt to unlock a door.

tuinal. a commonly abused barbiturate, usually taken orally or injected. Also called barb, downer, blue, yellow jacket and sleeping pill.

tumbler. a movable obstruction in a lock which must be adjusted to a particular position, as by a key, before the bolt can be thrown.

tuned circuit card. an access control card that contains radio frequency circuits "tuned" to disturb a frequency emitted by the card reader. The frequency fluctuations are interpreted by a processor to determine the access code in the card. The design of the card allows it to be read when placed in close proximity to the reader. There is no physical contact between the card and the reader. Also called a proximity card.

turn around. obtain the cooperation of a criminal in the acquiring of information or evidence concerning the criminal's accomplices.

turnkey. a person who has charge of the keys of a jail.

turnkey system. a fully installed, tested, and ready-for-operation system which is presented to the customer for use.

turnover. movement of individuals into, through, and out of an organization. The turnover rate can be statistically defined as the total number (or percentage) of separations within a given period of time. The turnover rate is an important indicator of the morale and health of an organization.

turn state's evidence. an agreement by a principal to a crime to testify against one or more other principals, usually in exchange for a reduced charge or immunity.

twenty-four hour circuit. a circuit that will initiate an alarm regardless of the system's arming status.

twisted pair. an electrical conductor consisting of two wires twisted around each other and sealed within an outer core. Twisted wire is used to reduce the possibility of induced alternating current in wire runs.

twisting and barbing. a type of selvage obtained by twisting adjacent pairs of wire ends together in a close helix equivalent to three full twists and cutting the wire ends at an angle to form sharp points.

twist off screw (or bolt). a screw or bolt designed to be tightened but once in place any attempt to loosen it will cause the head to twist off, leaving only a flat head that cannot be turned.

Two Factor Theory. a management theory which holds that two sets of factors determine a worker's motivation. The first set involves the worker's perceptions of job achievement, recognition, satisfaction, responsibility, and advancement. The second set concerns factors in the job environment such as company policies, competency of supervisors, compensation, personal relationships with supervisors, and working conditions in general.

two-man rule. a rule that requires, within highly sensitive areas, the presence of at least two authorized persons, each capable of monitoring the conduct of the other. Also called the two-person rule.

two-part explosive. a product used in blasting. It is composed of two chemicals each of which is not explosive until joined together.

two-party check. a check issued by one person to a second person who endorses it so that it may be cashed by a third person. A two-party check is most susceptible to fraud because the maker can stop payment at the bank.

TX-60. a term used by Underwriters' Laboratories to describe a combination-locked steel container offering 60 minute protection against an expert burglary attack utilizing cutting torches and high explosives.

TXTL-60. a term used by Underwriters' Laboratories to describe a combination-locked steel container offering 60 minute protection against an expert burglary attack utilizing common hand tools, cutting torches, high explosives, and any combinations thereof.

Tylenol With Codeine. the trade name for a product combining Tylenol with codeine, thereby subjecting it to regulation under the Controlled Substances Act.

Tyndall effect. the scattering of light by very small suspended particles. The smaller the particles, the greater is the polarization of the scattered light.

Type A error. an error of an access control system in which a valid card is rejected. Also called a Type 1 error.

Type B error. an error of an access control system in which an invalid card is accepted. Also called a Type 2 error.

type lines. in fingerprint classification, the two innermost ridges which start parallel, diverge and tend to surround the entire pattern area.

ulnar loop. a fingerprint pattern having a loop that flows in the direction of the ulnar bone of the forearm.

ultrahigh frequencies. radio frequencies in the approximate range from 300MHz to 3000 MHz. Commonly called UHF.

ultra-isolation transformer. a transformer having added electrical insulation and electrostatic shielding between its winding. Its function is to protect against line-to-ground leakage, such as common-mode noise.

ultrasonic. relating to sound waves, generally above 20 KHz, which are too high in frequency to be heard by the human ear.

ultrasonic alarm. an alarm system that operates by setting up a pattern of sound waves between two speakers which blanket the area to be protected. Any movement within the area causes the sound pattern to be distorted, resulting in an alarm.

ultraviolet fire detector. a sensor that detects a specific increase in ultraviolet radiation such as is generated by a flame.

ultraviolet light. light waves too high in frequency to be detected by the human eye. Commonly called UV.

ultra vires. a term meaning "beyond power." The acts of a corporation are ultra vires when they are beyond the power or capacity of the corporation as granted by the state in its charter; an act committed by a corporation through its agent which is not empowered or authorized by its charter.

umbrella policy. an all-encompassing insurance policy that provides increased coverage and/or broader coverage not provided by the basic policy.

unauthorized disclosure. a communication or physical transfer of classified information to an unauthorized recipient.

unbalanced line. a transmission line in which voltages on the two conductors are unequal with respect to ground.

uncompensated telephone line. a standard hard wire pair.

unconcealed walkout. in shoplifting, the taking of merchandise from store premises with no attempt at concealment.

underground economy. a term referring to illegal business practices in which commerce and the income derived from it are unreported. The practices are typically associated with bartering and the sale of goods and services for cash. Drug dealing, prostitution, and gambling are major segments of the underground economy.

underground press. clandestine publishing ventures which are frequently operated in support of minority ethnic and political interests.

underload. less than a normal amount of current flowing through an electrical device.

underside burn pattern. in arson investigations, charring seen on the underside of a very low object (such as the bottom of a door) which suggests that a burning liquid was on the floor's surface.

under the influence of alcohol. sufficient intoxicating liquor in the body system to impair faculties. A blood alcohol concentration of .10 grams of alcohol per 100 milliliters of blood, or per 210 liters of breath, constitutes the legal presumption for drunk driving under the laws of most jurisdictions.

Underwriters' Laboratories, Inc. a testing laboratory for manufactured items to determine their safety propensities.

undue influence. any threat or persuasion which overcomes or destroys a person's consent or will to act for himself.

unfounded offense. a criminal complaint in which the police determine that a criminal offense was not committed or did not occur.

unidentified dead. a deceased person whose true identity is unknown and whose relatives or friends cannot be immediately located.

Uniform Code of Military Justice. the code of law for the armed forces of the United States.

Uniform Commercial Code. a set of regulations governing business transactions, designed to unify methods of conducting business between the various states.

Uniform Controlled Substances Act. a model law based on Title II of the Comprehensive Drug Abuse Prevention and Control Act. Many states have adopted the model with only minor revisions, thereby helping to eliminate inconsistencies in drug enforcement in federal and state jurisdictions.

uniform crime index. an index of crime used for national crime reporting and evaluation purposes. The crimes listed in the index include murder, rape, robbery, aggravated assault, burglary, larceny, and auto theft. Except for murder, attempts are included. Attempted murder is listed as aggravated assault.

Uniform Crime Report. an annual report published by the FBI in which statistics are given for eight uniform crime index offenses.

uniform sentencing. the practice of imposing equal sentences for crimes of equal seriousness in the same relevant circumstances.

uninterruptible power supply (or system). a system that provides continuous power conditioning to an AC line within prescribed plus or minus tolerances. A UPS protects against overvoltage conditions and brownouts.

United States Code. the official law books that contain all federal laws.

United States Court of Appeals. an appellate court without power or jurisdiction to retry criminal cases. Its authority is limited to reviewing the trial court record and correcting errors of law that may have been committed. Thus, on an appeal from a judgment of conviction in the district court, the Court of Appeals will not hear cases anew.

United States vs. Robinson. a case in which the United States Supreme Court ruled that any person lawfully arrested by the police, regardless of the nature of the offense, may be subjected to a full search (sometimes called a field search), and whatever incriminating evidence is found on his person or in his clothing may be used against him.

unity of command. a concept that each individual in an organization should be accountable to only a single superior.

unity of direction. a concept that there should be only one head and one plan for each organizational segment.

unobtrusive measures. measures taken without the subject being aware that he/she is being observed.

unsolved case (or offense). a founded criminal offense in which the perpetrator could not be identified or that the available evidence is insufficient to support a charge against a known suspect.

upgrade. a determination that certain classified information requires, in the interest of national security, a higher degree of protection against unauthorized disclosure than currently provided, together with a changing of the classification designation to reflect such higher degree.

uranyl phosphate. a fluorescent tracing powder used to mark objects likely to be touched by a culprit. The powder fluoresces brilliantly in ultraviolet light.

user ID. a unique sequence of alphabetic or alphanumeric characters assigned to an authorized computer system user.

user password. in computer usage, a password that must be correctly supplied when an authorized user attempts to log in and be authenticated for access to the system.

user privileges. in computer usage, the privileges granted to a user by the system manager. Privileges might be granted to some files or functions but not to others.

usury. a rate of interest charged for the loan of money which is in excess of the rate authorized.

utter. to offer or pass as genuine; to declare that a counterfeit document is genuine.

V

vacate a judgment. to reverse a verdict or other decision of a court; to render void a prior verdict or decision.

vacate a plea. to withdraw a previously entered guilty plea.

vagueness doctrine. the principle that a statute written in an imprecise manner and capable of being invoked arbitrarily may violate due process and hence be unconstitutional, since it does not make clear what is and is not permitted.

Valium. the trade name of a commonly abused barbiturate, usually taken orally or injected. Also called barb, downer, blue, yellow jacket and sleeping pill.

value analysis. estimation of the present worth of the future benefits to be derived from an investment.

vanishing window. a larceny scheme in which a thief posing as a security guard stands next to a bank's night depository window and informs depositors that the window's mechanism is out of order and that he has been assigned by the bank to collect deposits.

vanity fire. a fire started for the purpose of attracting favorable attention, usually to the person who set it. A security officer, for example, who on his employer's premises starts and extinguishes a fire in order to make him appear diligent in his duties is said to have started a vanity fire.

vapor detector. a device that detects explosives by analysis of vapors.

variance. a nonstandard condition which technically varies from a requirement but provides essentially the same level of protection.

varying-density holographic card. an access control card fabricated of a translucent material that has areas of varying density. The variations in light transmission through the card are used to represent numerical values. A varying-density holographic card is appropriate for high-security applications because it is difficult to duplicate. Also called an optical-density card.

vault. a windowless closure with walls, floor, roof and one or more doors designed and constructed to delay penetration from forced entry.

vault-type room. in nuclear security, a room with one or more doors, all capable of being locked, protected by an intrusion detection system which creates an alarm upon the entry of a person anywhere into the room and upon exit from the room or upon movement of an individual within the room.

vehicle tracking system. a system of tracking vehicles in transit by using a computer, radio beacons, and predetermined travel routes.

vehicular manslaughter. causing the death of another by grossly negligent operation of a motor vehicle.

veiling reflection. a form of indirect glare produced when a light fixture in a protected area is directly above and in front of an intruder. Light from the fixture bounces off the surface on which the fixture is mounted. This reduces contrast rendition, making it difficult for the intruder to distinguish what is in front of him.

velocity of detonation. the speed with which the detonation wave progresses in an explosion.

vendor's lien. an unpaid seller's right to a prior lien on property until the purchase price has been recovered.

venireman. a juror or prospective juror.

venue. the geographical areas from which the jury is drawn and in which trial is held in a criminal action.

verdict. a decision by a jury to convict or acquit a defendant.

verification error rate. the rate of errors in an access control system which are attributable to rejection of a valid card or acceptance of an invalid card.

verification password. a password that must be entered when signing on to an electronic data processing system. Its purpose is to validate that the person who entered the user identification is the authorized individual. Once the user identification has been verified, further access is granted

vertical bolt lock. a lock having two deadbolts which move vertically into two circular receivers in the strike portion of the lock attached to the door jamb.

vertical footcandles. those footcandle values which are calculated perpendicular to a vertical surface. Vertical footcandles may or may not be in the same plane, and depending on the direction of the light rays, may or may not be cumulative.

vertical overcharging. a practice of some prosecutors in which a defendant's degree of culpability is raised by charging a higher offense. The practice is used to strengthen the prosecutor's negotiating position in plea bargaining.

vertical throw deadbolt lock. a lock with a deadbolt that enters a strike positioned at the top of the door frame or in the door sill.

very high frequency. a band of the radio spectrum operating in the approximate range from 30 to 300 megahertz. Commonly called VHF.

very low frequency. a band of the radio spectrum operating between 15-30 kilohertz.

vestibule training. training that prepares a new employee after acceptance of employment but before duties are assumed. For example, training given to new security officers after they are hired but before going on the job. The term has a derogatory connotation.

vet. examine legally or physically; inspect; inquire, as in a personnel security investigation.

vibrating bell. a bell that rings continuously as long as operating power is applied.

vibrating horn. an electrically operated horn in which the action of a vibrating armature working against a metal diaphragm produces a signal.

vibration fuze. a bomb fuze sensitive to minute movements or vibrations. The actual functioning of the fuze is caused by an influence from the target being exerted on a sensitive detecting device within the fuze itself.

vibration sensor. a detector pre-set for a degree of vibration which if exceeded will cause an alarm to be given. Commonly used for door and window protection.

vicarious liability. a legal principle which holds that not only is an employee civilly liable for his wrongful conduct, but his employer is also liable if the wrongfulness occurred while the employee was acting within the scope of his employment.

vice squad. a police unit dealing with prostitution, pornography, gambling, and other offenses deemed detrimental to the morals of a community. Also called a morals squad.

victim compensation. money or other assistance provided by the state to the victim of a crime.

victimization. the harming through criminal action of a single victim or victim class.

victimization theory. a means of measuring the crime rate by interviewing selected samples of people regarding their victimization or that of members of their families, households, or businesses. Such surveys are used to correct errors in statistics on crimes known to the police by estimating from victim reports the frequency of various types of crimes, injuries, and losses, as well as to learn other information about the acts, the offenders, and the victims.

victimless crime. a violation of law committed by or between two or more adults with the voluntary consent of each participant, as in adultery, sodomy, and gambling.

victimology. a subdiscipline of criminology that studies victims and victimization processes and techniques, victim-offender relationships, victim precipitation, victim vulnera-

bility, restitution, compensation, and similar issues.

victim precipitation. the initiation, encouragement, or escalation by the victim of a criminal act.

victim restitution. restoration of loss to the victim by the offender. This may be done voluntarily, perhaps in hopes of obtaining a more lenient sentence, or it may be ordered by a court as part of a sentence or as a condition of probation. Restitution does not necessarily relieve an accused of the necessity of standing trial and facing criminal sanctions, but it often does so in practice, or it acts to placate a victim and to reduce the severity of the sentence.

victim-witness assistance program. a program established in some jurisdictions to provide special services and support for victims, particularly of rape.

video comparison. a technique for access control verification. Typically, the authorized card holder is enrolled in the system by placing his photo image on a video disk. The image may also be coded by the height of the enrollee (correlated to the angle/tilt of the CCTV camera at the entrance point). To gain entry, the enrollee inserts his card in a reader; the stored image is found on the disk and projected on one-half of a split-screen CCTV monitor; the enrollee's actual image at the point of entry is projected on the other half of the screen; and a security officer matches the two images.

video graphic annunciator. a device that displays relevant alarm-related graphics and text for use by security personnel when an alarm is received. Some sophisticated units are capable of displaying a graphically represented intruder as alarms are sequentially tripped along the intruder's path.

video motion detector. a device used in conjunction with a CCTV system to detect movement within an area covered by a video camera. The video motion detector digitally analyzes a static picture several times a second. Any significant change in the picture triggers an alarm. Some video motion detectors allow the operator to select only portions (windows) of the video image for motion detection.

video switcher. an electronic device that routes video signals from multiple camera locations to one or more monitors. A switcher may also provide sequencing, homing, and bridging.

video window. a portion of a CCTV image in a video motion detection system that has been selected for constant analysis. Any movement or change in the window portion will produce an alarm. The window is typically a square or rectangle and may be bordered.

Vidicon. the trade name of a commonly used CCTV image-pickup tube. An advantage of the Vidicon design is the ability to control the target voltage. A Vidicon can be used indoors and outdoors in bright light.

view by jury. an on-site visit of a jury at the crime scene or other place having a material bearing on the issue to be decided.

vigilantism. action taken by the community, neighborhood, or other groups, without authorization by law, to frighten, contain, or take revenge on alleged, suspected, or would-be offenders.

vigorish. the portion of a bet withheld by a bookmaker.

vindictive vandalism. vandalism committed to express antagonism or hatred. Damage to company property by laborers on strike is an example.

vision panel. a fixed transparent panel of glazing material set into an otherwise opaque wall, partition, or door; a non-opening window.

vision-restricting dial. a type of safe dial constructed so only the person dialing the combination can easily see the numbers.

vis major. an accident for which no one is responsible; an act of God.

visual-display terminal. in electronic data processing, a terminal capable of receiving output data on a cathode ray tube and, with special provisions, of transmitting data through a keyboard.

vital equipment. in nuclear security, any equipment, system, device, or material, the failure, destruction, or release of which could directly or indirectly endanger the public health and safety by exposure to radiation.

vitreous fluid. in criminal investigation, a fluid taken from a deceased victim's eye for analysis to determine time of death.

vocal tract resonance. one of several criteria used in measuring speech for access control purposes.

vocoder. a voice scrambling device that converts speech into a sequence of pulses that are then scrambled by a digital data scrambler.

voice actuated switch. a switch that closes when conversation is impressed at its input. In electronic countermeasures, it is used to turn on and off clandestine listening and recording devices.

voice analysis. a technique of personnel identification that operates on the principle of voice-frequency patterns. A user's voice is digitized into a unique pattern and placed into the memory file of the identification system. When identification is required, the user provides a sample of speech. The sample is compared electronically with the known pattern on file.

voice answer-back. the response by a mechanically created voice from a computer upon an inquiry submitted by means of pushing buttons on a touch-tone telephone.

voice driver. an integrated circuit that creates a signal simulating a human voice. The voice is used to give instructions, deter an intruder, or alert response persons to an alarm condition.

voice grade. a telephone circuit suitable for transmitting band pass from 300 to 2700 Hz or greater, or having certain standards of noise and interference suppression to facilitate intelligible speech transmission.

voice pitch period. one of several criteria used in measuring speech for access control purposes.

voiceprint. a spectrographic sound representation of a person's voice. Voiceprints can be used for identification much like fingerprints, palmprints and footprints.

voice stress analyzer. a lie detector that can be used without the subject knowing that he/she is being tested. By analyzing the stress in a subject's voice it purports to tell whether or not the truth is being told.

voice verification recorder. a multichannel recorder that records all radio and telephone communications in a system, such as that used by a law enforcement or high-security agency to maintain a history of work events.

voir dire. preliminary examination which a court may make of one presented as a witness or juror where his competency or interest is objected to.

volatility. the tendency of a liquid to assume the gaseous state.

voltage booster. an amplifying circuit that raises alarm signal power to a higher level for transmission over leased lines or long wire runs.

voltage cell. a source of electrical energy depending on chemical action and complete in itself, e.g., a primary cell, or an accumulator.

voltage dip. a short-term decrease in line voltage, usually resulting from a short-circuit or a sudden increase in electrical load on the line. Also called a line dip or sag.

voltage drop. the drop in electric potential between two given points in an electric circuit.

voltage transient. a momentary surge or dip on an AC line, frequently caused by the shutdown or startup of motor-driven equipment sharing the same line. Also called a line transient.

volume. a mountable storage device such as

a disk pack, drum, mass storage system cartridge, or magnetic tape. Diskettes, cassettes, mag cards, and small system cartridges are not usually called volumes.

volume security erase. a feature of a computer system which upon command will erase entire volumes in memory by writing over them, as many as three times. Typically, the feature once started cannot be stopped until all volumes have been rendered irrecoverable.

volumetric sensor. a sensor with a protection pattern extending over a volume such as a room or an open field. Infrared and microwave sensors are volumetric in nature because they detect the presence of an intruder within a defined three-dimensional space.

voluntary manslaughter. intentionally causing the death of another with reasonable provocation.

voyeur. a person who derives sexual pleasure from viewing the genitalia or naked body of another.

V pattern. in arson investigations, a pattern of burn damage in the shape of a V, with the bottom of the V closest to the fire's point of origin.

vulnerability assessment. a methodology for evaluating the criticality of an entire system, a sub-system or an asset.

wage survey. a formal effort to gather data on compensation rates and/or ranges for comparable jobs within an area, industry or occupation.

waive. in law, to give up. For example, an arrested person might voluntarily give up his right to a preliminary hearing. Some rights may not be waived, such as the right not to suffer cruel and unusual punishment.

walk-in. a criminal who surrenders to law enforcement authorities and who usually co-operates by providing information or evidence.

walk test. a test of a space protection sensor (to ascertain its pattern of coverage) made by walking inside the protected area.

walk-under. a term referring to a deficiency of a volumetric sensor in which it is possible for an intruder to pass under the sensor's pattern of coverage.

wanted person. a person sought by law enforcement authorities because an arrest warrant has been issued or because he has escaped from custody.

war crime. an action ordered or authorized by leaders of a country engaged in a war, or carried out by its military personnel with or without such orders, that violates internationally accepted rules governing the conduct of war. War crimes include wanton killing of civilians, harsh treatment of prisoners, and use of chemical and biological weapons banned by treaties and agreements.

ward. an obstruction which prevents the wrong key from entering or turning in a lock.

warded lock. a lock with a simple mechanical cylinder containing a series of wards that move upon the application of a key with a slotted tab corresponding to the wards. A warded lock is easily defeated.

warrant. a process of criminal court which commands search or seizure of persons or property.

warranty. a collateral promise related to a contract.

watch list. a list of words, names, phrases, addresses, numbers and similar items which can be screened from a mass of data by a computer or human intelligence.

watchman's clock. a hand-held or shoulder-strapped clock device carried on prescribed rounds by a watchman or security officer. The device interfaces with watchman stations so that time entries are recorded to evidence that the rounds were made.

watchman's station. a designated point on the rounds made by a watchman or security officer. At the station is a key or similar device for inserting into a watchman's clock carried by the person making the rounds. The clock records the time and the station number as evidence that the round was made.

watered stock. corporate stock issued by a corporation for property at an overvaluation, or stock issued for which the corporation receives nothing in payment therefor.

water flow sensor. a device that detects the movement of water in a pipe. Typically, it consists of a paddle or vane suspended inside a pipe. Movement of water through the pipe moves the paddle, causing an electric switch (alarm) to actuate. A water flow sensor is frequently used to detect the activation of a fire sprinkling system.

water-soluble paper. paper that will rapidly disintegrate when immersed in water. Because it can be quickly destroyed, water-soluble paper is used in illegal gambling operations.

WATS line. a line that enables a user to telephone anywhere in a designated area for a flat monthly fee.

waveform envelope. one of several criteria used in measuring speech for access control purposes.

waveform generator. a device that develops the initial signal that is applied to a channel before data are inserted.

weapons offense. an offense that relates to the unlawful sale, distribution, manufacture, alteration, transportation, possession, or use of a deadly or dangerous weapon or accessory.

weapon system. a general term that describes a weapon or a combination of weapons and those components required for operation. The components required for operation typically include the weapon itself, the controlling system, and the carrier.

weight of evidence. the inclination afforded by credible evidence offered in a trial that supports one side of an issue. Weight is not a matter of mathematics but of inducing a belief.

wet cell battery. a rechargeable battery that has lead-acid or lead-calcium grids and a liquid electrolyte.

wheel search. a type of search made of an outdoor crime scene. The area to be searched is delineated by markers so as to form a large wheel with spokes radiating from the hub. The searchers begin at the hub and move outward within the lanes formed by the spokes. A disadvantage of this method is that the lanes become significantly wider as the searchers move away from the hub.

whistle blower. an individual who believes the

public interest overrides the interests of the organization and publicly reveals the organization's illegal, fraudulent or harmful activity.

white collar crime. nonviolent crime for financial gain committed by means of deception by persons whose occupational status is entrepreneurial, professional or semi-professional and utilizing their special occupational skills and opportunities; nonviolent crime for financial gain utilizing deception and committed by anyone having special technical and professional knowledge of business and government, irrespective of the person's occupation.

white intelligence. overt information such as that available in books, official reports and periodical literature available to any reader.

white noise. a noise whose spectrum density or level is substantially independent of frequency over a specified range.

white slavery. abduction and enforced prostitution of girls and women and, rarely, of young boys.

whorl pattern. one of the three basic groups of fingerprint patterns, the other two being the arch and loop. The whorl group has three sub-groups called the plain whorl, central pocket loop, double loop and accidental whorl.

wide area telephone service (WATS). a line that enables a user to telephone anywhere in a designated area for a flat monthly fee.

wide-gap contact. a special type of magnetic contact designed to work efficiently when the gap between the switch and magnet is greater than that suitable for standard magnetic contacts.

Wiegand card. a type of access card embedded with encodable ferromagnetic wires.

Wiegand Effect. the manner in which magnetic fields in specially prepared wire suddenly and forcibly reverse themselves when exposed to an external magnetic field. The special wire is a magnetically unstable ferromagnetic wire formed in a permanently tensioned helic twist. The magnetic reversals can be converted into distinct consistent electrical pulses. This effect is a basic operating principle in access control systems.

willful homicide. the intentional causing of death of another person, with or without legal justification.

willful misconduct. deliberate or intentional failure to comply with rules or regulations.

window assembly. a unit which includes a window, the anchorage between the window and the wall, and a portion of the surrounding wall extending at least 12 inches beyond the window frame.

window foil. thin metal tape applied to windows and similar breakable surfaces to detect breakage. The foil conducts a circuit which when interrupted triggers an alarm.

window frame. that part of a window which surrounds and supports the sashes and is attached to the surrounding wall. The members include side jambs (vertical), head jamb (upper horizontal), sill, and mullions.

window guard. a strong metal grid-like assembly which can be installed on a window or other opening. Types of window guards include metal bars, metal-mesh grilles, and sliding metal gates.

windowpane. LSD in the form of a thin square of gelatin.

wipe-through card reader. a card reader that accepts information from a card that is passed through it in a wiping motion. Because the card is not inserted into the reader, the possibility for jamming is reduced. This type of reader has a higher throughput rate and lower maintenance needs.

wired glass. glass consisting of wire meshing embedded between two layers of standard glass. Wired glass provides only slight resistance to impact but the mesh prevents the glass from shattering during intense heat.

Wire Fraud. a law that prohibits the devising of a scheme to defraud another or to obtain property by false pretenses when interstate communication facilities are used. The law is found in 18 USC, Section 1343.

wire glass. glass manufactured with a layer of wire mesh approximately in the center of the sheet.

wireless alarm system. an alarm system that does not use wires between sensors and the control panel. A radio frequency link is set up between each sensor, which has a transmitter, and the central controller, which has a receiver.

wiretap. a clandestine interception of a telephone conversation away from the target premises.

wire wrap. a method of temporarily connecting wires without solder.

withdrawal syndrome. the group of physical symptoms experienced by an addict when the addictive drug is withdrawn. The syndrome varies according to the drug abused. In narcotics abuse, the symptoms include watery eyes, runny nose, yawning, and perspiration from 8 to 12 hours after the previous dose. This is followed by restlessness, irritability, loss of appetite, insomnia, goose flesh, tremors, and finally yawning and severe sneezing. These symptoms peak at 48 to 72 hours, and are followed by nausea, vomiting, weakness, stomach cramps, and possibly diarrhea. Heart rate and blood pressure are elevated. Chills alternating with flushing and excessive sweating are characteristic. Pains in the bones and muscles of the back and extremities occur as do muscle spasms and kicking movements. Suicide is a possibility, and without treatment the symptoms may continue for 7 to 10 days. Also called the abstinence syndrome.

witness. a person who directly perceives an event or thing, or who has expert knowledge relevant to a case.

witness relocation program. a program administered by the Department of Justice in which witnesses who have testified against an organized-crime figure are given a change of name, identity, and place of residence.

woodblock core door. a door constructed of wood blocks glued together and wrapped in a face panel. It provides good protection against forced entry.

word processing. the manipulation of textual material through the use of a keyboarding device capable of controlled storage, retrieval, and automated typing.

work. in a numbers operation, the bet slips that are processed in a single day.

workers' compensation. cash benefits and medical care when a worker is injured in connection with work, and monetary payments to survivors in the case of death.

workhouse. a house of detention or correctional facility for short-term confinement of minor offenders.

working capital. the excess of current assets over current liabilities. Excess current assets are called working capital because they are used for carrying on business operations.

work measurement. any method used to establish an equitable relationship between the volume of work performed and the human resources devoted to its accomplishment.

work release program. a rehabilitation program in which prisoners are allowed to work and be gainfully employed outside of prison during the latter part of their sentences.

wounded bird ploy. a diversionary tactic used by an interviewee to lead the interviewer away from a subject that the interviewee does not want to discuss.

wrinkle wound. a cutting or stabbing wound that shows multiple cuts or punctures along the line of the blade, with interspersed areas of uninvolved skin. Wrinkle wounds are usually associated with obese or elderly victims.

writ. a paper issued by a judge which requires or forbids a specified act.

write, read and execute access right. a security feature of a computer system in which an authorized user is allowed to write, read, execute, modify and debug files.

writ of error. a document by which appellate review is requested on the ground that a lower court decision was based on one or more errors.

writ of habeas corpus. a document which directs the person detaining a prisoner to bring him or her before a judicial officer to determine the lawfulness of the imprisonment.

writ of mandamus. a document which orders a public official to perform an act that the law requires as his duty, such as to issue a license.

wrongful death action. a civil court suit brought by survivors against someone believed responsible, by negligence or intention, for another's death.

X

x-band. a radio frequency communications band in the 5200 to 11,000 MHz range.

x-bracing. cross-bracing of a partition or floor joist.

x-ray bomb. a bomb engineered to detonate if an x-ray machine is used to examine it.

x-ray radiography examination. a crime laboratory examination that uses x-ray radiography to reveal the interior construction of an object (such as a suspected bomb) and the presence or absence of defects, foreign matter and cavities.

x-ray spectrometer. an instrument for producing an x-ray spectrum and measuring the wavelengths of its components; a type of spectrometer used to measure the angles of diffraction of x-rays produced by reflection from the surface of a crystal.

XYY syndrome. a syndrome in men characterized by unusual aggression, caused by a genetic disorder in which the sufferer has an extra Y chromosome.

yellow-dog contract. any agreement between an employer and an employee that calls for the employee to resign from, or refrain from joining, a union.

yellow jacket. the street name for a commonly abused barbiturate, usually a Nembutal capsule.

yenhok. a needle-like device used to shape opium gum into pills.

yenshee. the opium residue which collects in the bottom of an opium pipe and which is frequently re-cycled by blending it with fresh opium gum.

yoking. a mugging technique in which the victim is grabbed from behind and held in a stranglehold while one or more accomplices remove the victim's valuables.

youthful offender. a person for whom special correctional commitments and special record sealing procedures are made available by statute.

Z

zebra line. a line, usually drawn on a floor, that demarcates an area that can only be entered after particular requirements have been met. Zebra lines are used to isolate bioclean areas such as a hospital's operating room or hazardous areas such as a nuclear radiation laboratory.

zero crossover point. in alternating current power circuits, the point at which the positive or negative voltage swing drops to zero before rising to its reversed value.

zinc-chloride battery. a heavy-duty battery designed for use in electronic applications. It is similar to the carbon-zinc battery, but has a longer life.

zip cord. a type of parallel wire that has two conductors. One side is ribbed and the other side smooth. The ribbed side is usually used to identify the positive circuit.

zip gun. a homemade gun, usually a pistol constructed of a short length of pipe attached to a handle or the frame of a toy gun. The firing mechanism is made of a nail head and elastic bands.

zone coding. a system in which each protection zone or sensor is uniquely identifiable, even when alarm signals share a common signal line. Pulses or frequency variations are used to differentiate between zones or sensors.

zone expander. a device in an alarm system that allows more than one individual zone to be monitored over a single pair of wires.

zone of comparison test. in polygraphy, a testing technique in which each relevant question is preceded and followed by at least one non-relevant question. For example, a 10 question test might follow this sequence: (1) neutral question, (2) sacrifice relevant question, (3) symptomatic question, (4) control question, (5) primary relevant question, (6) control question, (7) primary relevant question, (8) symptomatic question, (9) control question or guilt complex question, and (10) secondary relevant question. The polygraphist evaluates the resulting chart by comparing measurements in zones that correspond to the relevant/non-relevant questioning sequence. A zone of comparison test is helpful in disclosing any outside issues, detecting guilt concerning a separate crime, and reducing the subject's concern that surprise questions will be asked during the test.

zone search. a type of search conducted at an outdoor crime scene. The area to be searched is delineated by markers into quadrants. If the area is large, each quadrant may be further sectioned. One searcher is assigned to a quadrant or a subsection. Also called a grid search.

zoning. the process by which a protected structure is divided into zones or areas for security recognition purposes. An alarm initiating device installed in a given zone provides a means of identifying the location of the alarm condition.

zoom lens. a single lens with a variable focal range. A zoom lens can be manufactured to extend from wide-angle to telephoto viewing. Zoom lenses are usual components of CCTV systems.

ABBREVIATIONS

AAE. American Association of Engineers.
AAR. against all risk.
AAS. atomic absorption spectrometer.
ABA. American Bar Association; American Bankers Association.
ABC. Alcoholic Beverage Control.
ABCD. accelerated business collection and delivery.
ABS. American Bureau of Shipping.
AC. alternating current.
ACA. American Correctional Association.
ACDA. U.S. Arms Control and Disarmament Agency.
ACIA. asynchronous communications interface adapter.
ACL. access control list.
ACLS. advanced cardiac life support.
ACLU. American Civil Liberties Union.
ACM. Assistant Chief of Mission.
ACO. administrative contracting officer.
ACRS. accelerated cost recovery system.
ACS. access control system; American College of Surgeons; Assistant Chief of Staff.
ACSI. Assistant Chief of Staff for Intelligence.
ACV. actual cash value.
ADAD. automatic dialing and announcing device.
ADEA. Age Discrimination in Employment Act.
ADF. after deducting freight.
ADI. after date of invoice.
ADIT. Alien Documentation, Identification and Telecommunications (system).
ADM. atomic demolition munition.
ADP. automatic data processing.
ADPE. automatic data processing equipment.
ADPF. automatic data processing facility.
ADPRIN. Automatic Data Processing Intelligence Network.
ADPS. automatic data processing system.
ADR. alternative dispute resolution.
ADW. assault with a dangerous weapon; assault with a deadly weapon.
AFDC. aid to families with dependent children.
AFC. automatic frequency control.
AFE. authority for expenditure.
AFFF. aqueous film-forming foam.
AFI. Association of Federal Investigators.
AFL-CIO. American Federation of Labor-Congress of Industrial Organizations.
AFLETS. Air Force Law Enforcement Terminal System.
AFOSI. Air Force Office of Special Investigations.
AFOSP. Air Force Office of Security Police.
AFRAT. Air Force Radiation Assessment Team.

AFSC. Air Force Specialty Code.
AGC. automatic gain control.
AH. ampere-hour.
AIB. American Institute of Banking.
AIChE. American Institute of Chemical Engineers.
AICPA. American Institute of Certified Public Accountants.
AID. Agency for International Development.
AIE. American Institute of Engineers.
AIEE. American Institute of Electrical Engineers.
AIM. American Indian Movement.
AIPE. American Institute of Plant Engineers.
ALA. Associated Locksmiths of America.
ALARA. as low as reasonably achievable.
ALC. automatic level control.
ALE. annual loss expectancy.
ALSA. alarm line security attachment.
AMA. American Medical Association.
AMI. area of mutual interest.
AMS. aerial measuring system.
ANOVA. analysis of variance.
ANSI. American National Standards Institute.
Anti-C's. anti-contamination clothing.
AP. armor piercing.
APA. American Polygraph Association.
APB. all points bulletin.
API. American Petroleum Institute.
APO. Army Post Office.
APR. annual percentage rate.
AR. accounts receivable; acknowledgement of receipt; all rail; all risk; annual return; Arkansas; army regulation; autonomous republic.
ARAC. atmospheric release advisory capability.
ARC. American (National) Red Cross.
ARG. accident response group.
ARJIS. Automated Regional Justice Information System.
ASA. American Standards Association; Army Security Agency.
ASAC. assistant special agent in charge.
ASAP. Alcohol Safety Action Program; as soon as possible.
ASC. Airport Security Council.
ASCE. American Society of Civil Engineers.
ASCII. American Standard Code for Information Interchange.
ASD(C). Assistant Secretary of Defense (Comptroller).
ASET. Academy of Security Educators and Trainers.
ASIS. American Society for Industrial Security.
ASME. American Society of Mechanical Engineers.

ASPR. Armed Services Procurement Regulation.
ASSE. American Society of Safety Engineers.
ASTM. American Society for Testing and Materials.
ATBCB. Architectural and Transportation Barriers Compliance Board.
ATLA. American Trial Lawyers Association.
ATM. automatic teller machine.
ATRAP. air transportable radiac package.
ATSD(AE). Assistant to the Secretary of Defense for Atomic Energy.
AUTODIN. automatic digital network.
AUTOSEVCOM. automatic secure voice communications network.
AWG. American wire gauge.
AWOL. absent without leave.
ba. budget authority.
BAC. blood alcohol concentration.
B and E. breaking and entering.
BATF. Bureau of Alcohol, Tobacco and Firearms.
BBS. bulletin board system.
BCD. binary coded decimal.
BCLS. basic cardiac life support.
bd. baud.
BI. background investigation.
BIT. binary digit.
BJS. Bureau of Justice Statistics.
BL. bill of lading.
BLS. Bureau of Labor Statistics.
BOCA. Building Officials and Code Administrators.
BOLO. be on the lookout for.
BOMA. Building Owners and Management Association.
BOP. Bureau of Prisons.
BPA. blanket purchase agreement.
bps. bits per second.
BPU. badge processing unit.
BTBM. back-to-basics management.
CAB. Civil Aeronautics Board.
CAMI. commercial alarm monitor interface.
CAS. central alarm station.
CASA. court appointed special advocate.
CASO. central alarm station operator.
CBL. commercial bill of lading.
CBO. Congressional Budget Office.
CCD. charge-coupled device.
CCFA. Credit Card Fraud Act.
CCGD. CRT color graphic display.
CCMS. central control and monitoring system.
CCP. code of criminal procedure.
CCRS. capital cost recovery system.
CDR. critical design review.
CEO. chief executive officer.
CETA. Comprehensive Employment and Training Act.
CEU. card encoding unit.
CFG. cubic feet of gas.
cfi. cost, freight and insurance.

CFR. Code of Federal Regulations.
CHINS. child in need of supervision.
CID. criminal investigation division.
CLU. Chartered Life Underwriter.
CM. candidate material.
CMA. cash management account.
CMOS. complementary metal-oxide semiconductor.
CMT. crisis management team.
CN. chloroacetophenone (tear gas).
CNS. central nervous system.
CNWDI. critical nuclear weapon design information.
COB. close of business; chief of base; coordination of benefits.
COBOL. common business oriented language.
CODAP. client oriented data acquisition process.
COM. computer output micrographics.
COMINT. communications intelligence.
COMSEC. communications security.
CONUS. continental United States.
COO. chief operating officer; chief of outpost.
COPE. Community-Oriented Police Enforcement Program.
COR. central office of records.
COS. change of status; cash on shipment.
CP. command post.
CPM. counts per minute.
CPO. chief planning officer.
CPP. certified protection professional.
CPR. cardiopulmonary resuscitation.
CPS. crime prevention survey.
CPTED. crime prevention through environmental design.
CPU. central processing unit; crime prevention unit.
CPUSA. Communist Party of the United States of America.
CPX. command post exercise.
crim con. criminal conversation.
CRT. cathode ray tube.
CRU. crime reduction unit.
CSO. cognizant security office.
CSP. certified safety professional.
CSSO. computer system security officer.
CT. control transmitter.
CUSR. Central United States Registry.
DA. district attorney.
DAA. designated approval authority.
DAC. Department of Army civilian.
DAFC. Department of Air Force civilian.
DALE. Drug Abuse Law Enforcement.
DAPO. Drug Abuse Policy Office.
DAR. Defense Acquisition Regulation.
DAWN. Drug Abuse Warning Network.
db. decibel.
DBA. doing business as.
D&B. Dun and Bradstreet.
DBMS. data base management system.

DC. direct current.
DCAA. Defense Contract Audit Agency.
DCAS. Defense Contract Administration Service.
DCASR. Defense Contract Administration Service Region.
DCE. disaster control element.
DCID. Director of Central Intelligence Directorate.
DCII. Defense Central Index of Investigations.
DCM. Deputy Chief of Mission.
DCO. disaster control officer.
DDA. Deputy District Attorney.
DEA. Drug Enforcement Administration.
DES. data encryption standard.
DGP. data gathering panel.
DIA. Defense Intelligence Agency.
DIP. dual in-line package.
DIS. Defense Investigative Service.
DISC. defense industrial supply center.
DISCO. Defense Industrial Security Clearance Office.
DISCR. Director for Industrial Security Clearance Review.
DLA. Defense Logistics Agency.
DMA. direct memory access.
DMT. dimethyltryptamine.
DNA. Defense Nuclear Agency.
DNACC. Defense National Agency Check Center.
DOA. dead on arrival.
DOB. date of birth.
DOD. Department of Defense.
DOE. Department of Energy.
DOJ. Department of Justice.
DOL. Department of Labor.
DOM. display only monochrome.
DOT. Department of Transportation.
DOV. discreet observation vehicle.
DP. data processing.
DPAP. data processing asset protection.
dpdt. double-pole, double-throw.
DPF. data processing facility.
DPI. data processing installation.
DPM/m3. disintegrations per minute per cubic meter.
DPP. data project plan.
DPS. Department of Public Safety.
DPSD. data processing security department.
DRAM. dynamic random access memory.
DRF. disaster response force.
DRT. disaster response team.
DSI. Defense Security Institute.
DSO. data security officer.
DSP&P. Director for Security Plans & Programs.
DTE. data terminal equipment.
DTIC. Defense Technical Information Center.
DTSRK. data transmission system resynchronization kit.
DUI. driving under the influence.

DUSD. Deputy Under Secretary of Defense.
DWI. driving while intoxicated.
EACT. emergency action coordination team.
EAM. electronic accounting machine.
EAP. employee assistance program.
EAR. export administration regulation.
EAS. electronic article surveillance.
EDP. electronic data processing.
EEFI. essential elements of friendly information.
EEO. equal employment opportunity.
EEOC. Equal Employment Opportunity Commission.
EFT. electronic funds transfer.
EICC. Emergency Information and Coordination Center.
EIP. event initiated program.
ELSS. extravehicular life support system.
emi. electromagnetic interference.
emp. electromagnetic pulses.
EMS. energy management system.
EMT. emergency medical technician.
EMT. electrical metallic tubing.
ENAC. expanded national agency check.
ENTNAC. entrance national agency check.
EO. executive order.
EOC. emergency operations center.
EOD. explosive ordnance disposal.
EOM. end of month
emf. electromotive force.
emr. electromagnetic radiation.
EMT. emergency medical team.
EPA. Environmental Protection Agency.
EPROM. erasable programmable read only memory.
ERDA. Energy Research and Development Administration.
ERISA. Employee Retirement Income Security Act.
ESOP. employee stock ownership plan.
ETA. Employment and Training Administration.
EVD. electronic vibration detector.
EWS. early warning signal.
FAA. Federal Aviation Administration.
FACT. Fraud and Corruption Tracking System.
FAQ. fair average quality.
FBI. Federal Bureau of Investigation.
FCA. Farm Credit Administration.
FCBA. Fair Credit Billing Act.
FCC. Federal Communications Commission.
FCIP. Federal Crime Insurance Program.
FCL. facility clearance.
FCO. Federal Coordinating Officer.
FCPA. Foreign Corrupt Practices Act.
FCR. field contact report.
FCRA. Fair Credit Reporting Act.
FD. functional description.
FDA. Food and Drug Administration.
FDBA. formerly doing business as.
FDIC. Federal Deposit Insurance Corporation.

FEMA. Federal Emergency Management Agency.
FEPA. Fair Employment Practices Act.
FEPC. Fair Employment Practices Commission.
FERA. Federal Emergency Relief Administration.
FERPA. Family Educational Rights and Privacy Act.
f&fp. fraud and false pretenses.
FHA. Federal Housing Administration.
FHLBB. Federal Home Loan Bank Board.
FI. field interview; field inquiry.
FIAB. Foreign Intelligence Advisory Board.
FICA. Federal Insurance Contributions Act.
FIDLER. Field Instrument for the Detection of Low Energy Radiation.
FIDS. facility intrusion detection.
FIEPSS. fixed installation exterior perimeter sensor system.
FIFO. first in, first out.
FIO. free in and out.
FIPS. federal information processing standards.
FKA. formerly known as.
FLAIRS. Fleet Locating and Information Reporting System.
FLETC. Federal Law Enforcement Training Center.
FLSA. Fair Labor Standards Act.
FM. field manual.
FMB. Federal Maritime Board.
FMCS. Federal Mediation and Conciliation Service.
FMS. foreign military sales.
FOB. free on board.
FOCI. foreign ownership, control or influence.
FOIA. Freedom of Information Act.
FOIMS. Field Office Information Management System.
FOP. Fraternal Order of Police.
FORTRAN. formula translation (a computer language).
FOUO. for official use only.
FOV. field of view.
FPC. Federal Power Commission.
FPO. Fleet Post Office.
FRA. Federal Railroad Administration.
frag. fragmentation.
FRD. Formerly Restricted Data.
FRS. Federal Reserve System.
FSC. federal supply code.
FSLIC. Federal Savings and Loan Insurance Corporation.
FSO. foreign service officer; facility security officer.
FSP. Food Stamp Program.
FSS. federal supply schedule.
FTC. Federal Trade Commission.
FTS. Federal Telecommunications System.
FW&A. fraud, waste and abuse.

FY. fiscal year.
FYI. for your information.
GA. Gamblers Anonymous.
GAO. General Accounting Office.
GBL. government bill of lading.
GCI. gas chromatograph intoximeter.
GFE. government furnished equipment.
GFP. government furnished property.
GHz. gigahertz.
GIGO. garbage in, garbage out.
GMF. ground mobile force.
GOCO. government-owned, contractor-operated.
GOGO. government-owned, government-operated.
GOR. gas-oil ratio.
GP. general purpose.
GPBTO. general purpose barbed tape obstacle.
gpm. gallons per minute.
GPO. Government Printing Office.
GSA. General Services Administration.
GSOIA. general security of information agreement.
GSR. gunshot residue; galvanic skin response.
GSW. gunshot wound.
HE. high explosive.
HEW. Department of Health, Education, and Welfare.
hf. high frequency.
HHS. health and human services.
HID. high intensity discharge.
HOF. home office facility.
HMO. health maintenance organization.
HPR. highly protected risk.
HPS. high pressure sodium.
HUMINT. human intelligence.
HVAC. heating, ventilation and air conditioning.
IAAI. International Association of Arson Investigators.
IABTI. International Association of Bomb Technicians and Investigators.
IAC. intelligence advisory committee.
IACCI. International Association of Credit Card Investigators.
IACLEA. International Association of Campus Law Enforcement Administrators.
IACP. International Association of Chiefs of Police.
IACSS. International Association for Computer System Security.
IAEA. International Atomic Energy Agency.
IAHS. International Association for Hospital Security.
IASCS. International Association for Shopping Center Security.
IATA. International Air Transportation Association.
IBNR. incurred but not reported.
IC. integrated circuit.

ICAO. International Civil Aviation Organization.

ICAP. Integrated Criminal Apprehension Program.

ICBO. International Conference of Building Officials.

ICC. Interstate Commerce Commission.

IC&C. invoice cost and charges.

ICPC. International Criminal Police Commission.

IDCA. International Development Cooperation Agency.

IED. improvised explosive device.

IEEE. Institute of Electrical and Electronic Engineers.

IFB. invitation for bid.

IFIPS. International Federation of Information Processing Societies.

IMINT. imagery intelligence.

IMS. information management system.

INS. Immigration and Naturalization Service.

int. intelligence.

I/O. input/output.

IOB. Intelligence Oversight Board.

IUO. internal use only.

IPO. International Pact Organization.

ips. inches per second.

IRAC. Intelligence Resources Advisory Committee.

IRC. Internal Revenue Code.

IRF. initial response force.

IRS. Internal Revenue Service.

ISA. Instrument Society of America.

ISB. Industrial Security Bulletin.

ISCPP. International Society of Crime Prevention Practitioners.

ISCRO. Industrial Security Clearance Review Office.

ISIT. intensifier silicon, intensifier target.

ISL. Industrial Security Letter.

ISM. Industrial Security Manual.

ISO. International Standards Organization.

ISP. information security program.

ISR. industrial security regulation.

ITAR. international traffic in arms regulation.

ITC. investment tax credit; International Trade Commission.

ITSMV. interstate transportation of a stolen motor vehicle.

IVT. intensified vidicon tube.

JCAH. Joint Committee on Accreditation of Hospitals.

JCL. job control language.

JCS. Joint Chiefs of Staff.

JIC. joint information center.

JINS. juvenile in need of supervision.

JNACC. Joint Nuclear Accident Coordinating Center.

JRCC. Joint Radiological Control Center.

JSIIDS. joint services interior intrusion detection system.

KBO. keyboard only.

KeV. thousand electron volts.

KGB. Committee of State Security of the Soviet Union.

KHz. kilohertz.

KSA. knowledge, skill, and ability.

KT. kiloton.

LAAM. levo-alpha-acetylmethadol.

LAC. local agency check.

LAN. local area network.

LASER. light amplification by stimulated emission of radiation.

LCD. liquid crystal display.

LCL. less than carload.

LD. lethal dose.

LED. light emitting diode.

LEIU. law enforcement intelligence unit.

LF. low frequency.

LFC. local files check.

LIFO. last in, first out.

LIN. location identification number.

LLEA. local law enforcement authority.

LLL. low light level.

LLTV. low light television.

LMG. light machine gun.

LN. local national.

LNG. liquefied natural gas.

LOC. letter of consent.

LOS. limit of sensitivity.

LPG. liquefied petroleum gas.

LSD. lysergic acid diethylamine.

LSI. large scale integrated.

LSP. lump sum payment.

LTL. less than truckload.

MAAG. Military Assistance Advisory Group.

MAP. Mutual Aid Program.

MAT. mobile assistance team.

MBO. management by objectives.

MCE. multiplex central equipment.

MDAP. Mutual Defense Assistance Program.

ME. medical examiner.

MEI. management effectiveness inspection.

MER. maximum efficiency rate.

MeV. million electron volts.

MF. medium frequency.

MHz. megahertz.

MI. military intelligence.

MICR. magnetic ink character recognition.

MIL-STD. military standard.

MINS. minors in need of supervision.

MIS. management information system.

MLR. main line of resistance.

MO. modus operandi.

MODEM. modulator-demodulator.

MOS. military occupational specialty.

MOV. metal oxide varistor.

MPC. military payment certificate.

MPDC. multi-purpose dry chemical.

MPX. multiplex panel transponder.

MSD. mass storage device.

MSU. mass storage unit.

MT. megaton.
MTBF. mean time between failures.
MTMC. Military Traffic Management Command.
MTTR. mean time to repair.
MVR. motor vehicle record.
NA. National Academy (of the FBI); Narcotics Anonymous.
NAA. neutron activation analysis.
NAB. National Alliance of Businessmen.
NAC. national agency check.
NACI. national agency check and inquiry.
NAFS. National Academy of Forensic Sciences.
NAK. negative acknowledge character.
NAS. National Academy of Science.
NASA. National Aeronautics and Space Administration.
NATB. National Automobile Theft Bureau.
NATO. North Atlantic Treaty Organization.
NAU. narcotics assistance unit.
NAWAS. National Warning System.
NBDC. National Bomb Data Center.
NBFAA. National Burglar and Fire Alarm Association.
NBS. National Bureau of Standards.
NC. normally closed.
NCA. national command authority.
NCAIC. nuclear chemical accident/incident control.
NCCD. National Council on Crime and Delinquency.
NCIC. National Crime Information Center.
NCIC/AI. National Crime Information Center agency identifier.
NCJRS. National Criminal Justice Reference Service.
NCPC. National Crime Prevention Coalition.
NCPI. National Crime Prevention Institute.
NCS. National Crime Survey.
NCSC. National Communications Security Committee.
NDA. national defense area.
NEA. National Education Association.
NEC. national electrical code.
NEI. not elsewhere included.
NEMA. National Electrical Manufacturers Association.
NES. not elsewhere specified.
NEST. nuclear emergency search team.
NFPA. National Fire Protection Association.
ng. nanogram.
NHTSA. National Highway Traffic Safety Administration.
NIAAA. National Institute on Alcohol Abuse and Alcoholism.
NIC. National Institute of Corrections.
nicad. nickel cadmium.
NIDA. National Institue on Drug Abuse.
NILECJ. National Institute for Law Enforcement and Criminal Justice.

NIMH. National Institute of Mental Health.
NIS. Naval Investigative Service.
NLETS. National Law Enforcement Telecommunications System.
NLRA. National Labor Relations Act.
NLRB. National Labor Relations Board.
NLT. not later than.
NMCC. National Military Command Center.
NMI. no middle initial.
NMR. nuclear magnetic resonance.
NO. normally open.
NOC. not otherwise classified.
NOIBN. not otherwise indexed by name.
NORML. National Organization for Reform of the Marihuana Laws.
NOS. not otherwise specified.
NPD. no payroll division.
NPF. not provided for.
NPLO. NATO Production Logistics Organization.
NPV. net present value.
NRA. National Rifle Association.
NRC. Nuclear Regulatory Commission.
ns. nanosecond.
NSA. National Security Agency; National Sheriff's Association.
NSC. National Security Council.
NSF. National Science Foundation; not sufficient funds.
NST. not sooner than.
NSY. New Scotland Yard.
NT. no trace.
NTSB. National Transportation Safety Board.
NUREG. nuclear regulations.
NUWAX. nuclear weapon accident exercise.
OA. office applications.
OADAP. Office of Alcoholism and Drug Abuse Prevention.
OAS. Organization of American States.
OASD(C). Office of the Assistant Secretary of Defense (Controller).
OASD(PA). Office of the Assistant Secretary of Defense (Public Affairs).
OCC. Office of the Comptroller of the Currency.
OCDE TF. Organized Crime Drug Enforcement Task Forces.
OCR. optical character reader.
OCS. outer continental shelf.
ODC. Office of Defense Cooperation.
OEHL. Occupational and Environmental Health Laboratory.
OEO. Office of Economic Opportunity.
OFCCP. Office of Federal Contract Compliance Programs.
OHD. Office of Human Development.
OI. operating instruction.
OISI. Office of Industrial Security, International.

OJARS. Office of Justice Assistance, Research and Statistics.
OJCS. Office of the Joint Chiefs of Staff.
OMB. Office of Management and Budget.
OPD. Office of Policy Development.
OPEC. Organization of Petroleum Exporting Countries.
OPM. Office of Personnel Management.
OPSEC. operations security.
OPT. operator's terminal.
ORI. operational readiness inspection.
OS. operating system.
OSAC. Overseas Security Advisory Council.
OSC. on-scene commander.
OSD. Office of Secretary of Defense.
OSHA. Occupational Safety and Health Administration.
OSI. Office of Special Investigations, U.S. Air Force.
OTA. Office of Technology Assessment.
OTB. offtrack betting.
PAC. political action committee.
PBX. private branch exchange.
PCB. printed circuit board.
PCM. pulse code modulation.
PCO. procurement contracting officer.
PCP. phencyclidine.
PD. per diem; police department; postal district; potential difference; public domain.
PDD. past due date.
PDR. Physician's Desk Reference; preliminary design review.
PERF. Police Executive Research Forum.
PERT. Program Evaluation Review Technique.
PFOC. Prairie Fire Organizing Committee.
PILR. Property Insurance Loss Register.
PIN. personal identification number.
PINS. person in need of supervision.
PIR. passive infrared.
PKN. personal key number.
P&L. profit and loss.
PL. penal law.
PLSS. portable life-support system.
PM. provost marshal.
PMF. principal management facility.
PML. probable maximum loss.
PMLR. perimeter main line of resistance.
PNI. positive non-interfering.
PNIS. positive non-interfering and successive.
POC. port of call.
POD. pay on delivery; post office department.
POE. port of embarkation; port of entry.
POPI. protection of proprietary information.
POR. pay on return.
POS. point of sale.
POSDCORB. planning, organizing, staffing, directing, coordinating, record keeping, budgeting.
POST. peace officer standards and training.

POST. Protect Ownership of Software through Time stamping.
pot. potentiometer.
POT. peak of tension.
ppb. parts per billion.
ppd. postdate; prepaid.
ppm. parts per million.
ppt. parts per thousand; parts per trillion; precipitate.
PRCS. personal radio communications service.
PRESS. Program for assessing the Risk and Effectiveness parameters for Security Systems.
PROM. programmable read only memory.
PROMIS. Prosecution Management Information System.
PRP. Personnel Reliability Program.
PRR. preliminary requirements review.
ps. picosecond.
PSA. public service announcement.
PSC. physical security council.
PSCF. personnel security clearance file.
PSE. psychological stress evaluator.
psec. picosecond.
psf. pounds per square foot.
psi. pounds per square inch.
PSI. personnel security investigation; Permanent Sub-committee on Investigations, US Senate; physical security inspection.
PSQ. personnel security questionnaire.
PSS. physical security survey; protective security service.
PUD. pickup and delivery.
PWP. plasticized white phosphorus.
QD. quantity distance; questioned document.
QF. quick-firing.
RACES. Radio Amateur Civil Emergency Services.
RAD. radiation absorbed dose.
RADCON. radiological control.
RADIAC. radioactivity detection indication and computation.
RAM. random access memory; risk analysis management.
RAMT. radiological advisory medical team.
RAP. Radiological Assistance Program; random access programming.
RCA. radiological control area.
RCL. radiological control line.
RCMP. Royal Canadian Mounted Police.
RD. restricted data.
RDF. radio direction finding.
RDX. research department explosive.
REM. roentgen equivalent man/mammal.
rf. radio frequency.
rfi. radio frequency interference.
RFI. representative of a foreign interest.
RFP. request for proposal.
RFPA. Right to Financial Privacy Act.
RFQ. request for a quote.

RICO. Racketeer Influenced and Corrupt Organizations (statute).
RIM. relative impact measure; risk analysis management.
RJE. remote job entry.
R/O. reporting officer.
ROG. receipt of goods.
ROI. report of investigation; return on investment.
ROIT. remote input/output terminal.
ROM. read only memory.
ROPE. Repeat Offender Program Experiment.
ROR. release on own recognizance.
RPG. report program generator.
RPS. revolutions per second.
RRB. Railroad Retirement Board.
RRF. regional response force.
rsch. research.
RSO. Regional Security Officer.
RSP. render safe procedures.
RTU. remote transmission unit.
RW. radiological warfare.
S. secret.
SAAMS. special application alarm monitor system.
SAAR. seasonally adjusted annual rate.
SAF. standard ammunition file.
SAIC. special agent in charge.
SAM. secure access multiport.
S and M. sadism and masochism.
SAP. semi-armor piercing; statutory accounting principles.
SAS. secondary alarm station.
SAU. secure access unit.
SBA. Small Business Administration.
SBI. special background investigation.
SBN. standard book number.
S&C. search and clear.
S/C. suspicious circumstances.
SCD. security coding device.
SCI. sensitive compartmented information.
SDR. system design review.
SDS. Students for a Democratic Society.
SEC. Securities and Exchange Commission.
SHAPE. Supreme Headquarters Allied Powers Europe.
SHF. super high frequency.
SIDS. sudden infant death syndrome.
SIG. special interest group.
SIGINT. signal intelligence.
SII. special investigative inquiry.
SIOP. single integrated operational plan.
SIS. strategic information system.
SIT. silicon intensifier target.
SIW. self-inflicted wound.
SLATS. Safe, Loft and Truck Squad.
SLG. state and local government.
SLR. single lens reflex.
S&M. sado-masochism.
SMSA. standard metropolitan statistical area.

SN. serial number.
SNCC. Student Non-violent Coordinating Committee.
SNIE. special national intelligence estimate.
SOG. seat of government.
SOP. standard operating procedure.
SP. Shore Patrol.
SPP. standard practice procedure.
SRR. system requirements review.
SS. suspended sentence.
SSA. Social Security Administration.
SSN. social security number.
SSS. Signature Security Service; Selective Service System.
std. standard.
ST&E. security test and evaluation.
SVR. system validation review.
SWAT. Special Weapons and Tactics.
sync. synchronous or synchronize.
TAMS. tape archival management system.
TASER. Thomas A. Swift Electric Rifle.
TASO. terminal area security office.
TDB. temporary disability benefits.
TDY. temporary duty.
telex. telephone exchange.
THC. tetrahydrocannibinol.
THOR. target hardening/opportunity reduction.
THREATCON. terrorist threat condition.
TLC. thin layer chromatography.
TMD. trace metal detection.
TNT. transnational terrorism; trinitrotoluene.
TO. transportation officer.
TS. top secret.
TSEC. (U.S.) Telecommunications Security.
TVA. Tennessee Valley Authority.
twx. teletype communications; teletypewriter exchange.
U. unclassified.
UA. user agency.
UCC. Uniform Commercial Code.
UCI. Uniform Crime Index.
UCR. Uniform Crime Reporting (program).
UHF. ultrahigh frequency.
UIC. user identification code.
U.K. United Kingdom.
UL. Underwriters' Laboratories, Inc.
UNEP. United Nations Environment Program.
UNESCO. United Nations Educational, Scientific and Cultural Organization.
UNIDO. United Nations Industrial Development Organization.
UPS. uninterruptible power supply.
USACIDC. US Army Criminal Investigation Division Command.
USACIL. US Army Criminal Investigation Laboratory.
USAFSS. US Air Force Security Service.
USAINTA. US Army Intelligence Agency.
USC. United States Code.
USDA. US Department of Agriculture.

USDE. undesired signal data emissions.
USES. United States Employment Service.
USGS. United States Geological Survey.
USIA. United States Information Agency.
USIS. United States Information Service.
USMS. U.S. Marshals Service.
UV. ultraviolet.
UXB. unexploded bomb.
UXO. unexploded explosive ordnance.
VA. Veterans Administration.
VCAP. Violent Criminal Apprehension Program.
VD. vibration detector.
VDT. video display terminal.
VHF. very high frequency.
VLF. very low frequency.
VLLL. very low level light.
VLSI. very large scale integrated.
V&MM. vandalism and malicious mischief.

VOA. Voice of America.
VOM. volt-ohm-meter.
VOR. very-high-frequency omnidirectional radio range.
VP. variable pitch; various places; verb phrases; vice president.
VPP. voltage peak-to-peak.
VSA. voice stress analyzer.
VSS. video sequential switching.
VU. volume unit.
WATS. wide area telephone service.
WC. worker's compensation.
whr. watt-hour.
wi. when issued.
WP. white phosphorus.
WPS. word processing system.
WUO. Weather Underground Organization.
ZBB. zero based budget.

PROCEDURAL CONCEPTS

ALARM TERMINATIONS

There are four ways in which alarms are terminated:

• Local. An activated sensor will generate sound and/or light at the protected area.
• Central Station. An activated sensor will transmit a signal to a commercially operated central station. The central station operator will initiate a response in accordance with the customer's desires.
• Direct. An activated sensor will transmit a signal directly to a response agency, such as the police or fire department.
• Proprietary. An activated sensor will transmit a signal to a central point owned and operated by the owner of the protected area. The response may be to dispatch the owner's employees, security officers, or a public service response agency.

CARGO PROTECTION AT TERMINALS

Following are some standard measures for protecting cargo at terminals:

• Limit the number of entrances and exits. Ideally, there should be one place where all pedestrian and vehicular traffic enter and leave the terminal.
• Locate the security/police checkpoint and the dispatcher's office between the inbound and outbound lanes of the entry-exit point. This will allow superior coordination.
• Locate the parking lot for personal vehicles outside of the terminal. Eliminate situations that make it easy for employees to throw items over a fence in close proximity to parked personal vehicles.
• Enclose the terminal with a secure fencing system. All entrances through the fencing system should be controlled by the security/police force. Special entry points, such as rail leads, can be opened by electronically operated sliding gates.
• Install guard rails or concrete bumpers around the interior of the fence line to prevent large trucks from damaging the fence or creating holes that facilitate thefts. Place the rails or bumpers adjacent to the fence so that a walk-through corridor is created.
• Install at the exit point, under the control of the security/police, traffic signals, electronically operated gates and electronically operated road spikes.
• Install at appropriate locations in the terminal closed circuit television cameras that are mounted in weather-proof housings out of the reach of employees. Provide pan, tilt and zoom features, and a capability to make video tape recordings.

• Install throughout the terminal clusters of high pressure sodium vapor lights.
• Equip the dispatcher's office with a photoscope camera for photographing drivers, driving licenses and dispatch documents.

CASH HANDLING CONTROLS

At a minimum, cash should be handled with attention to the following procedures:

• The cash drawer should be closed after every transaction.
• Every customer should be given a receipt of the cash transaction.
• Unannounced audits of the cash drawer should be made regularly and with attention to detail.
• Over-rings and under-rings should be explained and verified.
• Ideally, the cash drawer should be accessed by only one person upon whom the responsibility rests for integrity of the contents.
• At the end of a shift, the cash drawer is counted and reconciled against sales activity for that shift. A supervisor should make a verifying count.
• With regard to employees who handle cash (or other valuables), there are these procedures to consider:
— Screen job applicants thoroughly. Use an employment application form that captures personal history facts concerning prior employment, former residences, drug and alcohol abuse problems, crime record, and other job-related circumstances. Verify facts given on the application form by conducting background investigations or administering polygraph tests.
— Provide surety bonding.
— Look for tell-tale employee behavior such as gambling, excessive drinking, drug abuse, debt, and social or domestic problems. Be concerned that these circumstances could lead to employee theft.
— Provide a means for periodically evaluating an employee's work behavior as it relates to safeguarding cash or other company property.
— Establish well-announced policies regarding company actions concerning employees who are caught stealing, and enforce those policies promptly and fairly.

COMPUTER FACILITY PHYSICAL SECURITY CONTROLS

Physical security controls for a computer facility should be sufficient to ensure that:

• access to the facility, equipment and data storage is limited to authorized persons.

- the risks of fire, flood and other hazards are minimized.
- environmental conditions are conducive to the efficient operation of the facility.
- any variations or failures of security safeguards are detected, reported and corrected in a timely manner.

COMPUTER OPERATIONS CONTROLS

Following are some general preventive measures appropriate for computer operations:

- Document all changes to computer programs before the changes are made. Changes that are made or attempted to be made without supervisory approval should be reported and acted upon.
- Access to the computer center should be controlled.
- The need to maintain a separateness of paying, receiving, accounting and payroll functions has applicability within the processes of computer operations.
- A continuous record should be made of data use.
- A record should be made of errors, restarts and running times.
- Important data files should be duplicated and stored in a separate, secure location.
- Hypothesize possible opportunities within the computer system for fraud and other losses, and take countermeasures for each.

COMPUTER SECURITY ACTION PLAN: LONG-TERM

A long-term plan to deal with computer-related risks should be flexible so as to accommodate changes in risks, technology, and the organization itself. A plan needs to be reviewed, coordinated with other organizational plans, and updated at planned intervals.

A long-term EDP strategy must be integrated with and operate in support of the organization's long-term operating/business goals. The elements of a long-term security strategy are:

- Define broad data processing security objectives.
- Allocate resources for implementation of the objectives.
- Establish an internal mechanism for providing management with continuous information about risks, their impact, and new solutions.
- Create an organizational environment that encourages resolution of computer-related problems.
- Ensure that security and control considerations are taken into account at the development and implementation stages of new systems and applications.
- Allow flexibility in the implementation of solutions to security problems so as to reduce negative reactions from users.
- Review the action plan on a regular basis.

COMPUTER SECURITY ACTION PLAN: SHORT-TERM

Management can take a number of actions in the short term to deal with computer risks. The actions focus on obtaining a clear understanding of risks specific to the organization so that a long-term strategy can be formulated. Short-term actions include:

- Make an up-to-date assessment of EDP risks and review the decisions already made to counter the risks.
- Review the current role of the EDP audit function, its capability and qualifications.
- Obtain information concerning EDP security controls, standards and procedures used in comparable organizations.
- Review existing EDP-related insurance coverage. Compare existing insurance with other available insurance coverage and self-insurance.

COMPUTER SECURITY POLICY MODEL

Many organizations rely heavily on electronic data processing to meet operational, financial, legal and informational requirements. Information and computer facilities must be safeguarded in a manner commensurate with their value. The purpose of a computer security policy is to:

- ensure that risks to computer-based information are identified, evaluated, recorded and managed.
- protect from loss, damage and disruption the assets, resources and personnel providing information services.
- protect computer-based information from disclosure and modification by controlling access to systems and data.
- ensure the continuity of operations in the event of a major disruption.

COMPUTER SYSTEM BASELINE REVIEW

This concept holds that the adequacy of security afforded to a computer system can be evaluated using a methodology as follows:

- Identify in gross form the facilities, people, equipment, supplies, computer pro-

grams, production processes, sources and destinations of data, data files, and locations where processed and stored.
• Identify and document all existing security controls and catalog them according to their purposes.
• Identify other security controls not in place but which have potential applicability. Catalog them according to their purposes.
• Visit similar computer facilities to identify security controls in place, controls tried and rejected, and controls considered and rejected.
• Synthesize the previous four steps and develop a baseline representation of controls and objectives of controls.
• Subject the baseline to potential threat, vulnerability and risk analysis. Develop recommendations based on findings.

COMPUTER SYSTEM AND DATA SECURITY CONTROLS

Security controls for computerized systems and data must be sufficient to ensure that:

• only authorized persons can access system facilities, application systems and data, systems libraries and data and communications facilities.
• all attempts to compromise the system are detected, documented and investigated.
• assignments of computer personnel provide sufficient segregation of duties to prevent compromise of the system and data.

CREDIT CARD OFFENSES

The rapid growth in the use of credit cards as a form of money has created a growing and lucrative criminal activity. The criminal's method of operation will change as technological changes make credit cards less susceptible to unauthorized use.

• Educate employees and customer card holders concerning the risks associated with credit card use.
• Maintain at the point of sale location up-to-date bulletins of cancelled and stolen credit cards and require sales clerks to use them.
• Obtain telephonic or electronic verification from the credit card issuer when the amount of purchase or other factor requires verification.
• Require the purchaser to provide identification.

CRIME PATTERN ANALYSIS

Crime pattern analysis seeks to determine what crimes are likely to impact particular targets, the criminals likely to commit the crimes, how the crimes are likely to occur and when they are likely to occur. The process of analysis typically includes the collection and processing of data related to:

• crime rate by opportunity.
• the varieties of attack methods, with emphasis on preferred methods.
• preferred times of attacks by day, week, month and other time variables such as holidays, seasons and special events.
• characteristics of suspects.
• general patterns of crimes.
• targets preferred by criminals, losses by types and values of losses.

CRIME PREVENTION ASSUMPTIONS

The underlying operating assumptions of crime prevention efforts are:

• Potential crime victims must be helped to take action which reduces their vulnerability to crimes and which reduces the extent of injury or loss should crime impact on them.
• Potential crime victims are limited in the actions they are able to take because of their inability to effectively exercise control over their environments.
• The environment to be controlled is that of the potential victim, not of the potential criminal.
• The direct control that a potential victim can exercise over his own environment can reduce criminal motivation. The absence of criminal opportunity means less temptation to commit crime and less chance that a criminal will develop criminal habits.
• Traditional approaches used by the criminal justice system, although response-oriented, do cause criminals to perceive personal risk and thus play an important role in preventing crime.
• Law enforcement agencies have a central but not dominant role in crime prevention.
• Many skill and interest groups in a community must act in concert if crime prevention is to have a comprehensive and lasting effect.
• Crime prevention activities can be both a cause and an effect of efforts to revitalize communities suffering from severe crime problems.
• Crime prevention doctrine is interdisciplinary in nature, is subjected to an ongoing process of discovery and change, and is useful to the extent that it is shared and applied.
• Crime prevention strategies and techniques are not absolutes. What succeeds in one situation may not succeed in other situations.

CRIME PREVENTION: A NEIGHBORHOOD APPROACH

The below listed action steps constitute a model approach to reducing crime at the neighborhood level:

• Obtain and analyze data relating to the neighborhood. Types of data worthy of analysis include crime and loss patterns, police patrol deployments, census tracts, terrain and topography descriptions, socio-economic and demographic patterns, and political infrastructures. The purpose of the analysis is to identify major crime locations, trends, sources of crime, cultural strengths and weaknesses of residents vis-à-vis the presence of crime, police effectiveness and efficiency, perceptions by the police and of the police, identify leaders and leadership groups in the community, identify resources that exist and that need to be acquired, and assess the divisiveness and/or cohesiveness of the neighborhood.
• Identify a comparable neighborhood not planned to be covered under the crime prevention program. Use the comparable neighborhood as a control area against which the success or failure of the program can be measured.
• Establish criteria for participation in the program. For example, what percentage of the neighborhood's population should be involved? What residents should be invited to perform organizing roles? What should those roles be? What kinds of projects are appropriate and likely to succeed, especially as first ventures? What kind of resistance can be expected? How do you neutralize it and turn it to your advantage? These are samples of issues to be addressed at this stage in the development of the program.
• Approach neighborhood leaders. Those who have been identified as having significant influence should be approached first. The local leaders should be invited to participate in the development of strategy and to act as a sounding board for program effectiveness. The program must be perceived as a neighborhood effort, with neighborhood involvement and direction.
• Educate residents through a wide variety of programs. Work through the neighborhood leaders and the groups they lead. Generate interest, support and an awareness of the program. The basic goal is to build a foundation for citizens and police to work together. This implies that police officials, from top on down, also need to be educated concerning program objectives.
• Provide feedback to residents and police. The residents need to know how the program is working (e.g., arrests made, convictions obtained, property recovered, victims assisted) and the police need to know how the residents regard the work they are performing (e.g., timeliness of responses, courtesy and visibility).
• Formulate crime specific tactics based on accumulating experiences. Ongoing analyses of crime data in the neighborhood will reveal times, places and methods of criminal attack. Preventive and response tactics can be inferred from the analyses.
• Implement crime specific tactics as they are developed. Existing tactics will call for modification, new tactics will emerge and combinations of tactics can be attempted. Whatever tactics are selected, they should be applied comprehensively so that criminals will simply not move to another location.
• Assess performance of the program's organizers, the residents, and the police. The purpose is not to pass final judgment but to determine what modifications are necessary to improve the program.
• Evaluate the impact of the program on crime in the covered neighborhood. The comparable neighborhood (mentioned previously) serves as a baseline for measurement.

CRIME PREVENTION OBJECTIVES

The overall goal of a crime prevention unit is to reduce crime in a given geographical area. This goal is achieved by planning, implementing and managing a comprehensive program. A program typically involves a wide range of projects and services that operate at three levels:

• At the client level, the objective is to design crime risk management systems that meet the needs of homes, businesses, institutions and other entities that are owned or managed by individuals or organizations.
• At the multiple client level, the objective is to design crime risk management projects through which many citizens in neighborhoods, shopping centers, industrial areas and similar localities can collectively work together to improve security.
• At the public policy level, the objective is to design crime risk management activities which units of government can carry out to improve security within a large jurisdiction and across jurisdictional lines.

CRIME PREVENTION PROGRAM EVALUATION

The impact of a crime prevention program can be evaluated by:

• measuring the degree of progress made in meeting specific objectives set for the program and progress toward the general goal of crime reduction.
• identifying weak and strong points of program operations and deriving suggestions for changes.
• comparing initial program assumptions against assumptions derived from the realities of program operations.
• suggesting new procedures and approaches.
• examining depletion of program resources and identifying new resources.

CRIME PREVENTION STRATEGIES

The strategies of crime prevention include many community-centered activities:

• Develop public awareness by informing citizens of crime problems and the services available to them for preventing crime.
• Develop specific courses of action to remediate crime problems impacting on specific persons, homes, businesses and organizations.
• Provide teaching and counseling services, with particular attention to key groups that hold leadership positions in the community.
• Develop group projects that harness collective efforts to achieve useful crime prevention activities.
• Interact with builders and code administrators to promote environmental design concepts that encourage active citizen involvement in neighborhoods and which at the same time discourage deviant behavior.
• Establish Neighborhood Watch programs and similar activities which encourage citizens to watch for crime and report observations to the police.

A CRIME PREVENTION STRATEGY FOR NEIGHBORHOODS

A program to reduce crime within a neighborhood might contain these objectives:

• Make the open areas more easily observable and increase human activity in them.
• Establish workable relationships between residents, businesses and police for the common purpose of eradicating crime.
• Promote a neighborhood identity, develop social cohesion and attract new financial investments to the community.
• Conduct no-cost security surveys to residents and businesses; and provide guidance for implementing survey recommendations.
• Hold public meetings; create special interest groups concerned with reducing particular crimes; and set up community-manned response units such as crisis hot line, rape crisis center, rumor control, rap line, child abuse center, etc.
• Improve the quality of police patrol operations by creating a dialogue between the police and community leaders.
• Encourage residents to report crimes and criminals.

CRIME RISK MANAGEMENT

This concept holds that all crime risks can be managed to an acceptable level through the application of one or more of five techniques:

• Risk Avoidance. The risk of losing an asset to criminal action is avoided to the extent that the asset is placed beyond the effective reach of the criminal. A coin collector, for example, applies the technique of risk avoidance when he places all of his coins in a safe deposit box.
• Risk Reduction. This technique is an extension of risk avoidance. Because it is not practical for an owner to place all of his assets under heavy protection, the owner leaves exposed those assets which he has immediate need of and places the remainder in safekeeping.
• Risk Spreading. This technique involves the application of physical and procedural safeguards to protect assets from criminal attack.
• Risk Transfer. In this technique, risk is transferred to someone else. The purchase of insurance is an example of transferring risk. Another form of risk transfer occurs when a storeowner raises his prices as a consequence of crime losses. In this way the risk is transferred to the customer.
• Risk Acceptance. The owner of an asset may choose to accept crime losses as a necessary cost of business. All or a portion of the maximum probable loss could be accepted.

CRIMINAL INFORMATION PROCESS

The criminal information process is a continuous cycle of interrelated activities directed toward converting raw data into information useful for law security purposes. The process has six steps:

• Collection. Needed information is identified and targeted for acquisition. Priorities are determined and communicated to the collectors (officers, investigators, special agents, et al.) The collectors gather from a variety of open and covert sources.
• Evaluation. The acquired information is evaluated at the collection level by the collectors (who are presumed to be in the best

position to judge the reliability of their information sources).

• Analysis. Information is analyzed on its own merits and in relation to other information. A central purpose is to answer the question, "What does this mean?" The information can be subjected to various statistical techniques and computer-assisted programs that manipulate the data in a search for trends and patterns.

• Collation. In this step, many types of information are combined and general hypotheses developed.

• Formatting. The processed information is placed into a variety of reports meaningful to the users. Distinctions are made between hard (corroborated) and soft (untested or hypothesized) information.

• Dissemination. Reports are channeled to users in a controlled fashion, e.g., with restrictions, protections and on a need-to-know basis.

CRIMINAL INTELLIGENCE AND LOSS PREVENTION

A loss prevention program can be assisted by the collection, processing and use of information pertaining to criminals and their methods of operation. The information used to create criminal intelligence can be collected from:

• undercover investigations.
• reports submitted by employees in other departments such as field representatives and salespersons.
• police reports and liaison with police officials.
• security department modus operandi and criminal personae files.
• informants.
• employees in "listening post" roles.
• feedback from specific reward offers and general "hot line" programs.
• liaison with security representatives from other organizations.

CRITICALITY RATING SCHEME

A criticality rating scheme offers a general approach for placing subjective values on particular loss events.

• Fatal to the Business. An event that would cause the company to go out of business.
• Extremely Serious. An event that would require major changes to insure survival and would have a major negative impact on balance sheet assets.

• Serious. An event that would have a noticeable impact on profits and would require considerable management attention.
• Less than Serious. An event that would normally be anticipated and would be provided for in normal reserves set aside for contingencies.

DISASTER RECOVERY FOR COMPUTER OPERATIONS

A disaster recovery plan for computer operations should address three major areas: backup facilities, data backup and off-site storage, and people and documentation.

Backup Facilities

• Determine the maximum amount of time the organization can function without data processing.
• Designate persons who will perform damage assessment during a disaster.
• Establish a decision-making mechanism, such as a crisis management team, to quickly decide whether or not to occupy the backup site.
• Make provisions for a tactical command post to be set up while disaster recovery operations are in effect.
• Establish at the off-site location an adequate store of supplies, such as preprinted check stock.
• Determine and make provisions for the manner in which data will move to and from the backup site. Assess the backup site's capacity to handle the volume and speed at which the data must flow in order for a recovery to be effected.
• Develop a testing capability so that the backup system can be checked out prior to live production.
• Determine if the backup site will be shared by other victims of a major disaster. If so, take steps to ensure that recovery efforts will be timely and capable of handling processing needs.
• Identify the critical business functions that are dependent upon microcomputers. To the extent that they are critical, arrange in the plan to replace them.
• Recognize that considerable rebuilding may be necessary. Designate employees who will be assigned to rebuilding duties.
• If the voice communications system does not have a backup, arrange for a replacement system. Do not wait until the disaster occurs. At that point it is too late.

Data Backup and Off-Site Storage

• Ensure that programs and files needed during disaster recovery are available at the off-site location.
• Establish a mechanism for monitoring the routine movement of backup tapes to the off-site facility for the purpose of reducing the chances that backup tapes would be destroyed by the disaster.
• Maintain an up-to-date accounting of backup tapes at the off-site storage location so as to not be missing any tapes and to identify the tapes that will be needed first at the backup site.
• Ensure that older program versions are available during disaster recovery to process data that were generated prior to program revisions.
• Include in the plan a requirement that during the initial phase of recovery all critical backup tapes will be copied before they are put to use.

People and Documentation

• Identify the persons who will play key roles during disaster recovery. List them in the plan and in specific procedures that facilitate implementation of the plan. Establish a mechanism for notifying key persons when a disaster occurs.
• Identify alternates to key persons and provide training to offset anticipated weaknesses.
• Establish a mechanism for contacting major vendors 24 hours per day, 7 days per week.
• Provide copies of the disaster recovery plan, procedures, notification lists and other associated documents to key persons for placement in their homes.
• Maintain in a safe location away from the data center up-to-date documentation of the operating system.

• Monitor changes to systems covered by the plan and when the systems are revised, revise the plan accordingly.
• Conduct periodic tests of the plan. The tests should be "hands-on" in which actual processing is conducted.
• Involve users in recovery plan development, approval, testing and revision.
• Describe in the plan what the users will be doing in support of disaster recovery while the systems are being restored.
• Assign relative priorities or a decision-making mechanism for assigning priorities that relate to the order in which processing work will be done.
• Identify a manpower pool from in-house and out-of-house resources to support key personnel as they manage the recovery operations.
• Designate responsibilities to qualified persons to handle functions related to the police and fire departments, medical services, local governmental officials, and the news media.

THE ENCRYPTION/DECRYPTION PROCESS

Encryption is the process of transforming intelligible information, known as plaintext, into a coded and therefore unintelligible form, known as ciphertext. The ciphertext is unintelligible except to those who possess the key to the code and the ability to apply the key in the prescribed manner. The process of applying the key is decryption. It is the reversal of encryption (See Figure 1).

In most cryptographic operations, the information that is encrypted is designed to be decrypted. In some cases, however, the extreme sensitivity of information may require that it never be available in plaintext form after its initial generation and distribution. When information of this type has been en-

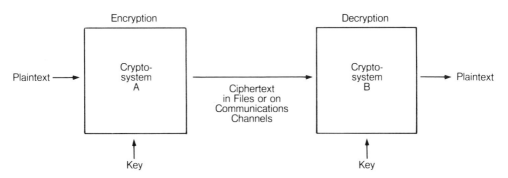

Figure 1   Schematic of the encryption/decryption process

crypted, it is not reversible even to authorized persons. This is called a one-way function.

The hardware, firmware, software, documents and associated procedures are called a cryptosystem.

EXTERIOR LIGHTING CONSIDERATIONS

Exterior lighting is intended to offset the advantages given to the criminal by the cover of darkness. The advantages of darkness to the criminal are:

• It is less likely that police patrols, residents or passersby will observe criminal activity in progress.
• The criminal is able to watch a target without being seen and to escape if detected.
• The natural fear that people have of being out-of-doors at night reduces the opportunity for detection of criminal activity in progress.
• The criminal has the element of surprise to gain control over his victims.

FALSE ALARM REDUCTION

False alarm problems can be overcome by:

• educating subscribers to properly use and care for alarm equipment.
• educating potential subscribers as to the proper applications of alarms and their limitations.
• warning potential subscribers concerning poor quality equipment and poor quality installation.
• enforcing licensing procedures to ensure that alarm dealers and installers meet the established criteria for workmanship, service and quality of equipment.
• placing controls on the quality and number of alarms that are in direct connection to the police department or other response agency.

FIRE SENSOR SELECTION

The type, number and placement of fire sensors can be determined by a careful consideration of these factors:

• The applicable state, county and municipal fire codes, and the advice of fire officials.
• The types of occupants; and the types of human activities in and around the structure.
• The composition of materials built into the structure; the types of materials stored or processed within the structure; and the composition of materials in furniture, draperies, carpeting and other accessorial materials.
• The size, configuration and internal layout of the structure; and in multi-building complexes, the interrelatedness of buildings, both physically and functionally.

• The structure's existing fire detection/suppression system, communications system and electrical wiring networks.

THE FOUR STAGES OF FIRE

Fire follows a progression through four stages:

• Incipient Stage. Invisible products of combustion are generated. There is no visible evidence of smoke, flame or heat.
• Smoldering Stage. Combustion products are visible as smoke. Flame and appreciable heat are not present.
• Flame Stage. Flames are visible. Appreciable heat is not present but will follow instantaneously.
• Heat Stage. Intense, uncontrolled heat is accompanied by rapidly expanding air.

FRAUDULENT CHECK OFFENSES

Two conditions can contribute to excessive loss from bad checks: the absence of check cashing procedures, and the failure of cashiers to follow the procedures.

• Develop tight but sensible check cashing procedures. The procedures should be good enough to prevent most types of check cashing frauds but not so tight as to discourage employees from following them and customers from tolerating them.
• Provide employees with initial, refresher and remedial training in check cashing procedures.
• Set a limit on the amount of a check proferred for cashing.
• Require the check casher to provide identification.
• Establish a check cashing station or approval desk.
• If economies permit, photograph each transaction.
• For large transactions, such as a check for the amount of a large purchase, verify the customer's address, phone number or bank account.
• Subscribe to bad check services for up-to-date information concerning active criminals and their methods of operation.
• Be on the lookout for unusual check features such as counter checks, post-dating, erasures, writeovers, unusual endorsements and differences between numerical and written amounts.

Figure 2 is a model of a check cashing policy.

HIGH VALUE SHIPMENTS

High value goods in transit and in storage while being transported require special attention:

1. Name and address must be printed on the check.

2. Look for the correct date.

3. Check number is very important.

4. State I.D. Number
5. Bank I.D. Number
6. Federal Reserve I.D. Number

7. The numerals and written value must be the same.

8. The signature must be the same as pre-printed on the check.

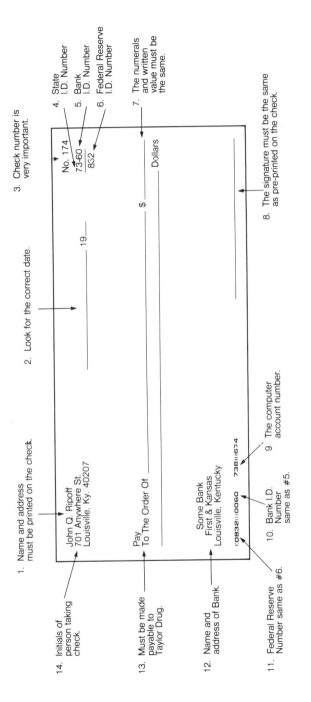

No. 174
73-60
832

John Q. Ripoff
701 Anywhere St.
Louisville, Ky. 40207

19___

Pay To The Order Of ___ $___

___ Dollars

Some Bank
First & Kansas
Louisville, Kentucky

⑈0832⑈0060 738⑈674

14. Initials of person taking check.

13. Must be made payable to Taylor Drug.

12. Name and address of Bank.

11. Federal Reserve Number same as #6.

10. Bank I.D. Number same as #5.

9. The computer account number.

*1. Accept only those checks with the *name and address pre-printed* on the check. The address must be a street, *not a Post Office Box.*
2. *Accept only those checks with the correct date.* Checks over 30 days old are not covered by the bad check law. Never accept a post-dated check . . . a check that has a future date on it.
*3. Watch for low sequence numbers—Numbers 200 or less. It is a proven fact that a large number of "cold" checks have a check number of 200 or less.
4. Each state has an identification number. Kentucky is #73; Louisville #21.
5. Each bank has an identification number. *Some Bank* is #60. The bank number is shown in 2 places on the check—#5 and #10.
6. Identifies the geographical location within the Federal Reserve System.
*7. The amount of the check in *numerals and written value must be the same.* If they do not agree, the bank will favor the written amount.

*8. The signature should be the same as the pre-printed name—#1.
*9. Each account has its own computerized account number. Never accept a check without this pre-printed number on the check. A check without this number is called a Counter Check.
10. Bank I.D. number appears here and should be the same number as #5.
11. Federal Reserve number here should be the same number as #6.
*12. The name and address of the Bank is here. It must be local. *Do not* accept an out-of-town or out-of-state check.
*13. The check must be made payable to *Taylor Drugs.* A check made payable to anyone else is a third party check. *You must not accept a third party check* under any circumstances.
14. Place your initials in the upper left hand corner. If the check is returned you may be able to remember something that will help locate the writer.

Figure 2 Check cashing policy—accepting a check

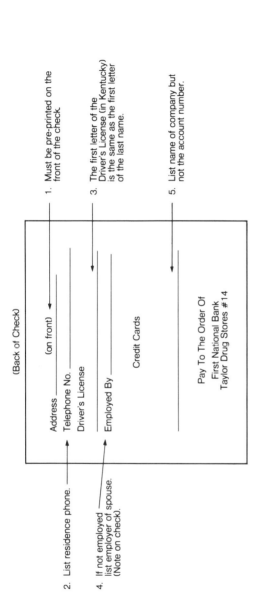

(Back of Check)

2. List residence phone.

4. If not employed list employer of spouse. (Note on check).

Address _____ (on front)
Telephone No. _____
Driver's License _____
Employed By _____

Credit Cards

Pay To The Order Of
First National Bank
Taylor Drug Stores #14

1. Must be pre-printed on the front of the check

3. The first letter of the Driver's License (in Kentucky) is the same as the first letter of the last name.

5. List name of company but not the account number.

*Place the store check stamp on the back of the check *immediately*. This is exactly like an endorsement for *Taylor Drug Stores*, Inc. If the check was stolen it could not be cashed.
1. Be certain a complete address is pre-printed on the front of the check.
2. Copy the residence phone number here. The exchange (first three numbers) should be familiar to you. Think of your store phone number. Is this number in your area?
3. Copy the driver's license number carefully. The first letter of the number should be the same as the first letter of the last name of the check writer (Kentucky). Look at the photo on the driver's license. Is it the same person who is writing the check?
4. List here the name of the company where the writer is employed. If not employed list spouse's employer.
5. Request a credit card. List the name of the company but do not copy the account number. If the account is *not* in the name of the check writer, note the name of account on the check.

Important General Information Regarding the Handling of Checks
1. A check is *exactly like cash*. Protect the check the same way you protect cash.

2. Accept a check only for the amount of the purchase.
3. Refer any check over $25.00 to the Manager-on-Duty for approval. If it is the policy of the store to have all checks approved, you must adhere to this policy.
4. Never accept a third party check. This is a check that was written by someone (a person, company, etc.), other than the person who is presenting the check to you.
5. Never accept an altered check. This is a check that has been changed in some way, the amount may have been written over, an erasure may have been made, etc.
6. Never accept a money order. *Exception:* A money order bought at your store and returned because it was not used for the purpose intended may be accepted.
7. You may accept a Traveler's Cheque in denominations under $25.00. You must be sure the writer signs the Traveler's Cheque in your presence. Compare the two signatures on the cheque carefully. Both signatures must have been made by the same person.
8. Willful violation of the Standard Procedure for accepting and protecting a check will result in *immediate dismissal*.

Figure 2—(continued) Check cashing policy—protecting a check. Courtesy of Taylor Drug Stores.

• Schedule the arrival of shipments so as to permit quick delivery to final consignees.
• Assign honest, dependable drivers.
• Provide radio equipment and a system for reporting trip status.
• If circumstances warrant, use a convoy, chase cars and checkpoints.
• Use special equipment such as truck alarms, high security locks and tracking devices.

IDENTIFICATION DOCUMENTS CRITERIA

The minimum specifications for identification documents are that they be:

• distinctive in appearance and easy to read/ understand.
• resistive to counterfeiting and unauthorized changes.
• unique to each authorized holder.
• codable by adding a distinctive marking or feature.
• adaptable for carrying and wearing.
• valid for a limited period.

INFORMAL SOCIAL CONTROL

This concept holds that crime in a small community or neighborhood can be reduced through:

• intensified use by residents of streets, parks and land around the structures in which they live.
• increased watchfulness of residents for intruders who manifest unacceptable behavior.
• an increased tendency of people to look out for the property and well-being of their neighbors and to interact with law enforcement.
• an enhanced ability to discriminate between outsiders and residents, and an ability to communicate by actions that deviant behavior will not be allowed.
• a strong sense of shared interests in improving and maintaining the quality of life in the physical environment and social climate of the area.

THE INTELLIGENCE CYCLE

The intelligence cycle consists of four steps through which information is assembled, converted into intelligence, and made available to users.

• Direction. The determination of intelligence requirements, preparation of a collection plan, tasking of collection agencies, and a continuous monitoring of collection productivity.
• Collation. The exploitation of information

sources and the delivery of collected information to the intelligence processing unit for use in producing intelligence.
• Processing. The production of intelligence through evaluation, analysis, integration and interpretation of information.
• Dissemination. The distribution of information or intelligence products (in oral, written, graphic or other forms) to users.

INTERVIEWING AND INTERROGATING OBJECTIVES

Although physical evidence plays a key role in any investigation, it has been consistently true that the most prolific and valuable sources of information are the people involved. The investigator interviews or interrogates people to achieve at least four objectives:

• Obtain valuable facts.
• Eliminate the innocent from consideration as suspects.
• Identify persons who are guilty.
• Obtain confessions from guilty persons.

As the investigator moves from the preliminary task of gathering facts to obtaining confessions there is an increase in the difficulty of acquiring information. That difficulty, however, is rewarded by an increase in the value of the information. Figure 3 illustrates these relationships.

Figure 3   Objectives of interviewing and interrogating

INTERVIEWING AND INTERROGATING ZONES

The distance between a questioner and a respondent can influence the success or failure of an interview or interrogation. Four zones are hypothesized:

• Public Zone. This is an open area, more

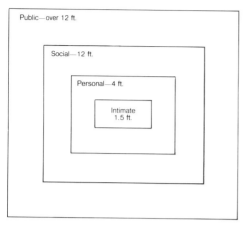

Public—over 12 ft.

Social—12 ft.

Personal—4 ft.

Intimate
1.5 ft.

Figure 4   Interviewing and interrogating zones

than 12 feet in any direction and larger than an average room. This zone is suitable for casual interviewing.
• Social Zone. In this setting, the surrounding space is roughly equivalent to an average room. It is confining, but not restricting. A social zone is suitable for interviewing.
• Personal Zone. The surrounding space is not larger than an average room; the questioner and respondent are close, but not touching. This zone is appropriate for controlled interviewing and light, or non-intensive, interrogating.
• Intimate Zone. This is a more confined space, perhaps half the size of an average room. The questioner is face-to-face with the respondent, well within touching distance and touching as circumstances of the dialogue dictate. This zone is intended for intensive interrogating.

INTRUSION DETECTION SYSTEM COMPONENTS

An intrusion detection system has three components: sensor, control and annunciator.

• A sensor detects a condition; it is not able to determine if the condition is in fact an intrusion. Sensors can be grouped according to principles of operation:
— Touch sensors respond to movement, pressure and vibration.
— Taste/Smell sensors detect changes in the chemical makeup of the air or surrounding substance.
— Hearing sensors detect changes in airborne sound.
— Sight sensors detect changes in light patterns.

• The control component of an intrusion detection system usually contains the following subcomponents:
— Power sources to provide operating energy.
— Circuitry to carry the system's signals.
— Energizing devices to turn the system on and off, program it and test it.
• The annunciator component receives signals from the control component and initiates a programmed response. There are four general forms of annunciation.
— Local alarms such as bells, horns, sirens and flashing lights that activate at the protected area.
— Central station alarm service provided by commercial companies on a subscription basis.
— Direct connection to a response agency such as the police department, fire department, ambulance service, hospital, civil defense, etc.
— Proprietary station service provided by the owner of the protected area. The owner or his employees receive the alarms at a central point.

INTRUSION DETECTION SYSTEM DESIGN CONSIDERATIONS

The principal considerations in designing an intrusion detection system are:

• The asset or assets to be protected.
• Existing barrier systems, security procedures, security guard force, security equipment/hardware and surveillance systems.
• The degree of skill and technical competence required by those who will operate the intrusion detection system.
• The speed and quality of response that can be given by the responding agency.
• The extent of protection appropriate for maintaining the integrity of the alarm monitoring station.
• The need to maintain a record of door openings and closings.
• The need for key access, card access, personal recognition access and other techniques for controlling the movement of people.
• The desires and sensitivities of the user groups that work in the protected area.
• The feasibility of integrating the intrusion detection system with the safety system and energy management system.
• The constraints imposed by cost, time, code restrictions and public attitude.

OPPORTUNITY REDUCTION

This concept holds that three ingredients must be present for a crime to be committed.

• There must be a desire or motivation on the part of the criminal to commit the crime.
• The criminal must possess the skills, knowledge and tools needed to commit the crime.
• There must be an opportunity for the criminal to act.

The first two ingredients are difficult to affect in any meaningful preventive way. The third ingredient, however, can be impacted through a variety of preventive actions.

PERSONAL RECOGNITION

The concept of personal recognition for access control applications requires:

• prior familiarity, by the person exercising control, with the persons who use the facility.
• an opportunity to observe without disruption and with regularity.
• low turnover among the observers and the observed.
• a means for speedy notification (to persons exercising control) concerning removal of authorizations to enter.

PERSONNEL IDENTIFICATION SYSTEM PERFORMANCE CRITERIA

A system for identifying persons entering or leaving a protected area should meet certain performance requirements:

• Validity. The system should positively differentiate the identities of persons.
• Reliability. The system should work every time or within a tolerable margin for error.
• Simplicity. The system should be easy to use, simple to operate and free of delay.
• Resistivity. The system should be able to withstand attempts to penetrate and defeat it.
• Durability. The system should hold up over an extended period, both in terms of equipment and human endurance.

PURCHASING CONTROLS

A purchasing agent is in a position to victimize his or her employer. The following general controls can be effected to reduce this possibility.

• Centralize the purchasing function. This will allow stricter management monitoring and control.
• Pre-number purchase order forms; account for the forms; and insure that all copies of completed forms reach the appropriate departments (e.g., accounts payable, receiving, etc.).

• Maintain a separateness between purchasing, receiving and accounting. Do not let one or a few persons handle all functions.
• Insure that purchasing agents do not own or hold interests in companies they buy from. Establish a strong conflict of interest policy and enforce it.
• Require supporting documentation for each purchase and cancel or mark the documents so they cannot be paid twice.
• Use numbers or codes on payment checks so that purchase expenditures can be tracked to purchase orders and supporting documentation.

RAPE AVOIDANCE

The best overall strategy to keep from becoming a rape victim is to avoid situations in which a rape can occur.

• Never admit a strange man to a home when alone.
• Keep doors and windows locked when alone at home or in a car.
• Keep shades and curtains drawn.
• Use exterior lighting around the home at night.
• Avoid walking alone.
• Do not ask for a ride nor accept a ride from a stranger.
• Avoid dark places.
• Be careful of social companions.
• Be conscious of surroundings at all times.

If in doubt, decide on the side of personal safety.

RAPE RESISTANCE

Following are some tactics that can be taken to resist a rape attack. Not all tactics will work in all situations, and not all victims will have the capacity to effect them. They are provided for illustrative purposes.

• Flight. The victim should flee to a place of safety if it is possible to do so.
• Scream. The victim should cry for help.
• Behave assertively. The victim should try to conceal her fear, not permit herself to be intimidated and demonstrate to the rapist that he will be resisted.
• Resist physically. The purpose of physical action is to immobilize the rapist long enough to allow the victim to escape.
• Use a weapon. Tear gas or a firearm might be used to immobilize or frighten off the rapist.
• Manipulate. The victim can pretend to desire submission for the purpose of creating an opportunity to escape.
• Submit. If all else fails, the victim may

choose to submit on the rationale that she may spare herself harm beyond the rape act itself.

All of the above tactics are fraught with danger for the victim. If a tactic does not succeed, the rapist may raise his level of violence.

RECEIVING FUNCTION CONTROLS

The receiving function offers many opportunities for crime-related loss. Here are some suggested controls:

• Use physical safeguards and barriers to isolate the receiving area. The use of a security officer at the receiving area would be appropriate when the size and complexity of operations dictate and economies permit.
• Channel the movement of delivery persons and employees so that the receiving area itself does not become a staging area for theft of property. Do not allow employees to leave the premises from the receiving area, and do not allow vehicles owned by employees to park at the receiving area.
• Count all goods received and compare the count against shipping documents before verifying receipt. Assign two people to verify receipt, and rotate them on at least a weekly basis. Periodically use a supervisor to make unannounced third party verifications.
• Do not accept damaged materials, and file claim forms as appropriate.
• Use numbers or codes on receiving forms so that received materials can be tracked to purchase orders and supporting documentation.
• Separate the receiving function from purchasing and accounting.

RISK ASSESSMENT

Risk assessment procedures provide a framework for identifying, evaluating and documenting for each facility and system:

• the risks to which the facility and system are vulnerable.
• the control measures available to counter the identified risks.
• the value attached to the facility and system.

RISKS IN THE PHYSICAL ENVIRONMENT

There are certain common and observable risks in the physical environment. The conditions that produce these risks are:

• inadequate lighting.
• inadequate physical barriers to individual structures.
• places of concealment from which criminal attacks can be launched and to which criminals can flee and find refuge within.
• situations (social, political and otherwise) which create access difficulties for law enforcement.
• a growing number of community areas which are difficult for the police to patrol, such as construction sites, transportation depots, shopping malls, parking complexes, parks, playgrounds and housing projects.

RISK SPREADING

In this concept, physical, electronic and procedural measures are applied singly or in combination to directly oppose criminal attack. The objectives of risk spreading are to:

• deter or discourage the criminal from attacking.
• detect the criminal if an attack is made and initiate a response.
• delay the criminal so that the response action can be consummated.
• deny the criminal access to the protected targets.

ROBBERY AND PERSONAL SAFETY

Some steps to take when confronted by a robber are:

• Do not attempt to overcome the robber, either with physical force or a weapon.
• Regard a robber's firearm as if it were loaded.
• Do not defy, challenge, "stare down" or provoke the robber in any way.
• Do not volunteer to do anything the robber does not mention.
• Cooperate, but only to the point where you believe your continued cooperation will bring personal harm, such as being taken from the place of the robbery. If you sense the need to resist, do so in a persuasive, non-threatening way.
• Activate an alarm only if you can do so without detection.

ROBBERY PREVENTION

Robbery prevention techniques are aimed at the potential robber. They seek to convince the robber that the personal risks to him are high and that the possible gain from a robbery is low.

• Keep in the cash drawer the smallest amount of cash needed to operate. Use a drop safe or similar robbery-resistive container to store excess cash.

• Make bank deposits at least daily. Do not allow unneeded cash to build up. To the extent possible, use two people to make bank deposits or use a courier service. If a courier service is not used, the time of the trip to the bank and the route taken should be varied.

• Place notices in prominent places on the premises which announce the cash protection procedures.

• Arrange for maximum visibility of the cashier's counter from outside the premises. Remove signs and provide lighting as needed.

• Provide initial and refresher training to store personnel concerning excess cash, warning signs and cashier visibility. Also provide training on what to do when a robbery occurs.

• Maintain liaison with local law enforcement, especially with those officers who patrol in the immediate neighborhood.

• Commensurate to the perceived crime risk, install alarm equipment and CCTV or a capability to photograph a robbery in progress. Post warning signs that such equipment is installed and mount cameras so they will serve as psychological deterrents.

SHIPPING CONTROLS

The shipping function is a principal risk area. The normal processes of a shipping department provide an ideal cover for theft. The following controls can help reduce criminal opportunity.

• Allow nothing to leave unless it is clearly documented.

• Shipping documents should be keyed to and easily tracked to billing and storage removal documents.

• Goods that are being assembled into a shipment should be checked by a second person. Goods that are being packed should be checked by a second person.

• After goods have been assembled and packed, they should be sealed in cartons. The sealing should be of a type that reveals an opening after sealing. If a sealed carton is opened and resealed, an entry should be made on the shipping document.

• Make a tally and check of goods as they are loaded onto the carrier.

• Loaded trucks, railroad cars and other transport vehicles should be locked and under supervision until they depart the premises.

• A method should be in place to monitor the movement of goods in transit and to provide protection of goods at points along the route where travel is interrupted for refueling, maintenance, rest, transshipment, etc.

SHOPLIFTING CONTROLS

These procedures can help cut back on losses from shoplifting:

• Understand the characteristics of shoplifters and the methods they use.

• Communicate understanding of shoplifters and shoplifting methods to sales employees through orientation and refresher training.

• Display high-value items so that customer access must be made through a sales clerk.

• Arrange merchandise neatly and orderly. This helps to highlight merchandise removed without the sales clerk's knowledge.

• At the sales point, check larger items to ensure that smaller items are not concealed inside.

• Apply price tags that are not easily altered or switched to another item.

• Give to each purchaser a sales receipt and require that it be presented if the item is to be returned. This will keep shoplifted items from being returned for cash or credit.

• Establish a legally sound procedure for detaining, questioning and requesting an arrest of a suspected shoplifter and for safeguarding evidence of the offense.

• Vigorously prosecute shoplifters and make this policy widely known.

STORAGE CONTROLS

Poor controls on goods in storage offer opportunities for dishonest employees. Here are some suggested procedures:

• Apply access controls to storage areas. Unauthorized persons should not be allowed inside. This is a safety measure as well as a security measure.

• Arrange stock neatly and in an organized fashion. This will allow visual notice to be made of stock that has been removed.

• Count the stock on hand in at least two intervals. A perpetual inventory system based on a first-in/first-out system can be used for daily accounting, supplemented with weekly or monthly inventories. Unannounced physical counts by company auditors and supervisors can also be used.

• Establish restricted areas within the general storage area to provide an extra level of protection for high-value items. The restricted areas can be separate, lockable rooms; large cages constructed of heavy duty wire mesh; permanently affixed, lockable shipping containers; or vaults.

• Maintain some form of responsible supervision over the storage area. In the absence of human supervision, use electronic supervision.

- Maintain records of stock in and out movements.

TELEPROCESSING SYSTEM SECURITY

Several general security conclusions can be made with respect to almost all teleprocessing systems:

- The need for security measures is in direct proportion to the value of the information to persons not authorized access to the system.
- The potential loss from system infiltration should determine the degree to which security is applied.
- Data volume and type, transmission method, and network size are important determinants in the selection of security measures.
- The personal integrity of authorized system users will have a profound effect on the success or failure of security measures.
- The opportunity to infiltrate the system increases as one gets closer to the terminal equipment.

THEFT PREVENTION THROUGH PHYSICAL SAFEGUARDS

Losses that result from theft can be reduced through physical safeguards that address these general considerations:

- Make it difficult for thieves to obtain access to assets.
- Identify and uniquely mark assets.
- Limit the amount or concentration of assets in any one place at any one time.

THEFT PREVENTION THROUGH PROCEDURAL MEASURES

Theft losses can be controlled by implementing procedural measures that incorporate these actions:

- Report all losses to a central point.
- Give priority attention to high risk loss items.
- Establish accountability and hold employees responsible for losses.

- Test the system of procedures and modify accordingly.
- Establish an audit trail capability.

VULNERABILITY ASSESSMENT

A methodological approach exists for assessing an organization's vulnerability by examining the separate criticalities of the organization's components. An approach might feature these steps:

- Identify the components that are minimally essential in order for the organization to operate.
- Determine the reliability of each component to function up to full capacity.
- Identify alternates or substitutions to components that would permit continued operation in the event of component breakdown or loss.
- Identify those key elements of a component (e.g., equipment, materials or persons) that are critical to the functioning of the component or entire organization.
- Identify the extent of exposure (risk) to damage or loss of critical elements.
- Identify the extent of interdependence among components and how interdependence might be reduced or made resistant to negative influences.

VULNERABILITY TO TERRORISM

A business organization is more likely to be a target of terrorists when:

- its revenues are substantial and generally known.
- its senior executives have high visibility in the media.
- its senior executives are generally known to be highly paid.
- the organization operates internationally or operates in a troubled geographical area.
- the organization is perceived to have a high concern for the well-being of its employees, particularly senior staff and executives.
- the organization is believed by the terrorists to have insurance coverage regarding kidnapping and other terroristic crimes.

LEGAL CONCEPTS

229

CORPUS DELICTI

The term corpus delicti means "body of the crime." It is often used erroneously to describe the corpse of the victim in a homicide case. Actually, the term relates to the essence of an offense and thus implies that every offense must have a corpus delicti.

In proving an accused's guilt of a specific crime the prosecution establishes three general facts:

• that an injury or loss particular to the crime involved has taken place.
• that the injury or loss was brought about by somebody's criminality, meaning that the injury or loss resulted from a criminal act as opposed to an accident or other cause.
• that the accused possessing the requisite state of mind (i.e., intent) was the person who caused the injury or loss.

The first two facts described above constitute the corpus delicti. The third fact simply establishes the identity of the offender.

For example, the corpus delicti in a larceny would be (1) the loss of property (2) by an unlawful taking. In an arson offense, it would be (1) a burned house (2) caused by a deliberately set fire.

CRIME CLASSIFICATIONS

When considering the vast and growing number of crimes it helps to classify offenses along certain broad lines.

In Order of Seriousness

• Treason is a crime against one's country. Under early common law it was a breach of faith to the king (high treason) or a killing of a lord by his vassal (petit treason).
• Felonies have their roots in the common law crimes of murder, rape, arson, burglary, larceny, robbery and sodomy. In earlier times most felonies were punishable by death. At the present time, whether a crime is classified as a felony or a misdemeanor depends upon the extent of punishment provided by the statute defining the offense.
• Misdemeanors were originally known as transgressions and continue today to be regarded as lesser offenses. A misdemeanor is generally defined as an offense not constituting a felony.

By Social Harm Involved

• Offenses against the person include murder, manslaughter, rape, assault, kidnapping, and the like.

• Offenses against the habitation include arson, breaking and entering and burglary.
• Offenses against property include the various forms of larceny and robbery.
• Offenses against morals and public health include sodomy, adultery, incest, lewdness, illicit cohabitation, abortion, prostitution, indecent exposure, obscenity, nonsupport, desertion, gambling and drug offenses.
• Offenses against public authority and government include escape, rescue, perjury, bribery involving public officials, resisting arrest, bail jumping, obstructing justice, misprision, compounding a crime, misconduct in office, criminal contempt, and the like.

In the Order of Nature

• Mala in se crimes are those which are so inherently wrong in their nature that they may be said to be evil in themselves. Crimes like murder, rape, robbery and arson are regarded as mala in se crimes.
• Mala prohibita crimes are those which are wrong because statutes declare them to be wrong. Examples would be to violate traffic laws or licensing laws.
• Infamous crimes are generally felonies and they relate to conduct which call for punishment by loss of civil and political rights, or by imprisonment in a penitentiary or imprisonment at hard labor.
• Crimes involving moral turpitude are acts of baseness, vileness or depravity in the social and private duties a person owes to society in general. The element of moral turpitude may be important in cases involving disbarment of attorneys, revocation of medical licenses and the deportation of aliens.

CRIME CONSTITUENTS

There are two essential constituents to every crime: an external physical action and an internal mental action.

• The external physical action is the conduct of the offender and its result. The forbidden conduct is set out in the definition for each particular crime. For example, in the crime of murder the conduct is the unlawful killing and the result is the death of the victim. In larceny, it would be the unlawful taking and the permanent loss to the victim of the property taken.
• The internal mental action is the intent of the offender to act. Common to all crimes is the requirement that the offender willfully determines to do an act which the law forbids. Although general criminal intent will suffice for many crimes, certain offenses require ad-

ditional mental intention. For example, the crime of unlawful taking is established when an offender intends to take someone else's property without permission and does so. For the crime to be larceny, a more serious offense, proof must be shown that the offender intended to permanently deprive the owner of the property taken.

There can be no crime unless an external act and an internal mental state are present. If a person possesses a criminal intention but does not act on it, he has not committed a crime. If a person commits a forbidden act but does so without intent, there is no crime. A person duped into or insane at the time of performing an unlawful act has not committed a crime. Not only must the external and internal actions be present, they must be united at one and the same time.

CRIMES AND TORTS

A crime is a public wrong and a tort is a private wrong. A public wrong is remedied in a criminal proceeding and a private wrong is remedied in a civil proceeding. A single act in some instances will constitute both a crime and a tort. For example, if a person commits an assault and battery upon another, he commits a crime (a public wrong) and a tort (a private wrong). The law will seek to remedy both wrongs, but it will do so in different ways.

The State will move on its own authority to do justice by bringing a criminal action against the offender. The victim is also entitled to bring action against the offender in a civil suit. Tort law gives the victim a cause of action for damages in order that he may obtain sufficient satisfaction. The victim, however, pursues a civil remedy at his own discretion and in his own name.

Whether the victim wins his lawsuit or not, the judgment will not prevent prosecution of the offender by the State.

The civil injuries involved in tort cases usually arise from acts of negligence. The fact that the victim by his own negligence contributed to the harm done may afford the offender a defense in a civil action of tort, but it does not constitute a defense to the offender in a criminal prosecution.

CRIMINAL INTENT

Criminal intent is the state of mind of the offender, and is generally regarded as falling into two categories: general criminal intent and specific criminal intent.

• General criminal intent is an essential element in all crimes. It means that when the offender acted, or failed to act, contrary to the law, he did so voluntarily with determination or foresight of the consequences. For example, general criminal intent is shown in the offense of assault and battery when the offender voluntarily applies unlawful force to another with an awareness of its result.

• Specific criminal intent requires a particular mental state in addition to that of general criminal intent. The laws relating to certain crimes may describe an additional, specific mental purpose. For example, the crime of murder has a general criminal intent in that the offender voluntarily applies unlawful force with an awareness of its result. In addition, the crime of murder in a particular jurisdiction may require a showing that the offender acted with premeditation to commit murder.

CRIMINAL LAW: A DISTINGUISHING FEATURE

The single characteristic that differentiates criminal law from civil law is punishment. Generally, in a civil suit the basic questions are:

• how much, if at all, has the defendant injured the plaintiff, and

• what remedies, if any, are appropriate to compensate the plaintiff for his loss.

In a criminal case, the questions are:

• to what extent has the defendant injured society, and

• what sentence is appropriate to punish the defendant.

CRIMINAL LAW SOURCES

There are two sources of the criminal law: judicial decisions of the courts and express enactments of the legislatures.

• Judicial decisions of the courts are frequently referred to as the common law. The law enunciated by the authority of courts is also called case law and unwritten law. The term case law derives from the cases decided by judges, and the term unwritten law derives from the idea that judicial decisions are not written as statutes. In truth, common law is well documented in the reports of decisions handed down since the 13th century. These decisions, and the reasons on which they are based, act as controlling precedents. The actual words of the opinions explaining the principles applied by the courts are not the law itself but an exposition of it.

• Express enactments of the legislatures are usually called statute law. A legislature may affirm, extend, abolish or modify any common law doctrine laid down by the courts. When conflict exists between common law and statute law, the statute prevails. All of the States have put their common law crimes into some statutory form. Many statutes are simply re-statements of the common law. The criminal statutes are the imperative commands of elected lawmakers.

DAMAGES: COMPENSATORY AND PUNITIVE

When one person's tortious act injures another's person or property, the remedy for the injured party is to collect damages. The common law rules of damages for physical harm contain three fundamental ideas:

• Justice requires that the plaintiff be restored to his pre-injury condition, so far as it is possible to do so with money. He should be reimbursed not only for economic losses, but also for loss of physical and mental well-being.
• Most economic losses are translatable into dollars.
• When the plaintiff sues for an injury he must recover all of his damages arising from that injury, past and future, in a lump sum and in a single lawsuit.

If the defendant's wrongful conduct is sufficiently serious, the law permits the trier of fact to impose a civil fine as punishment and to deter him and others from similar conduct in the future. Punitive damages (also called exemplary or vindictive damages) are not really damages at all since the plaintiff has been made whole by the compensatory damages awarded in the same action. Punitive damages are justified as:

• An incentive for bringing the defendant to justice.
• Punishment for offenses which often escape or are beyond the reach of criminal law.
• Compensation for damages not normally compensable, such as hurt feelings, attorneys' fees and expenses of litigation.
• The only effective means to force conscienceless defendants to cease practices known to be dangerous and which they would otherwise continue in the absence of an effective deterrent.

DEFENSES IN CRIMINAL CASES

The law allows many defenses to charges of crime and it is the right of the accused to use any and all of them. The concept of defenses against prosecution may be viewed from two aspects: the basic capacity of the accused to commit the crime charged, and the applicability of certain legal defenses such as the statute of limitations.

Capacity to Commit Crime

• The infancy defense holds that children are incapable of committing any crime below a certain age; that at a higher age there is a presumption of an incapacity to commit crime; and at an even higher age certain crimes are conclusively presumed to be beyond the capability of a child. For example, it may be presumed that a 13 year old boy is incapable of committing the crime of rape.
• The corporation defense holds that because a corporation is an artificial creation it is considered incapable of forming the requisite criminal intent. This defense has been largely overcome in recent years. Some crimes, such as rape, bigamy and murder, cannot logically be imputed to a corporation.
• The insanity defense holds that a person cannot be held liable for his criminal act if he was insane at the time of the act. The defense goes to the heart of the fundamental principle of intent, or guilty mind. If the accused did not understand what he was doing or understand that his actions were wrong, he cannot have criminal intent and without intent, there is no crime.
• The intoxication defense is similar to that of the insanity defense. It argues that the accused could not have a guilty mind due to intoxication. The fact of voluntary intoxication is generally not accepted as a defense. Involuntary intoxication produced by fraud or coercion of another may be a defense, and insanity produced by intoxicants may be acceptable. Intoxication can also be offered as evidence that an accused was incapable of forming the intent to commit a crime, e.g., the accused was too drunk to entertain the idea of breaking and entering into a house at night for the purpose of committing an offense.

Specific Defenses

• The alibi defense seeks to prove that the accused was elsewhere at the time the offense occurred.
• The compulsion or necessity defense argues that a person should not be charged with a crime when the act was committed in response to an imminent, impending and overwhelmingly coercive influence. For example, a person who is ordered to drive a getaway car under the threat of immediate death would not be punishable as a principal to the crime.
• The self-defense protection against prosecution relies on the premise that every person

has a right to defend himself from harm. The general rule is that a person may use in self-defense that force which, under all the circumstances of the case, reasonably appears necessary to prevent impending injury.

• The condonation defense is used in some rare cases where the law allows an accused to be not prosecuted if certain conditions are met. For example, a charge of seduction might be dropped if the parties involved subsequently marry.

• The immunity defense grants protection from prosecution in exchange for cooperation by the accused. The required cooperation might be a full disclosure of all facts and testimony at trial.

• The consent defense may be used when consent of the victim is involved. Where consent is offered as a defense, the consent must have been given by a person legally capable of giving it and it must be voluntary.

• The entrapment defense argues that an accused should not be charged if he was induced to commit a crime for the mere purpose of instituting criminal prosecution against him. Generally, where the criminal intent originates in the mind of the accused and the criminal offense is completed by him, the fact that a law enforcement officer furnished the accused an opportunity for commission does not constitute entrapment. But where the criminal intent originates in the mind of the officer and the accused is lured into the commission, no conviction may be had.

• The withdrawal defense may sometimes be used in a prosecution for conspiracy. A conspirator who withdraws from the conspiracy prior to commission of the requisite overt act may attempt a defense based on withdrawal.

• The good character defense may seek to offer evidence that the accused is of such good character that it was unlikely he committed the crime charged. This is not a defense as a matter of law, but an attempt to convince a jury it was improbable for the accused to have committed the crime.

• The defense of ignorance or mistake of fact argues that the accused had no criminal intent. This defense seeks to excuse the accused because he was misled or was not in possession of all facts at the time of the crime. For example, this defense might be used in a case where a homeowner injured someone who he thought was a burglar in his home but who in fact was the invited guest of another member of the family.

• The former jeopardy defense is founded on the principle that a case once terminated upon its merits should not be tried again. Double jeopardy can only be claimed when the second prosecution is brought by the same government as the first. When the act is a violation of the law as to two or more governments, the accused is regarded as having committed separate offenses.

• The statute of limitations defense seeks to prevent prosecution on the grounds that the government failed to bring charges within the period of time fixed by a particular enactment. Not all crimes have time limitations for seeking prosecution, and some crimes, such as murder and other major crimes, have no limits whatsoever. As a rule, statutes of limitations are made applicable to misdemeanors and some minor felonies.

FEDERAL CRIMES

There can be no federal crime unless Congress first makes an act a criminal offense by the passage of a statute, affixes punishment to it, and declares what court will have jurisdiction. This means that all federal crimes are statutory. Although many of the statutes are based on common law, every federal statute is an express enactment of Congress. Nearly all crimes are defined in Title 18 of the United States Code.

Generally speaking, federal crimes fall into three large areas: crimes affecting interstate commerce, crimes committed in places beyond the jurisdiction of any State, and crimes which interfere with the activities of the federal government.

• Crimes affecting interstate commerce are described in a variety of acts, e.g., the Mann Act, the Dyer Act, the Lindbergh Act, the Fugitive Felon Act, etc. They cover a wide variety of offenses over which Congress has plenary control.

• Crimes committed in places beyond the jurisdiction of any State might include, for example, murder on an American ship on the high seas or on a federal enclave such as a military reservation ceded to the United States by a State. It should be noted that when an offense, not covered by a federal statute, is committed on a federal enclave, the case can be tried in a federal court under the laws of the State where the enclave is located. The offense of murder, for example, is not defined in a federal statute. If murder occurs on a military reservation in Texas, the federal government can prosecute the case using the Texas statute covering murder. This procedure is authorized by the Assimilative Crimes Act.

• Crimes which interfere with the activities of the federal government include fraudulent use of the mails, robbery of a federal bank, violation of income tax laws, espionage and many similar offenses. Federal courts have no jurisdiction over crimes against the States, and vice versa. It can happen, however, that an offense will violate both a State law and a federal law, e.g., robbery of a federally insured State bank. In such a case, both the federal and State court will have jurisdiction.

FORESEEABILITY

This concept holds that two key factors determine an organization's liability for a crime committed against invitees on the premises. The factors are:

• whether the crime was reasonably foreseeable, and if so,
• whether there was reasonably adequate security in place to prevent the crime.

THE INTENTIONAL TORT OF INTRUSION

Interference with the right to be "let alone" can be grouped into four categories: intrusion, appropriation of one's name or likeness, giving unreasonable publicity to private facts, and placing a person in a false light in the public eye. The latter three of these are founded upon improper publicity, usually in the public press or electronic media. They are beyond the scope of this concept and will not be discussed.

Intrusion is an intentional tort closely related to infliction of emotional distress. Both torts protect a person's interest in his mental tranquility or peace of mind. Privacy is a basic right of a person to choose when and to what extent he will permit others to have knowledge of his personal affairs.

Essentially, intrusion is an intentional, improper, unreasonable, and offensive interference with the solitude, seclusion or private life of another. It embraces a broad spectrum of activities. It may consist of an unauthorized entry, an illegal search or seizure, or an unauthorized eavesdropping, with or without electronic aids.

The tort is complete when the intrusion occurs. No publication or publicity of the information obtained is required. It is, of course, essential that the intrusion be into that which is, and is entitled to remain, private.

Additionally, the harm must be substantial. The intrusion must be seriously objectionable, not simply bothersome or inconvenient.

LAW DIVISIONS

The total body of law consists of systems of rules laid down by the power of government to regulate the conduct of people in society.

The law is divided, sometimes arbitrarily, into separate sections.

With reference to its subject matter, the law is either private or public.

• Private law deals with those relations between individuals with which the government is not directly concerned. It is subdivided for practical purposes into many branches such as:
— property law.
— domestic relations law.
— trust law.
— tort law.

• Public law is that part of the law which deals with the government either by itself or in its relations with individuals. Some of its branches are:
— constitutional law.
— administrative law.
— public health law.
— vehicle and traffic law.
— criminal law.

The criminal law is one of the most important branches of public law. It is divided into two main parts: substantive and procedural.

• Substantive law defines what varying types of conduct will constitute crimes, provides for punishments, and lays down rules on such matters as the capacity of persons to commit crimes and the defenses that may be legally employed by charged persons.
• Procedural law provides the means and methods by which rights and obligations created by the criminal law are to be vindicated and enforced. In other words, procedural law defines the manner in which criminal cases are prosecuted. Whereas substantive law tells us what is just, procedural law tells us how justice is to be carried out.

MILITARY LAW

Military law consists of the rules governing military personnel as prescribed by Congress pursuant to its constitutional authority to regulate the armed forces.

Offenses against military law are found in the Uniform Code of Military Justice, Title 10 of the United States Code. Violations of rules and regulations which are merely disciplinary in nature, such as absent without leave, are not considered crimes in the usual sense of the word. Military law does, however, cover a wide range of criminal offenses. Breaches of military law are heard and determined by courts-martial.

Military persons are bound equally with civilians to strict observance of the criminal laws and are answerable to the ordinary courts for their acts.

Military law is different than martial law. Martial law is imposed during extreme emergencies that threaten public order. It is applied equally to civilians and military personnel. Martial law supersedes civil law, and the will of the military commander is supreme.

MISFEASANCE VERSUS NONFEASANCE

The law of negligence distinguishes between liability for the consequences of affirmative acts (misfeasance) and liability for merely doing nothing (nonfeasance).

Almost any inaction can be characterized as "misfeasance" if the court is so disposed, and often inaction is substantially the equivalent of active misconduct. The failure to repair defective brakes may be seen as active negligence. A fundamental question is whether there is a sufficient relationship between the one who failed to act and the one injured as a result.

A common example is the absence of a duty to go to the aid of someone needing help (when such help is not required by some pre-existing status or relationship). A person skilled in administering cardiopulmonary resuscitation is not required to aid a victim needing such assistance, unless the person happens to also be a paramedic hired for that purpose.

Duties of affirmative action which would not otherwise exist may be voluntarily assumed. It is commonly held that one who freely undertakes to render aid to another assumes a duty to act with reasonable care, and once the duty is assumed it may not be abandoned. This rule is thought by many to have the negative effect of discouraging rescuers.

MOTIVE VERSUS INTENT

Motive and intent are separate concepts in criminal law. Motive is the desire or inducement which tempts or prompts a person to do a criminal act. Intent is a person's resolve or purpose to commit the act. Motive is the reason which leads the mind to desire a certain result. Intent is the determination to achieve the result.

Motive is an important investigative consideration, but is not an essential element of a crime. Intent must be established for a crime to exist. A good motive (as might be represented in a mercy killing) does not keep an act from being a crime, and an evil motive will not necessarily make an act a crime. Furthermore, an accused would not be acquitted simply because a motive could not be discovered.

The basic urge that led the offender's mind to want the result of the forbidden act is immaterial as to guilt. Proof of motive, however, may be relevant and admissible on behalf of either side at trial. Motive can be especially pertinent where the evidence in a case is largely circumstantial.

In some statutes, proof of motive may be required.

NEGLIGENCE DEGREES

Tort law has attempted to refine the negligence concept by subdividing negligent conduct into narrower categories. Degrees of care and degrees of negligence are closely-related but separate approaches.

• Degrees of Care. The amount of care which is reasonable for a given situation depends on various factors, including the relationship between the parties and the nature and extent of the risk inherent in that situation. Transporting school children requires a higher degree of care than hauling watermelons.

• Degrees of Negligence. The notion that negligence may be classified as slight or gross is a persistent theme in tort law and criminal law. There are statutes in which the term "negligence" is preceded by some adjective, such as "slight" or "gross." In most cases, the statute applies only to a particular situation or activity.

— Slight negligence is the failure to exercise great care. It is not a slight departure from ordinary care. Technically, it is the failure to exercise greater care than the circumstances would ordinarily require.

— Gross negligence is something more than ordinary negligence but only in degree. It is less than recklessness, which is a different kind of conduct showing a conscious disregard for the safety of others. The distinction is important since contributory negligence is not a defense to wanton misconduct but is to gross negligence. A finding of reckless misconduct will usually support an award of punitive damages whereas gross negligence will not.

NEGLIGENT CONDUCT

Negligence describes that form of negligent conduct which is an element of various tort causes of action. The components of the cause of action for negligence are:

• A duty owed by the defendant to the plaintiff. More accurately, the absence of any rule limiting the general duty of ordinary care.

• A violation of that duty by defendant's

failure to conform to the required standard of conduct.
• A sufficient causal connection between the negligent conduct and the resulting harm.
• Actual loss or damage. The plaintiff's contributory negligence, if any, will reduce or defeat a claim. In many jurisdictions, contributory negligence is a defense to be pleaded and proved by the defendant, but in some jurisdictions the plaintiff must allege and prove his freedom from contributory negligence as a part of his case.

NEGLIGENT HIRING

In this concept an employer can be held directly liable for employee conduct on grounds that the employer failed to exercise reasonable care in hiring and retaining an employee who proves to be a danger to others.

Although similar to respondeat superior, this concept can extend to situations that occur outside of the workplace. Assume that during working hours a male security officer makes a date with a female employee. During the date (off the employer's premises and during non-working hours) the security officer rapes the other employee. She learns that the employer was aware that this same security officer had assaulted other women whom he had met at work, but had hired him anyway without warning her or other female employees. The employer can be charged with failure to exercise reasonable care in the hiring and retention of a dangerous employee.

PARTIES TO CRIME

The parties to a felony crime fall into four categories:

Principals in the First Degree

Generally, a principal in the first degree is the actual offender who commits the act. If the offender uses an agent to commit the act for him, he is still a principal in the first degree. There may be more than one principal in the first degree for the same offense.

Principals in the Second Degree

A principal in the second degree is one who, with knowledge of what is afoot, aids and abets the principal in the first degree at the very time the felony is being committed by rendering aid, assistance or encouragement. A principal in the second degree is typically at the crime scene, nearby or situated in such a way as to render assistance. Under the concept of "constructive presence," a principal in the second degree could be a considerable distance removed from the crime while it is being committed. An example might be a lookout who monitors police radio communications at a remote location and calls his burglar accomplices at the crime scene to alert them of police patrol movements.

Accessories Before the Fact

An accessory before the fact is a person who, before the time a crime is committed, knows of the particular offense contemplated, assents to or approves of it, and expresses his view of it in a form which operates to encourage the principal to perform the deed. There is a close resemblance between an accessory before the fact and a principal in the second degree. The difference relates to where the accessory was and the nature of the assistance rendered at the time the crime was committed. If a person advises, encourages and gives aid prior to the act but is not present at the act and not giving aid at the time of the act, he would be regarded as an accessory before the fact.

Accessories After the Fact

An accessory after the fact is a person who, knowing that a person has committed a felony, subsequently aids the felon to escape in any way or prevents his arrest and prosecution. He may help the felon elude justice by concealing, sheltering or comforting the felon while he is a fugitive, or by supplying him with the means of escape or by destroying evidence. An accessory after the fact must have an intention to assist the felon and must actually do so. Mere knowledge of the felon's offense and a failure to report it does not make a person an accessory after the fact.

PRELIMINARY CRIMES

There are three crimes which are preparatory in nature and serve as part of a larger purpose. Each of them is a means of reaching a criminal end. These so-called preliminary crimes are: solicitation, attempt, and conspiracy.

• Solicitation consists of the offender's oral or written efforts to activate another person to commit a criminal offense. The essence of the crime is to incite by counsel, enticement or inducement. The offense of solicitation is complete if the offender merely urges another to violate the law and otherwise does nothing himself.
• Attempt has two elements. First, there must

be a specific intent to commit a particular offense, and second, there must be a direct ineffectual overt act toward its commission. There must be some act moving directly toward the act. Mere preparation, such as obtaining tools or weapons, may be insufficient to establish the crime, especially when made at a distance in time or place.

• Conspiracy is the combination of two or more persons working in some concerted action to accomplish some criminal or unlawful purpose, or to accomplish some purpose in a criminal or unlawful manner. If there is a common understanding among the participants to achieve a certain purpose or to act in a certain way, a conspiracy exists without regard to whether there is any formal or written statement of purpose, or even though there is no actual speaking of words. There may be merely a tacit understanding without any express agreement.

PRIVATE SEARCH

This concept holds that:

• searches undertaken by private persons are not subject to constitutional regulation.
• the Bill of Rights, including the Fourth Amendment, apply only to actions of the federal government.
• the unlawfulness of a private search is irrelevant to the issue of a defendant's entitlement to an exclusionary remedy in criminal proceedings.
• a wrongful search or seizure conducted by a private party does not deprive the government of the right to use evidence it has acquired lawfully.

PUNISHMENT PURPOSES

The purposes of punishment allowed in the criminal law are reformation, restraint, retribution, and deterrence.

• Reformation is regarded by many criminologists as the most worthwhile goal of punishment. The real criticism of reformation, however, is simply that it hasn't worked. This criticism is supported by much evidence. It can be persuasively argued that the very nature of the prison system is contradictory to reformation.
• Restraint is not a debatable proposition. It is necessary to protect society from unreformed criminals. One argument suggests that restraint should be either permanent (life imprisonment) or be coupled with meaningful rehabilitation. The force in this argument is that the penal system should attempt to both

reform and restrain rather than merely keep criminals in custody.

• Retribution is frequently challenged as a proper purpose of punishment. Opponents contend it is barbaric and inappropriate for a civilized society. Proponents contend it is morally correct to hate criminals and to inflict retribution upon them for their misdeeds. Whether retribution is or is not morally justifiable, most citizens demand it in some fashion. Some experts point out that in the absence of institutionalized retribution there is a danger that people will seek private revenge against criminals.
• Deterrence aims at precluding further criminal activity by a defendant. The concept holds that positive sanctions imposed upon one convicted criminal will deter others with similar propensities.

THE REASONABLE PERSON CONCEPT

In judging whether conduct is negligent, the law applies objective standards of reasonableness. The law does not make special allowance for the particular weaknesses of the person acting negligently. Conduct which creates an unreasonable risk of harm is no less dangerous because the actor lacked the capacity to conform to an acceptable level of performance. While it may seem unfair to hold some people to standards they cannot always meet, it would be more unjust to require the innocent victims of substandard conduct to bear the consequences.

The standard is usually stated as "ordinary care" or "due care" or "reasonable care" measured against the hypothetical conduct of a hypothetical person, i.e., the reasonable man of ordinary prudence.

The reasonable person is not the average or typical person, but an idealized image. He is a composite of the community's judgment as to how the typical citizen ought to behave in circumstances where there is a potential or actual risk of harm.

The reasonable person is not perfect or infallible. He is allowed mistakes of judgment, of perception, and he may even be momentarily distracted. Above all, he is human and prone to errors, but such errors must have been reasonable or excusable under the circumstances.

RESPONDEAT SUPERIOR

Respondeat superior means "let the superior reply." The concept holds the master (employer) responsible for the acts of the servant (employee). It is based on the doctrine that the employee is acting on the employer's behalf as the employer's agent. Another term used in this connection is "vicarious liability," so called because the employer assumes liability for acts performed by someone else.

The courts have developed over the years a doctrine of time, place and purpose. If the employee's harmful conduct occurred during the employee's normal working hours at a place considered appropriate for the job, and if it resulted from an act whose purpose was to serve the employer's interest, then there is a legal basis for holding the employer accountable under respondeat superior.

For example, if a security officer on duty at his employer's premises uses excessive force to capture an intruder, the employer could be held liable on the basis of time (normal working hours), place (employer's premises), and purpose (serving the employer's interests).

A related doctrine is ratification. An employee may have injured someone outside the scope of employment, but if the employer knows about it and in some fashion indicates approval, there can be grounds for imposing liability.

SECTION 1983 SUIT

As gathered from the law (Section 1983 of Title 42, USC, called "Civil Action for Deprivation of Civil Rights") and from court decisions, four elements must be present for the suit to succeed.

• The defendant must be a natural person (not a company or corporation) or a local government.
• The defendant must be acting under color of law.
• The violation must be of a constitutional or a federally protected right as opposed to a state protected right.
• The violation must reach constitutional level.

STRICT LIABILITY

In criminal law the general requirement is that a crime must have an external physical act coupled with an internal mental intent. However, there are some statutory offenses where this doctrine is not applied. They are found in the regulatory areas of public health, safety and welfare which categorically forbid certain acts and omissions without regard to the offender's state of mind.

These strict liability statutes are based on a view that it is in the best interests of the community to place the burden upon individuals to act or not act at their own peril. Even though a person might not intentionally do or fail to do something, there is no one else in a better position to prevent the violation. Whether a violator acted intentionally or with knowledge of wrongdoing is immaterial to the question of guilt.

Strict liability statutes usually carry relatively light penalties, offenders are not generally regarded as criminals in the true sense of the word, and mitigating circumstances are frequently taken into account in assessing penalties.

Examples of strict liability offenses are failure to comply with motor vehicle regulations, food handling violations, alcohol dispensing violations, noncompliance with fish and game laws, licensing violations, etc.

TORT LAW PURPOSES

Tort law has three main purposes:

• To compensate persons who sustain a loss as a result of another's conduct.
• To place the cost of that compensation on those responsible for the loss.
• To prevent future harms and losses.

Compensation is predicated on the idea that losses, both tangible and intangible, can be measured in money.

If a loss-producing event is a matter of pure chance, the fairest way to relieve the victim of the burden is insurance or governmental compensation. But where a particular person can be identified as responsible for the creation of the risk, it becomes more just to impose the loss on the responsible person (tortfeasor) than to allow it to remain on the victim or the community at large.

The third major purpose of tort law is to prevent future torts by regulating human behavior. In concept, the tortfeasor held liable for damages will be more careful in the future, and the general threat of tort liability serves as an incentive to all persons to regulate their conduct appropriately. In this way, tort law supplements criminal law.

ORGANIZATIONAL CONCEPTS

ACTION RESEARCH

Action research is the process of systematically collecting research data about an ongoing system relative to:

• some objective, goal or need of the system.
• feeding the collected data back into the system.
• taking actions by altering selected variables within the system based both on the data and on hypotheses.
• evaluating the results of actions by collecting more data.

ASSESSMENT CENTER MODEL

The term assessment center does not refer to a place, but to the process by which employees are evaluated so that they may be given appropriate training and development assignments. The process typically involves placing the subject under intense observation in a variety of simulations and stress situations over a period of several days. (See Figure 5.)

CAREER NEGOTIATION

Career negotiation is that point in an individ-

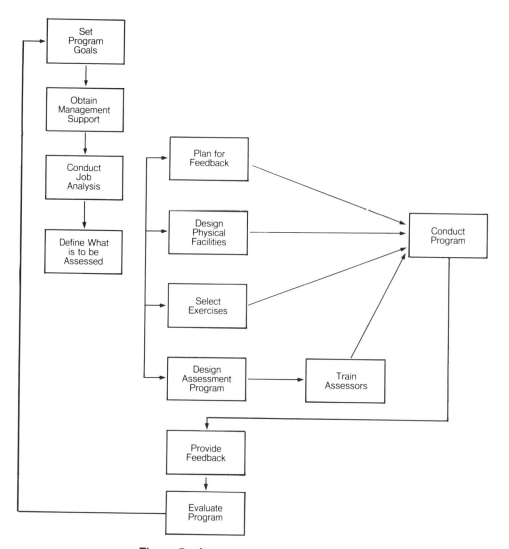

Figure 5   Assessment center model

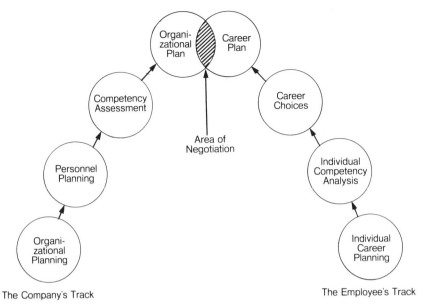

Figure 6   Career negotiation

ual's career where he/she and the organization, in the light of their respective interests and needs, develop or negotiate a career plan that serves both parties. (See Figure 6.)

DECISION TREE CONCEPT

A decision tree is a graphic technique for presenting decision alternatives so that the various risks, information needs and courses of action are visually available to the decisonmaker. (See Figure 7.)

The various decisional alternatives are displayed in the form of a tree with nodes and branches. Each branch represents an alternative course of action or decision, leading to a node which represents an event.

Thus, a decision tree shows both the courses of action available as well as their possible outcomes.

The steps in constructing a decision tree are:

• Identify the points of decision and alternatives available at each point.
• Identify the points of uncertainty and the type or range of alternative outcomes at each point.
• Estimate the values needed to make the analysis, especially the probabilities of different events or results of action and the costs and gains of various events and actions.
• Analyze the alternative values to choose a course of action.

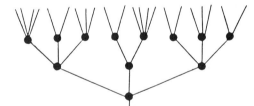

Figure 7   Decision tree

DELPHI TECHNIQUE

The Delphi Technique is a methodology that pieces together various opinions in order to arrive at a consensus on the probability of a future event. The concept involves:

• asking various informed individuals or groups as to their opinions concerning a possible future event.
• evaluating the responses by one or more factors such as the respondents'
— relative importance or influence on the situation.
— expertise or understanding of the situation.
— past forecasting accuracy.
• calculating from the aggregate of opinions an event probability.

FATIGUE CURVE

A fatigue curve is a graphic presentation of

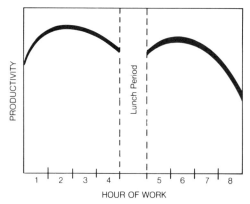

Figure 8   Fatigue curve

productivity increases and decreases influenced by fatigue. (See Figure 8.) As workers get settled into their job tasks, productivity increases; thereafter fatigue sets in and productivity drops off. After coffee breaks or lunch, productivity may rise slightly, but thereafter continue to decline to the end of the day. The pattern varies with different kinds of work and organizational settings.

A monotony factor can be present. It is usually observable as a productivity drop in the middle of the work period, with a tendency to show a spurt of productivity at the end due to a feeling of relief that the work period is almost over.

GANTT CHART

The Gantt Chart was developed during World War I by Henry L. Gantt. It is a planning and control document which graphically presents work planned and work done in relation to each other and in their relation to time. A chart which uses this concept to compare planned and actual progress on a time continuum could be called a Gantt Chart. (See Figure 9.)

HUMAN RESOURCES ACCOUNTING

In this concept employees are viewed as capital assets similar to plant and equipment. The cost of replacing an employee can be computed as shown in Figure 10.

JOHARI WINDOW

The Johari Window model is used as a visual aid for explaining the concepts of interpersonal feedback and disclosure. (See Figure 11.) The model consists of four quadrants.

• The first quadrant is the public self. It contains knowledge known to the individual and others.
• The second quadrant is the blind self. It contains knowledge known to others and unknown to the individual.
• The third quadrant is the private self. It contains all of those things that an individual keeps secret.
• The fourth quadrant is the unknown area. It contains information that neither the individual nor others know.

LAW OF EFFECT

This is a fundamental concept in learning theory which holds that, all other things being equal, an animal (person) will learn those habits leading to satisfaction and will not learn (or learn with greater difficulty) those habits leading to dissatisfaction.

LAW OF THE SITUATION

In this concept one person should not give orders to another person, but both should agree to take their action cues (orders) from

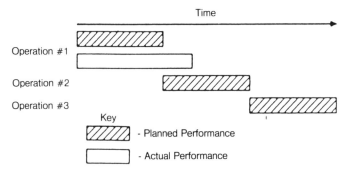

Figure 9   Gantt chart concept (simplified)

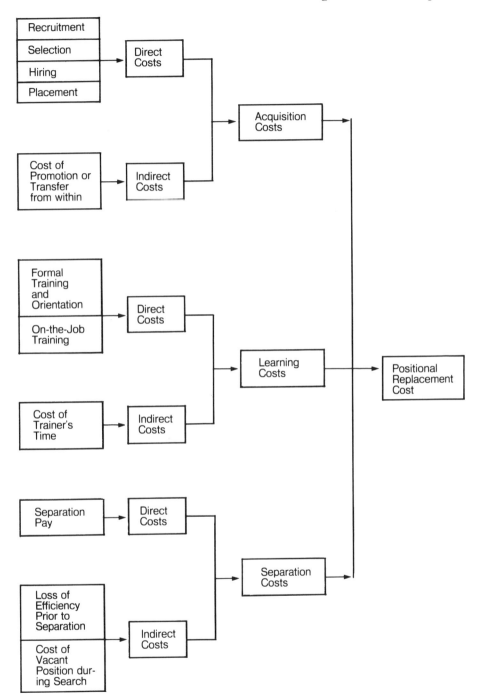

Figure 10   Model for measurement of human resource replacement costs

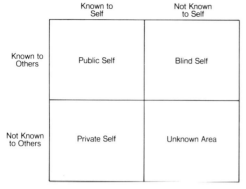

	Known to Self	Not Known to Self
Known to Others	Public Self	Blind Self
Not Known to Others	Private Self	Unknown Area

Figure 11   Johari window

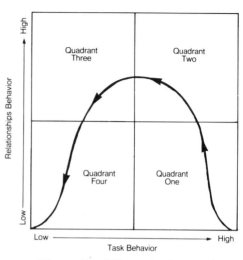

Figure 12   Life cycle theory of leadership

the situation. To the extent that workers will accept the notion that orders are simply part of the situation, the question of someone giving and someone taking orders does not come up.

LIFE CYCLE THEORY

This is a concept of leadership which holds that the appropriate management style for a particular situation should be primarily dependent upon the maturity level of the employee. (See Figure 12.)

Maturity is defined as a function of the employee's general level of education, experience, motivation, desire to work, and willingness to accept responsibility.

Leadership is seen as a combination of two types of behavior: directive and supportive.

If an employee is assessed to be immature, the theory suggests that the manager's supervisory style should be high in directive behavior and low in supportive behavior. As the employee matures, the manager's behavior should shift to low direction and high support.

LIKERT SCALE

Theough this concept, management can obtain useful feedback concerning employee perceptions of the organization. The Likert Scale (named for Rensis Likert) presents a respondent with a statement calling for a reaction/opinion in one of five or more possible responses. for example,

The vacation benefits of this company are not generous enough.

1. strongly agree
2. agree
3. no opinion
4. disagree
5. strongly disagree

My supervisor is a good leader.

1. strongly agree
2. agree
3. agree somewhat
4. not sure
5. disagree somewhat
6. disagree
7. strongly disagree

MANAGERIAL GRID

The managerial grid is an organizational development measurement tool. It evaluates a manager in terms of how he balances the needs of production with the needs of employees.

The grid has 81 blocks: 9 blocks on the horizontal axis represent concern for production; and 9 blocks on the vertical axis represent concern for people.

Respondents who score the grid can place themselves (or others) in one of the blocks, as shown in Figure 13.

MANAGERIAL OPERATIONS (POSDCORB)

Classical management theory holds that managers carry out their responsibilities by performing tasks associated with the functions of planning, organizing, staffing, directing, coordinating, record keeping, and budgeting. The first letters of the functions form the acronym POSDCORB.

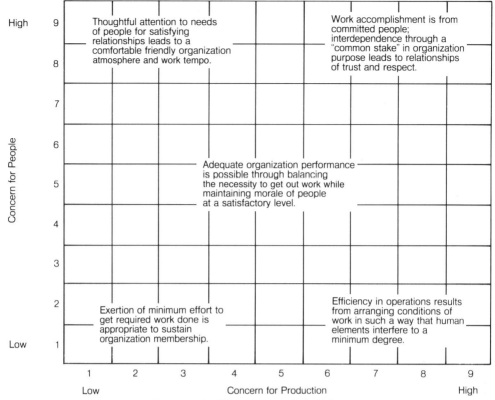

High 9

Thoughtful attention to needs of people for satisfying relationships leads to a comfortable friendly organization atmosphere and work tempo.

Work accomplishment is from committed people; interdependence through a "common stake" in organization purpose leads to relationships of trust and respect.

Adequate organization performance is possible through balancing the necessity to get out work while maintaining morale of people at a satisfactory level.

Exertion of minimum effort to get required work done is appropriate to sustain organization membership.

Efficiency in operations results from arranging conditions of work in such a way that human elements interfere to a minimum degree.

Concern for People

Low

Low   Concern for Production   High

Figure 13   The managerial grid

• Planning is a continuous process that involves gathering information, analyzing the information, and developing a problem statement. Goals are established which address the problem.

• Organizing is the process of creating an organizational structure consistent with the achievement of established goals.

• Staffing is the function of identifying, selecting and assigning human beings to the positions that make up the organizational structure.

• Directing is to apply the organization's resources to the achievement of established goals. The resources are both human and non-human. Directing implies policies, procedures, training, continuous evaluation, and the use of positive and negative incentives to influence the workforce.

• Coordinating is the process of insuring that the various groups and sub-groups of the organization are working toward the same goals, in harmony, and cost-effectively.

• Record keeping is the maintenance of information in useful and meaningful formats.

It is not simply the retention of all information, but of information that has a known or potential value. This process also implies that kept data is to be shared with other managed groups.

• Budgeting is the preparation of a request for resources to carry out plans, programs and projects already decided upon. A budget covers a specific period, usually one year.

THE MECHANISTIC ORGANIZATION

This is a form of organizational structure suitable under stable conditions. (See Figure 14.) It is characterized by:

• a high degree of task differentiation and specialization with a precise delineation of rights and responsibilities.

• a high degree of reliance on the traditional hierarchical structure.

• a tendency for the top of the hierarchy to control all incoming and outgoing communications.

• an emphasis on vertical interactions between superiors and subordinates.

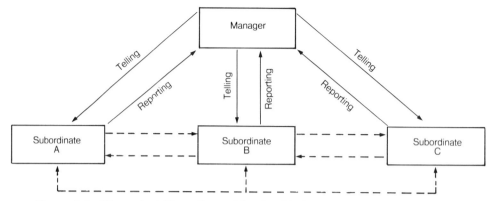

Figure 14 Characteristic pattern of leadership in a mechanistic system

- a demand for loyalty to the organization and to superiors.
- a greater importance placed on internal (local) knowledge, experience and skill, as opposed to more general (cosmopolitan) knowledge, experience and skill.

MOTIVATION-HYGIENE THEORY

Frederick Herzberg is the principal architect of a theory which holds that five factors are the chief determinants of job satisfaction: achievement, recognition, the work itself, responsibility, and advancement.

Factors associated with job dissatisfaction were empirically observed to be company policy and administration, supervision, salary, interpersonal relations and working conditions.

The use of the term hygiene in the title of the theory derives from job-content satisfiers such as achievement, advancement and responsibility. The term hygiene is analogous to the medical use of hygiene to control conditions in the environment.

NEEDS HIERARCHY

Abraham Maslow's concept of human needs asserts that humans have five sets of goals or needs arranged in a hierarchy of prepotency:

- physiological needs.
- safety needs.
- love or affiliation needs.
- esteem needs.
- the need for self-actualization.

Once lower needs are satisfied they cease to be motivators of behavior. Conversely, higher needs cannot motivate until lower needs are satisfied.

THE ORGANIC ORGANIZATION

This is a form of organizational structure suitable for operating under unstable, changing conditions. (See Figure 15.) It is characterized by:

- Constant reassessment of tasks, assignments and the use of organizational expertise.
- Authority, control and communications are frequently exercised on an ad hoc basis depending upon specific commitments and tasks.
- Communications and interactions between members are both very open and extensive.
- Leadership that stresses consultation and group decisional processes.
- Greater commitment to the organization's tasks and goals than to traditional hierarchical loyalty.

PAY SATISFACTION

Pay satisfaction is affected by the difference between pay and the person's belief about what his pay should be. If employees find themselves assuming substantially similar duties and responsibilities as co-workers who, because of seniority or education, have higher paying classifications, they are going to be dissatisfied with their pay. (See Figure 16.)

It is very difficult to convince employees that their pay is determined fairly if they have before them on a daily basis other more highly paid employees who serve not as role models that one should strive to emulate, but as glaring examples of the inequities of the pay program.

PROGRAM EVALUATION AND REVIEW TECHNIQUE (PERT)

PERT is an approach to planning, organizing, directing, coordinating, and controlling the

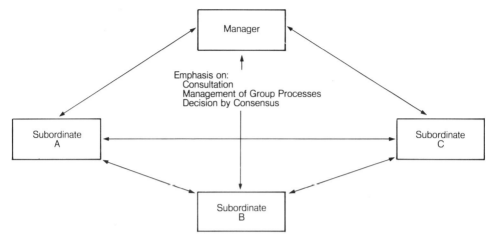

Figure 15   Characteristic pattern of leadership in an organic system

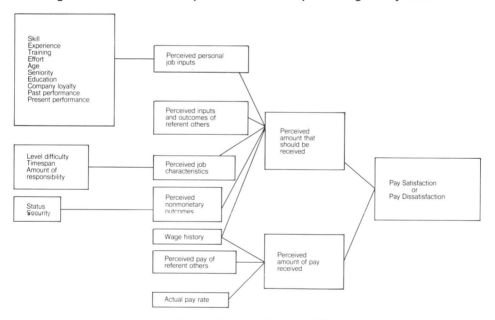

Figure 16   Determinants of pay satisfaction

work efforts required to achieve an established goal. Typically, PERT is used in projects of finite duration, such as the design of
a security system or the installation of alarms.

PERT helps management identify and correct problems that arise during a project. The
chief value of the technique is the information
that it generates concerning a project's current status. The project manager uses the
generated information in exercising control of
project activities.

The PERT methodology requires an identification of events that must be passed through
in order to complete the project. The events
represent clusters of work tasks that must be
performed according to established specifications. The tasks are delineated as to sequence, timing, and in some cases, costs. A
PERT chart will depict in a graphical format
the project's planned chain of events, the
work activities, and time/cost of getting from
event to event.

PSYCHOLOGICAL CONTRACT

The concept of a psychological contract holds that the individual has a variety of expectations of the organization and that the organization has a variety of expectations of him. These expectations not only cover how much work is to be performed for how much pay, but also involve the whole pattern of rights, privileges and obligations between worker and employer. For example, the worker may expect the company not to fire him after he has worked there for a certain number of years and the company may expect the worker will uphold the company's public image by adhering to a particular lifestyle. Expectations such as these are not written into any formal agreement between employee and employer, yet they operate powerfully as determinants of behavior.

SECURITY COST-BENEFIT RELATIONSHIP

A security system seeks reasonable, but not absolute assurance that its objectives will be accomplished. While security aims at preventing and detecting losses, absolute prevention and detection is costly and most probably impossible to achieve. Since controls have a cost in both time and money, management must always make economic judgments as to whether a further degree of risk reduction is worth the cost of providing it.

The security cost-benefit relationship is affected by these circumstances:

• That the level of acceptable risk is arrived at through a subjective process.
• That the costs of particular security controls are not always measurable in dollars.
• That the benefits of security controls are especially difficult to measure, if they can be measured at all.
• That subjective knowledge, experience, specific industry and business conditions, management style and similar factors will usually and improperly influence the selection of security controls.

SKILLS INVENTORY PROGRAM

A skills inventory program is the comprehensive collection and examination of data on the workforce to determine the composition and level of employees' skills, knowledges and abilities so that they can be more fully utilized and/or developed to fill the staffing needs of the organization.

To be useful, skills data must be arranged in such a manner that the information gathered can be readily accessible for management use. (See Figure 17.)

SPAN OF CONTROL

Span of control is usually expressed as the number of subordinates that a manager should supervise. Studies support an assertion that a supervisor can be effective in handling from 3 to 6 subordinates.

As the number of subordinates increases arithmetically, the number of possible interpersonal interactions increases geometrically.

THEORY X AND THEORY Y

Douglas McGregor describes contrasting sets of assumptions made by managers about the people they direct.

Theory X holds that:

• the average human being has an inherent dislike of work and will avoid it if possible.
• because people inherently dislike work, they must be coerced, controlled and threatened with punishment to get them to put forth adequate effort toward the achievement of company objectives.
• the average human being prefers to be directed, wishes to avoid responsibility, has relatively little ambition, and wants security above all.

Theory Y holds that:

• the expenditure of physical and mental effort in work is as natural as play and rest.
• external control, and the threat of punishment are not the only means for bringing about effort toward company objectives.
• commitment to objectives is a function of the rewards associated with their achievement. The most significant types of rewards are ego satisfaction and self-actualization.
• the average human being will learn, under proper conditions, not only to accept but to seek responsibility.
• the human capacity to exercise a relatively high degree of imagination, ingenuity and creativity in the solution of company problems is widely, not narrowly, distributed in the population.
• under the conditions of modern industrial life, the intellectual potentialities of the average human being are only partially utilized.

TIME MANAGEMENT

Time management experts often say that people tend to spend about 80 percent of their time on tasks that produce 20 percent of the results. Too many people work diligently on

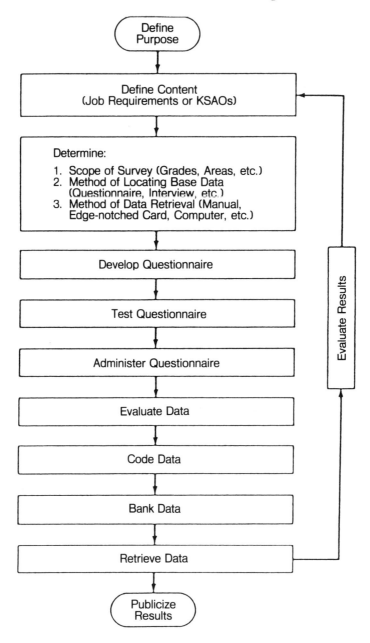

Source: U.S. Civil Service Commission, *The Skills Survey: What It Is and How It Works* (Washington, D.C.: U.S. Government Printing Office, October 1977), p. 24.

Figure 17 Skills survey process flow chart

low-value activities. The activities may make the worker feel a sense of accomplishment, but they are not significantly productive. Techniques that have been found to be effective in raising productivity include the following.

• Determine the time of day you are most productive and schedule your important work during those hours.
• Keep a log of how you spend your time. If the log shows wasted time and lack of self-discipline in how you apply yourself, develop a schedule and stick to it until it becomes a habit.
• Keep a calendar, preferably covering a week at a time, and plan your activities. Try to schedule the important activities during your most productive hours.
• Do similar tasks at one time. For example, make all of your telephone calls or write all of your letters at one sitting. Do the routine tasks during your least productive hours.
• Identify work you are presently doing which can be done by subordinates. Delegate that work.
• When you are traveling or waiting for an appointment, catch up on your routine tasks, such as figuring your expense account or reading trade literature.
• Resist the urge to read the mail the instant it arrives. Save it for the least productive hours.
• Control the flow of paperwork. Keep your records simple and look for ways to streamline.
• Don't call meetings that are unnecessary and avoid attending unproductive meetings.
• Establish quiet times for planning and thinking.
• Attach priorities to tasks. Do not spend more time on a project than it is worth.

• Make notes of things that need to be done. Prioritize and do them as you find time.
• Hold your unscheduled and social visits to a minimum.
• When a subordinate brings you a problem, expect him to also present a suggested solution.
• Do a job right the first time so you don't have to do it again.

TRANSACTIONAL ANALYSIS

Transactional analysis (TA) is an approach to psychotherapy first developed by Eric Berne.

TA defines the basic unit of social intercourse as a transaction. Transactions emanate from three ego states: parent, adult and child. A transactional stimulus is any action that consciously or unconsciously acknowledges the presence of other individuals.

The transactions between individuals can be classified as complementary, crossed, simple or ulterior, based upon the response that an individual receives to a stimulus.

The TA framework can be used to help managers assess the nature and effectiveness of their interpersonal behavior. By concentrating on developing adult-to-adult transactions, a manager may eliminate many of the "games people play" in work situations.

ZONE OF ACCEPTANCE

In this concept, authority in an organization stems from the bottom up and is based on a willingness of subordinates to hold in abeyance their own critical faculties and accept the directives of superiors.

The zone of acceptance is a theoretical range of tolerance within which organizational members will accept orders without question.

APPENDICES

TERRORIST GROUPS

This list contains the names of organizations believed to be responsible either by claim or attribution for terrorist acts. Some acts may have occurred without the approval or even the foreknowledge of the leaders of the organizations identified.

Certain of the claims of responsibility are probably false. Some of the names listed may be fictional ones invented by persons or organizations not wishing to accept responsibility for particular actions or by criminals or mentally disturbed persons for their own purposes. In some cases, the group names listed may be merely different English versions of the same group names. In other cases, organizations may have claimed credit for, or have been blamed for, actions they did not take.

The inclusion of any group should not be interpreted as an evaluation of that group's goals, motives or policies.

Name of Group	Also Known as	Place of Origin or Operating Location
Abu Nidal Group		Iraq
Acilciler		Turkey
Action Directe		France
Action Front of National Socialists	ANS	West Germany
Action Group for Communism		Portugal
Afghan Collective		Undetermined
African National Congress	ANC	South Africa
Ahwaz Liberation Front		Palestine
Alacran	Scorpion	Cuba
Albanian National Democratic Organization		Albania
Al Jihad al Islami	Islamic Holy War	Lebanon
Al Jihad al Jadid		Egypt
Al Sadr Brigade		Lebanon
Al Saiqua		Palestine
Al Zulfiqar		Pakistan
American Indian Movement		US
Ananda Marg		India
Andreas Baader Brigade		West Germany
Angels		Philippines
Anti-Communist Latin American Army		Cuba
American Army Anti-Fascist Movement		Undetermined
Anti-Imperialist Fighters for a Free Palestine		Palestine
Anti-Imperialist Group		Italy
Anti-Imperialist Resistance Group of 4 May 1979		West Germany
Anti-Terrorist Liberation Group		Spain
April 2nd Movement		Argentina
April 6th Liberation		Philippines
April 19 Movement	M-19	Colombia
Arab Communist Organization		Palestine
Arab National Action Organization		Worldwide
Arab Nationalist Youth Organization for the Liberation of Palestine		Palestine
Arab People		Saudi Arabia
Arab Revolutionary Brigades		Iraq
Arab Revolutionary Movement		Palestine
Arab Socialist Unifiers		Undetermined

Name of Group	Also Known as	Place of Origin or Operating Location
Argentine Liberation Front		Argentina
Armed Arab Struggle		Undetermined
Armed Forces of National Liberation	FALN	Puerto Rico
Armed Forces of National Liberation		Venezuela
Armed People's Revolutionary Army	ORPA	Guatemala
Armed Proletarian Nuclei		Italy
Armed Proletarian Power		Italy
Armed Radical Groups for Communism		Italy
Armed Resistance Unit	ARU	US
Armed Revolutionary Forces	FAR	Guatemala
Armed Revolutionary Nuclei		Italy
Armed Revolutionary Party of the People		El Salvador
Armed Struggle of the Communist Party		Peru
Armenian Liberation Army		Armenia
Armenian Liberation Front		Armenia
Armenian Secret Army for the Liberation of Armenia	ASALA	Armenia
Army of National Liberation	ELN	Undetermined
ASEAN Moslem Liberation Front		Southeast Asia
Autonomous Anti-Capitalist Commandos		Spain; France
Autonomous Intervention Collective		France
Autonomous Resistance		Greece
Autonomy Front		The Netherlands
Avengers of the Armenian Genocide		Armenia
Azad Hind Sena		India
Baader-Meinhof Gang		West Germany
Bande des Rats	Rat Pack	Soviet Union
Bandera Roja		Venezuela
Basque Anti-Capitalist Autonomous Commandos		Spain; France
Basque Battalion		Spain; France
Basque Fatherland and Liberty	ETA	Spain; France
Basutoland Congress Party		Lesotho
Batallon Vasco Espanol		Spain
Bakunin-Gdansk-Paris-Guatemala-Salvador		Undetermined
Bazargan Brigades		Undetermined
Black Argus		US
Black Block		West Germany
Black Brigade		Liberia
Black Crescent		Undetermined
Black December Movement		Undetermined
Black Guerilla Family		US
Black June Organization	BJO	Palestine
Black Liberation Army	BLA	US

Name of Group	Also Known as	Place of Origin or Operating Location
Black March Organization	BMO	Palestine
Black September Organization		Palestine
Black Workers Congress		US
Benchella Column		France
C-4		US; Cuba
Caribbean Revolutionary Alliance		Undetermined
Carlos Apparat		Undetermined
Carlos Aguero Echeverria Command		Costa Rica
Casa Cuba		US
Casa El Salvador		US
Casa Farabundo Marti		US
Catalan Socialist Party for National Liberation		Spain
Cayetano Carpio Movement		El Salvador
Central African Movement of National Liberation	MCLN	Central Africa
Charles Martel Group		Undetermined
Charter 77		Czechoslovakia
Christos Kassimis Group		Greece
Chukaku-ha	Nucleus Faction	Japan
Cinchoneros		Honduras
Coalition of National Liberation Brigades		Haiti
Combatants for Communism		Italy
Commanda Benno Ohnesborg		West Germany
Commandos for Revolutionary Solidarity		Costa Rica
Committee for Revolutionary Integration		Venezuela
Communist Fighting Nuclei		Italy
Communist Labor Organization		Lebanon
Communist Patrols for Territorial Counter-power		Italy
Condor		Undetermined
Confederation of Iranian Students-National Union	CISNU	Iran
Coordination of United Revolutionary Organizations	CORU	Cuba
Croatian Freedom Fighters		Croatia
Croatian National Liberation Front		Croatia
Croatian National Liberation Army in Germany		Croatia
Croatian National Resistance		Croatia
Cuban Action Communists		Cuba
Dawa		Lebanon
Democratic Front for the Liberation of Palestine	DFLP	Palestine
Dev Sol	Revolutionary Left	Turkey
Direct Action Group, Section Belgium		Belgium
Dominican Popular Movement		Dominican Republic
Eagles of the Palestine Revolution		Palestine
El Condor		Cuba

Name of Group	Also Known as	Place of Origin or Operating Location
El Poder Cubano		Cuba
Eritrean Liberation Forces		Eritrea
Ethiopian Socialist Movement		Ethiopia
Extraparliamentary Group for Communism		Italy
Eylem Birligi Faction	United for Action	Turkey
Farabundo Marti Popular Liberation Front		El Salvador
Fatah		Palestine
Fatah Revolutionary Front		Palestine
Fedayeen of the Iraqi People		Iraq
Fidas Besa Bes		Albania
Fighting Communist Cells		Belgium
Fighting Unit for Communism		Italy
First of August Group		West Germany
First of October Group of Anti-Fascist Resistance		Spain
Forcas Populares de April 25	FP-25	Portugal
Free Arabia		Undetermined
Free Nasserite Revolutionaries		Lebanon; Palestine
Frente Revolucionaria Anti-Fascista y Patriotica	FRAP	Spain
Front for the Liberation of Aceh from Sumatra		Indonesia
Front for the Liberation of Angola		Angola
Front for the Liberation of Lebanon from Foreigners		Lebanon
Front for the Liberation of the Enclave of Cabinda	FLEC	Cabinda
Front Line	Prima Linea	Italy
GRAPO		Spain
Greek Anti-Dictatorial Youth		Greece
Greek Armed Group for the Support of the North Ireland Struggle		Greece
Greek Military Resistance		Greece
Greek People		Greece
Group 15		Armenia
Group of Martyrs of Issam Sartawi		Palestine
Grupo Arabe Palestino		Bolivia
Gruppo Internazionalista		Italy
Guadeloupe Liberation Army		Guadeloupe
Guerilla Army of the Poor	EGP	Guatemala
Guerilla Resistance Unit	GRU	US
Guerillas of Christ the King		Spain
Gush Emunim		Israel
Hector Riobe Brigade		Haiti
Halkin Kurtulusum	People's Liberation	Turkey
Holy War	Islamic Jihad	Lebanon
Imam Musa Sadr Command of the Black Brigades		Lebanon
Independent Revolutionary Armed Command		Puerto Rico

Name of Group	Also Known as	Place of Origin or Operating Location
International Brigade Against Repression in Europe		Italy
International Communist Brigade, Command Che Guevara		Undetermined
International Revolutionary Movement		Worldwide
Iranian People's Fedayee Guerillas	OIPFG	Iran
Iranian Peoples Strugglers		Iran
Iranian Students Assn		Iran
Iraqi Democratic Front		Iraq
Iraqi Islamic Action		Iraq
Iraqi Liberation Army Command		Iraq
Iraqi Liberation Army-General Command		Iraq
Iraultza		Spain
Irish National Liberation Army INLA		N. Ireland
Irish Republican Army	IRA	Ireland
Islamic Amal		Iraq
Islamic Amal		Lebanon
Islamic Call Party	ICP	Iraq
Islamic Call		Lebanon
Islamic Dawa Party		Iraq
Islamic Front for the Liberation of Bahrain		Bahrain
Islamic Guerillas of America	IGA	US
Islamic Holy War		Spain; Saudi Arabia
Islamic Jihad		Iraq
Islamic Jihad		Lebanon
Islamic Revolutionary Guard		Undetermined
Islamic Revolutionary Organization in the Arabian Peninsula		Saudi Arabia
Islamic Struggle Organization		Lebanon
January 31 Popular Front	FP-31	Guatemala
Japanese Red Army		Japan
Jewish Armed Resistance		US
Jewish Brigades		Israel
Jewish Committee of Concern		Israel
Jewish Defense League		Israel
John Brown Anti-Klan Committee	JBAKC	US
Juan Rayo Guerillas		Honduras
July 14th Movement		Iraq
Justice Commandos of the Armenian Genocide	JCAG	Armenia
Justice for Palestine Organization		Undetermined
Kakurokyo	Revolutionary Workers Assn	Japan
Karen National Union		Burma
Kexel-Hepp		West Germany
Kurdish Liberation Army		Iran
Kurdish Workers Party		Kurdistan
Latin American Anti-Communist Army		Cuba

Name of Group	Also Known as	Place of Origin or Operating Location
Lebanese Armed Revolutionary Faction	LARF	Undetermined
Lebanese Cedar Force to Free Lebanon from Lebanese Terrorists		Lebanon
Lebanese Liberation		Lebanon
Lebanese Revolutionary Guard		Lebanon
Left Acapulco Guerillas		Mexico
Liberal Nasserite Organization		Lebanon
Liberation Army of Kurdistan		Kurdistan
Liberation Movement of the Central African People	MLPC	Central Africa
Libyan Revolutionary Committee		Libya
Lorenzo Zelaya People's Revolutionary Command		Honduras
Luis Boitel Commandos		Cuba
Makhons Anarchist Army		Undetermined
Manuel Rodriguez Patriotic Front	FPMR	Chile
Martyr Arif Basari Command		Iraq
Marxist-Leninist Armed Propaganda Unit	MLAPU	Turkey
Mavi Front for the Liberation of Northern Iprios		Greece
May 15 Organization		Palestine
May 1 Sandigan of the April 6th Liberation Movement		Philippines
Militant Autonomy Front		Netherlands
Montoneros	Peronist Montonero Movement-MPM	Argentina
Morazinist Front for the Liberation of Honduras		Honduras
Moroccan Patriotic Front		Morocco
Moro National Liberation Front		Philippines
Moslem Students Organization	MSO	Iran
Movement Brothers of Palestine		France
Movement for the Autonomy and Independence of the Canary Archipelago	MPAIAC	Canary Islands
Movement of 18 October		Netherlands
Movement of the 19th of April		Colombia
Movement of the Revolutionary Left	MIR	Chile
Movement of the Revolutionary Left	MIR	Peru
Mujahedin of the People of Iran	OMPI	Iran
Mujahidin		Iraq
Murabitun Movement		Palestine
Muslim Brotherhood		Syria
National Democratic Popular Front		Undetermined
National Front		Greece
National Front for the Liberation of Congo	FLNC	Congo
National Front for the Liberation of Corsica		Corsica

Name of Group	Also Known as	Place of Origin or Operating Location
National Liberation Army		Bolivia
National Liberation Army	ELN	Colombia
National Liberation Front		Brazil
National Organization of Cypriot Fighters	EOKA-B	Cyprus
National Socialist Organization of the Panhellenes	ESOP	Greece
National Union for the Total Independence of Angola	UNITA	Angola
Neo-Nazi Groups		West Germany
New Armenian Resistance		Armenia
New International Brigade		Ireland
New Jewish Defense League		Israel
New Joint Command	NJC	Palestine
New Movement in Solidarity with Puerto Rico Independence and Socialism	NMSPRIS	Puerto Rico
New People's Army		Philippines
Nineteenth of April Movement	M-19	Colombia
Nordic Terrorist Front		Netherlands
November 17		Greece
Nuclei di Avanguardia Comunista		Italy
October 1 Anti-Fascist Revolutionary Group	GRAPO	Undetermined
Omega 7		Cuba
Organization for the Vengeance of the Martyrs of Sabra and Shatila		Lebanon
Organization of Avengers of Palestine Youth		Palestine
Organization of National Restoration		Greece
Organization of Popular War Vanguards		Syria
Organization of Revolutionaries		Venezuela
Organization of the Sons of Southern Lebanon		Lebanon
Orly Group		Armenia
Oulen 44		Greece
Pakistan Liberation Army		Pakistan
Palestine Front Against Qatar		Undetermined
Palestine Liberation Organization	PLO	Palestine
Palestinian Revolutionary Armed Forces		Palestine
Party Islam		Malaysia
Pasdaran	Revolutionary Guard	Iran
Peace Conquerors		Belgium
Peace Conquerors		West Germany
Pedro Luis Botero Commando Group		Cuba
People's Army of the Oppressed in Zaire	APOZA	Zaire
People's Defense Committee	CDP	Mexico
People's League of Free Palestine		Palestine
People's Liberation Army	EPL	Colombia

Name of Group	Also Known as	Place of Origin or Operating Location
People's Progressive Party		Guyana
People's Resistance Army		Greece
People's Revolutionary Armed Forces		Mexico
People's Revolutionary Army	ERP	Argentina
People's Revolutionary Army		El Salvador
People's Revolutionary Army in Puerto Rico		Puerto Rico
People's Revolutionary Front		Philippines
People's Revolutionary Solidarity Organization		Undetermined
People's Revolutionary Struggle	ELA	Greece
People's Sacrifice Guerillas		Iran
People's Strugglers		Undetermined
Peronist Armed Forces		Argentina
Petra Kraus Group		Undetermined
Polisario		Undetermined
Poor People's Army		Mexico
Popular Army Force	FAP	Undetermined
Popular Forces of April 25	FP-25	Undetermined
Popular Front for the Liberation of Palestine	PFLP	Palestine
Popular Front for the Liberation of Palestine-General Command	PFLP-GC	Palestine
Popular League-28 February	LP-28	El Salvador
Popular Liberation Army	EPL	Undetermined
Popular Liberation Forces	FPL	El Salvador
Popular Liberation Movement		Djibouti
Popular Resistance		Chile
Popular Revolutionary Bloc		El Salvador
Popular Revolutionary Forces	Lorenzo Zelaya	Honduras
Popular Revolutionary Movement		Undetermined
Popular Revolutionary Resistance		Greece
Popular Revolutionary Struggle		Greece
Popular Revolutionary Vanguard		Brazil
Popular Struggle Front	PSF	Libya
Progressive Socialist Party		Lebanon
Progressive Socialist Party		Syria
Proletarian Justice		Worldwide
Proletarian Squad		Italy
Proletarian International		Italy
Provisional Irish Republican Army	PIRA; Provos	Ireland
Puerto Rican Armed Resistance		Puerto Rico
Puerto Rican Solidarity Committee		Puerto Rico
Puerto Rico Popular Army	Macheteros	Puerto Rico
Puerto Rico Revolutionary Workers Organization		Puerto Rico
Quebec Liberation Front	FLQ	Quebec
Red Army Faction	RAF	West Germany
Red Brigades	Brigate Rossi	Italy
Republic of New Africa	RNA	US
Revolutionary Action		Greece
Revolutionary Action Front		Honduras
Revolutionary Action Movement	RAM	US

Name of Group	Also Known as	Place of Origin or Operating Location
Revolutionary Armed Forces of Columbia	FARC	Colombia
Revolutionary Armed Squads	SAR	Italy
Revolutionary Cells	RZ	West Germany
Revolutionary Cells for a Free Palestine		Undetermined
Revolutionary Commandos of Solidarity		Costa Rica
Revolutionary Commandos of the People		Puerto Rico
Revolutionary Core-International Group		Netherlands
Revolutionary Left		Greece
Revolutionary Marxist League		West Germany
Revolutionary Organization for the Liquidation of Agents and Reactionaries		Lebanon
Revolutionary Organization of the People		Colombia
Revolutionary Organization of the People in Arms	ORPA	Guatemala
Revolutionary Party of Central American Workers		El Salvador
Revolutionary People's Army		Greece
Revolutionary People's Struggle		Undetermined
Revolutionary Student Front	FER	Undetermined
Revolutionary Union to Overthrow the Government of the US		Puerto Rico
Revolutionary Youth Union	Dev Genc	Undetermined
Ricardo Franco Front	FRF	Colombia
Robert E.D. Straker Commando of the Territorial Resistance Army		West Germany
Sabi Lillah		Thailand
Sandinista National Liberation Front	FSLN	Nicaragua
Secret Armenian Army		Armenia
Secret Armenian Liberation Army		Armenia
Self-Defense Against All Authority		France
Sendero Luminoso	Shining Path	Peru
Senki-shuryuha	Mainstream Battle Flag	Japan
Sixth Armenian Liberation Army		Armenia
Soldiers of the Algerian Opposition Movement		Algeria
Solidarist Resistance Movement		France
Somali Salvation Front	SSF	Somaliland
Sons of the Occupied Land Organization	SOLO	Bahrain
Sons of the South		Lebanon
Spear of the Nation	MK	South Africa
Sudanese People's Liberation Army		Sudan
Symbionese Liberation Army	SLA	US
Takfir wa Hijra	Repudiation and Renunciation	Egypt

Name of Group	Also Known as	Place of Origin or Operating Location
Terrorist Group of Badizardegun		Iran
Towhid		Iran
Tunisian Revolutionary National Organization		Tunisia
Tupac Amaru Revolutionary Movement	MRTA	Peru
Tupumaros		Uruguay
Turkish Islamic Revolutionary Army		Turkey
Turkish People's Liberation Army	TPLA	Turkey
Turkish People's Libertion Front	TPLF	Turkey
Turkish Revolutionaries		Turkey
Turkish Revolutionary Youth Federation		Turkey
Uganda Freedom Movement		Uganda
Ukrainian Nationalist Group		Ukraine
Ulster Defense Assn		N. Ireland
United Freedom Front	UFF	US
United Front Guerilla Action		Colombia
United Jewish Underground		
United Liberation Front for New Algeria		Algeria
United Popular Action Front		Undetermined
Upheaval Movement		Palestine
Vanguardia Falangista		Spain
Venceremos Brigade		US
Venezuelan Revolutionary Party		Venezuela
Voice of the People	Halkin Sesi	Undetermined
Warriors of Christ the King		Spain
Weather Underground	WUO	US
We Must Do Something		France
Western Somali Liberation Front		Ethiopia
White Warriors		El Salvador
Worker's Direct Action		France
Workers Party of Guatemala		Guatemala
Workers Self-Defense Movement		Colombia
Young Armenians in the US		US
Young Militants		Ireland
Young Proletarian Organization for Communism		Italy
Youth Action Group		France
Zionist Resistance Fighters		France
2 June Movement		West Germany
3 July Revolution Force		Iraq
3 October Group		Armenia
9 June Group		Armenia
14 September Workers Self-Defense Force		Colombia
20 December Movement		West Germany
23 September Communist League		Mexico
24 September Group		Armenia
28 May Organization		Armenia

ELECTRONIC SECURITY SYSTEM SYMBOLS

LETTER DESIGNATORS

A:	Police/Fire Connect	PN:	Pan
AL:	Access Control	Q:	Listen-In
B:	Direct (Central Station) Connect	R:	Remote
C:	Digital Communicator	S:	Sound Detector/Discriminator
D:	Digital Keypad	SQ:	Sequential
E:	Emergency Power Supply/Battery	T:	Toggle/Pushbutton
F:	Flush	TL:	Tilt
G:	Glass Break Detector	U:	Ultrasonic
H:	Capacitance/Proximity Sensor	V:	Vibration/Shock
I:	Passive Infrared	W:	Wireless
J:	Multiplex	X:	Transformer
K:	Keyswitch	Y:	Supervised Wireless
L:	Tape Dialer	Z:	Zone
M:	Microwave	ZM:	Zoom
O:	Outdoor/Weatherproof	n:	Number
P:	Photoelectric		

FIRE PROTECTION SYMBOLS

Manual Station (Call Point)

Manual Alarm Box (Pull Station and Pull Box)

Telephone Station (Telephone Call Point)

Automatic Detection and Supervisory Devices

Projected Beam Smoke Detector

Smoke Detector

Heat Detector (Thermal Detector)

Speaker/Horn (Electric Horn)

Bell (Gong)

Vibrating Bell

Single Stroke Bell

Buzzer

Horn with Light

Light (Lamp, Signal Light, Indicator Lamp)

Gas Detector

Flame Detector (Flicker Detector)

Flow Detector/Switch

Pressure Detector/Switch

Level Detector/Switch

Tamper Detector/Switch

Valve with Tamper Detector/Switch

Control Panel

Door Holder

Illuminated Exit Sign

Illuminated Exit Sign with Direction Arrow

Emergency Light, Battery Powered (one lamp)

Emergency Light, Battery Powered (two lamps)

Emergency Light, Battery Powered (three lamps)

262

INTRUSION ALARM SYMBOLS

- ◼ Control Unit
- Ⓩ Zoned Control Unit
- Slave Digital Communicator
- Slave Tape Dialer
- Slave Zone Board/Control/ Annunciator
- Remote Zone Annunciator
- Remote Control—Digital Keypad
- Remote Control— Keyswitch
- ◈ Ultrasonic Transceiver
- ▷▪ᵤ Ultrasonic Transmitter
- ◁▪ᵤ Ultrasonic Receiver
- ◆ Dual-Technology Device
- ◈ Photoelectric, Self-Contained
- ▷▪ Photoelectric Transmitter
- Remote Control— Toggle/Pushbutton
- Signal Processor
- Signal Processor— Microwave
- Signal Processor— Ultrasonic
- Signal Processor— Passive Infrared
- Signal Processor— Vibration/Shock
- Signal Processor— Sound Detector
- Signal Processor— Listen-In
- ⬦ Hold-Up/Panic Device
- ⬦ Hold-Up/Panic Button
- ⬦ Cash Drawer Money Clip
- ⬦ Foot Rail

- Ⓔ Emergency Power Supply/Battery
- ◇ Contact Switch (Surface)
- ◇ᶠ Contact Switch (Flush)
- ◆ Contact Switch, Balanced
- ◈ Glass Breakage Detector
- ◈ᵥ Vibration/Shock Sensor
- ◈ₛ Sound Detector/Discriminator
- ⊠ Transformer
- ◻◁ Horn/Siren Speaker
- ◻ Buzzer
- ✕ Light/Strobe
- ⁾⁾ʷ Wireless Transmitter
- ◁⁽ʷ Wireless Receiver
- ⊓ Foil Tape
- ⋈ Laced Wire
- ⊏ Floor Mat
- ◇ Space Protection Device
- ◇ᵢ Passive Infrared Detector
- ◇ₘ Microwave Transceiver
- ▷▪ᴹ Microwave Transmitter
- ◁▪ᴹ Microwave Receiver
- ⁾ᵛ Supervised Wireless Transmitter
- ◁⁽ᵛ Supervised Wireless Receiver
- ◁▪ʳ Photoelectric Receiver
- --▸- Photoelectric Beam Path
- ◻◯ Bell

ACCESS CONTROL AND CCTV SYMBOLS

Digital Keypad

Card Reader

Digital Keypad and
Card Reader

Monitor

Manual Switcher

Sequential Switcher

Door Strike

Door Bolt

Parking Gate

Video Tape Recorder

Zoom Lens Control

Pan Control Unit

Access Control Unit

Film Camera

CCTV Camera

Pan and Tilt Control Unit

Remote Control Unit

CCTV Camera with
Zoom Lens

Pan Unit

Pan and Tilt Unit

CONVERSION TABLE—
CUSTOMARY TO METRIC*

When You Know	Multiply by	To Find	Symbol
inches	25	millimeters	mm
inches	2.5	centimeters	cm
feet	0.3	meters	m
yards	0.9	meters	m
fathoms	1.8	meters	m
miles	1.6	kilometers	km
square inches	6.5	square centimeters	cm²
square feet	0.093	square meters	m²
square yards	0.84	square meters	m²
acres	0.4	hectares	ha
square miles	2.6	square kilometers	km²
cubic inches	16.4	cubic centimeters	cm³
cubic feet	0.028	cubic meters	m³
cubic yards	0.76	cubic meters	m³
ounces (fluid)	30	milliliters	mL
pints } liquid	0.47	liters	L
quarts } liquid	0.95	liters	L
gallons	3.8	liters	L
pints } dry	0.55	liters	L
quarts } dry	1.1	liters	L
bushels	35	liters	L
bushels	0.035	cubic meters	m³
avoirdupois ounces	28	grams	g
avoirdupois pounds	0.45	kilograms	kg
short tons (2000 lb)	0.91	metric tons	t
long tons (2240 lb)	1.0	metric tons	t

(Fahrenheit temperature − 32) × 0.56 = Celsius temperature

*Approximate to within 2%.

CONVERSION TABLE—
METRIC TO CUSTOMARY*

When You Know	Multiply by	To Find
millimeters	0.04	inches
centimeters	0.4	inches
meters	3.3	feet
meters	1.1	yards
kilometers	0.62	miles
square centimeters	0.155	square inches
square meters	10.8	square feet
square meters	1.2	square yards
hectares	2.5	acres
square kilometers	0.39	square miles
cubic centimeters	0.06	cubic inches
cubic meters	35	cubic feet
cubic meters	1.3	cubic yards
milliliters	0.034	ounces (fluid)
liters	2.1	pints } liquid
liters	1.06	quarts }
liters	0.26	gallons
liters	1.8	pints } dry
liters	0.9	quarts }
cubic meters	2.8	bushels
grams	0.035	avoirdupois ounces
kilograms	2.2	avoirdupois pounds
metric tons	1.1	short tons (2000 lb)
metric tons	1.0	long tons (2240 lb)

(Celsius temperature × 1.8) + 32 = Fahrenheit temperature

*Approximate to within 2%.

266

MEASUREMENT TABLES

Length (Long)

12 inches	= 1 foot		1 rod	= 16½ feet
3 feet	= 1 yard		1 chain	= 66 feet
5½ yards	= 1 rod		1 furlong	= 660 feet
4 rods	= 1 chain		1 furlong	= 220 yards
10 chains	= 1 furlong		1 mile	= 5280 feet
8 furlongs	= 1 mile		1 mile	= 1760 yards
3 miles	= 1 league		1 knot	= 6080 feet
1 meter	= 39.37 inches		1 inch	= 2.54 centimeters
1 meter	= 3.28083 feet		1 foot	= 0.3048 meters
1 meter	= 1.09361 yards		1 yard	= 0.9144 meters
1 kilometer	= 0.62137 miles		1 mile	= 1.6093 kilometers

Surface (Square)

144 square inches	= 1 square foot		1 square yard	= 1296 square inches
9 square feet	= 1 square yard		1 square rod	= 272.25 square feet
30¼ square yards	= 1 square rod		1 acre	= 10 square chains
160 square rods	= 1 acre		1 acre	= 4840 square yards
640 acres	= 1 square mile		1 acre	= 43560 square feet

An acre equals a square whose side is 208.71 feet.

1 square centimeter	= 0.155 square inch		1 square inch	= 6.452 square cm.
1 square meter	= 10.764 square feet			
1 square meter	= 1.196 square yards		1 square yard	= 0.8361 sq. meter
1 square kilometer	= 0.386 square miles		1 square mile	= 2.59 sq. kilometers

Volume (Cubic)

1728 cubic inches	= 1 cubic foot		128 cubic feet	= 1 cord (wood)
27 cubic feet	= 1 cubic yard		24¾ cubic feet	= 1 perch (masonry)
40 cubic feet	= 1 U.S. shipping ton		= 32.14 U.S. Bushels	
42 cubic feet	= 1 British shipping ton		= 33.75 U.S. Bushels	
1 cubic centimeter	= 0.061 cubic inch		1 cubic inch	= 16.387 cubic cm.
1 cubic meter	= 35.314 cubic feet		1 cubic yard	= 0.7646 cubic mt.
1 cubic meter	= 1.308 cubic yard			

MEASUREMENT TABLES—*Continued*

Liquid

4 gills = 1 pint	1 U.S. gallon = 231 cubic inches
2 pints = 1 quart	1 British gallon = 277.274 cubic in.
4 quarts = 1 gallon	1 British gallon = 1.2003 U.S. gal.
1 liter = 61.023 cubic inches	1 U.S. gallon = 3.785 liters
1 liter = 0.03531 cubic foot	1 cubic foot = 28.317 liters
1 liter = 0.2642 U.S. gallon	

Dry

2 pints = 1 quart	1 U.S. bushel = 2150.42 cubic in.
8 quarts = 1 peck	1 U.S. bushel = 1.2445 cubic feet
4 pecks = 1 bushel	1 British bushel = 2218.192 cu. in.

Avoirdupois (Commercial)

16 drachms = 437.5 grains	1 stone = 14 pounds
16 drachms = 1 ounce	2000 pounds = 1 short ton
437.5 grains = 1 ounce	2240 pounds = 1 long ton
16 ounces = 1 pound	2204.6 pounds = 1 metric ton
7000 grains = 1 pound	
1 gram = 15.432 grains	1 grain = 0.0648 gram
1 gram = 0.03527 ounces	1 ounce = 28.35 grams
1 kilogram = 2.2046 pounds	1 pound = 0.4536 kilogram
1 metric ton = 2204.6 pounds	1 long ton = 1.016 metric ton

Comparison of Thermometers

Freezing Point	= 32 degrees Fahrenheit	= 0 degrees Centigrade.
Boiling Point	= 212 degrees Fahrenheit	= 100 degrees Centigrade.
Temperature F.	= 9/5 (Temperature C. + 32)	
Temperature C.	= 5/9 (Temperature F. − 32)	

CONVERSION FACTORS

To Obtain	Multiply	By
Circumference of a circle	Diameter of circle	3.14160
Area of a circle	Diameter squared	.78540
Area of a circle	Radius squared	3.14160
Diameter of a circle	Circumference	.31831
Surface of a sphere	Diameter squared	3.14160

To Convert From	To	*Multiply By
Lengths		
Centimeters	Inches	.39370
Fathom	Feet	6.00000
Kilometers	Miles	.62100
Meters	Inches	39.37000
Meters	Feet	3.28100
Miles	Feet	5,280.00000
Miles	Varas (Texas)	1,900.80000
Nautical miles	Feet	6,080.20000
Nautical miles	Miles	1.15150
Varas (Mexico)	Inches	32.99200
Varas (Texas)	Inches	33.33000
Volumes		
Barrels	U.S. gallons	42.00000
Barrels	British imperial gallons	34.97500
Barrels	Cubic Feet	5.61500
Barrels	Liters	158.96000
Barrels	Cubic Meters	.15897
British imperial gallons	Cubic Inches	277.41800
Cubic Feet	Gallons	7.48060
Liters	Cubic Inches	61.02300
U.S. gallons	Liters	3.78500
U.S. gallons	Pounds of water	8.34300
U.S. gallons	British imperial gallons	.83270
U.S. gallons	Cubic inches	231.00000
Weights		
Cu. ft. of water at 60°F.	Pounds	62.36600
Pounds	Grams	453.60000
Pounds	Kilograms	.45360
Pounds	Ounces	16.00000
Tons (short)	Pounds	2,000.00000
Tons (long)	Pounds	2,240.00000
Tons (short)	Barrels of water (1.0 sp. gr.)	5.71100
Tons (long)	Barrels of water (1.0 sp. gr.)	6.39700

CONVERSION FACTORS—*Continued*

To Convert From	*To*	*Multiply By*
Rate and Velocity		
Cubic feet per second	Gallons per minute	449.00000
Feet per second	Centimeters per second	30.48000
Feet per second	Miles per hour	.68180
Feet per second	Kilometers per hour	1.09800
Gallons per minute	Barrels per day	34.29000
Gallons per minute	Barrels per hour	1.42900
Gallons per hour	Barrels per day	.57140
Gallons per minute	Liters per minute	3.78500
Knots	Miles per hour	1.15150
Energy and Pressure		
Btu	Foot pounds	778.1000
Feet of water	Pounds per square inch	.4335
Horsepower	Ft.-lbs. per second	550.0000
Horsepower	Ft.-lbs. per minute	33,000.0000
Horsepower	Kilowatts	.7460
Horsepower-hour	Btu	2,544.0000
Inches of mercury	Pounds per square inch	.4912
Inches of water	Pounds per square inch	.0361
Kilowatts	Horsepower	1.3400
Kilowatt-hour	Btu	3,413.0000

To convert Specific Gravity to Baumé, divide 140 by the Specific Gravity and subtract 130 from the result.

To convert Baumé to Specific Gravity, divide 140 by the Baumé Gravity plus 130.

*Divide by factor to convert in opposite direction.

WIND-CHILL CHART

Estimated Wind Speed MPH	Actual Thermometer Reading, °F.											
	50	40	30	20	10	0	—10	—20	—30	—40	—50	—60
	Equivalent Temperature °F											
Calm	50	40	30	20	10	0	—10	—20	—30	—40	—50	—60
5	48	37	27	16	6	—5	—15	—26	—36	—47	—57	—68
10	40	28	16	4	—9	—21	—33	—46	—58	—70	—83	—95
15	36	22	9	—5	—18	36	15	—58	—72	—85	—99	—112
20	32	18	4	—10	—25	—39	—53	—67	—82	—96	—110	—124
25	50	16	0	—15	—29	—44	—59	—74	—88	—104	—118	—133
30	28	13	—2	—18	—33	—48	—63	—79	—94	—109	—125	—140
35	27	11	—4	—20	—35	—49	—67	—82	98	—113	—129	—145
40	26	10	—6	—21	—37	—53	—69	—85	—100	—116	—132	—148

Wind speeds greater than 40 MPH have little additional effect

LITTLE DANGER FOR PROPERLY CLOTHED PERSON

INCREASING DANGER

GREAT DANGER

DANGER FROM FREEZING OF EXPOSED FLESH

To use the chart, find the estimated or actual wind speed in the left-hand column and the actual temperature in degrees F in the top row. The equivalent temperature is found where these two intersect. For example, with a wind speed of 10 mph and a temperature of —10°F., the equivalent temperature is —33°F. This lies within the zone of increasing danger of frostbite, and protective measures should be taken.

CLASSIFICATION OF FIRES AND RATING OF PORTABLE FIRE EXTINGUISHERS

Classification of Fires

Fires can be divided into four basic types:

Class A: Fires involving ordinary combustible materials (such as wood, cloth, paper, rubber, and many plastics) requiring the heat-absorbing (cooling) effects of water, water solutions, or the coating effects of certain dry chemicals which retard combustion.

Class B: Fires involving flammable or combustible liquids, flammable gases, greases, and similar materials where extinguishment is most readily secured by excluding air (oxygen), inhibiting the release of combustible vapors, or interrupting the combustion chain reaction.

Class C: Fires involving energized electrical equipment where safety to the operator requires the use of electrically non-conductive extinguishing agents. (Note: When electrical equipment is deenergized, the use of Class A or B extinguishers may be indicated.)

Class D: Fires involving certain combustible metals, such as magnesium, titanium, zirconium, sodium, potassium, etc., requiring a heat-absorbing extinguishing medium not reactive with the burning metals.

Rating of Fire Extinguishers

Based upon the preceding classification of fires and also upon fire extinguishment potentials as determined by physical testing of fire extinguishers by Underwriters' Laboratories, Inc., ratings have been established for portable fire extinguishers.

These ratings consist of a NUMERAL, a LETTER or combinations thereof. They appear on the labels affixed to the extinguishers listed by Underwriters' Laboratories of Canada. These NUMERALS and LETTERS connote the following:

a. In the case of Extinguishers suitable for use on Class A fires, the NUMERAL is indicative of the approximate relative fire extinguishing potential of various sizes of the different suitable extinguishers available, e.g., a 4-A extinguisher can be expected to extinguish approximately twice as much fire as a 2-A EXTINGUISHER.

b. In the case of extinguishers suitable for use on Class B fires, the NUMERAL is also indicative of the approximate relative fire extinguishing potential of various sizes of the different suitable extinguishers available, and in addition, the NUMERAL is an approximate indication of the square foot area of deep layer flammable liquid fire which an average operator can extinguish, e.g., a 10-B unit can be expected to extinguish 10 square feet of deep layer flammable liquid fire when used by an average operator.

c. In the case of extinguishers suitable for use on Class C fires, no NUMERAL is used since Class C fires are essentially either Class A or B fires involving energized electrical wiring and equipment. The size of the different suitable extinguishers installed should be commensurate with the size and extent of the area involving the electrical hazard or containing equipment being protected.

d. The LETTERS refer to the classes of fire on which the use of the particular extinguisher is most effective for fire extinguishment.

Examples:

Foam extinguisher, rated 2-A, 5-B. This extinguisher should extinguish approximately twice as much Class A fire as a 1-A extinguisher, and five times as much Class B fire as a 1-B extinguisher. Also, the extinguisher should extinguish a fire in a deep layer flammable liquid, such as a dip tank having a surface area of 5 square feet, when used by an average operator.

Dry chemical extinguisher, rated 10-B, C. This extinguisher should extinguish approximately ten times as much Class B fire as a 1-B unit and should successfully extinguish a deep layer flammable liquid fire of 10 square feet area when used by an average operator. It also is safe to use on fires involving energized electrical equipment.

A multi-purpose extinguisher, rated 4-A, 20-B, C. This extinguisher should extinguish approximately four times as much Class A fire as a 1-A extinguisher, 20 times as much Class B fire as a 1-B extinguisher and a deep layer flammable liquid fire of 20 square feet when used by an average operator, and it is also safe to use on fires involving energized electrical equipment.

From NFPA-10, Standard for Installation of Portable Fire Extinguishers.

PROPERTIES OF FLAMMABLE LIQUIDS AND GASES

	Flash Point (Deg. F)	Ignition Temperature (Deg. F)	*Flammable Limits (percent by volume in air)		Boiling Point (Deg. F)
			Lower	Upper	
Acetylene	gas	581	2.5	81.0	−118
Ammonia (anhydrous)	gas	1204	16.0	25.0	−28
Benzene (benzol)	12	1040	1.3	7.1	176
Benzine (pet. ether)	0	550	1.1	5.9	95– 140
Butane	gas	761	1.9	8.5	31
Carbon Disulphide	−22	194	1.3	50.0	115
Carbon Monoxide	gas	1128	12.5	74.0	−314
Ethyl (grain) Alcohol	55	689	3.3	19.0	173
Ethylene Glycol (glycol)	232	752	3.2		387
Gasoline (100 Octane)	−36	853	1.4	7.4	
Hydrogen	gas	752	4.0	75.0	−422
Kerosene	100	410	0.7	5.0	304– 574
Methane	gas	1004	5.0	15.0	−259
Methyl (wood) Alcohol	52	725	6.7	36.0	147
Natural Gas		900– 1170	3.8– 6.5	13.0– 17.0	
Petroleum Crude	20–90	———— Varies Widely ————			
Propane	gas	842	2.2	9.5	−44
Toluene (toluol)	40	896	1.2	7.1	231
Turpentine	95	488	0.8		300
Varsol (No. 1)	108	560	1.1	6.0	320– 390
Vinyl Acetate	18	800	2.6	13.4	161

*Based upon normal atmospheric conditions. The general effect of increase of temperature or pressure is to lower the lower limit and raise the upper limit. Decrease of temperature or pressure has the opposite effect.

Flash Point of the liquid is the temperature at which it gives off vapor sufficient to form an ignitable mixture with the air near the surface of the liquid or within the vessel used.

Ignition Temperature of a substance, whether solid, liquid, or gaseous, is the minimum temperature required to initiate or cause self-sustained combustion independently of the heating or heated element.

Boiling Point of a liquid is the temperature of the liquid at which its vapor pressure equals the atmospheric pressure.

From NFPA—325-M 1969, Fire Hazard Properties, etc.

BIBLIOGRAPHY

Air Force Regulation 125-22, Department of the Air Force, Washington, D.C., 1976.

Air Force Regulation 205-1, Department of the Air Force, Washington, D.C., 1982.

Air Force Regulation 205-16, Department of the Air Force, Washington, D.C., 1984.

Air Force Regulation 205-32, Department of the Air Force, Washington, D.C., 1982.

Air Force Regulation 208-1, Department of the Air Force, Washington, D.C., 1982.

Alcohol Abuse in the Hard-to-Reach Work Force, National Institute on Alcohol Abuse and Alcoholism, Rockville, MD, 1982.

Allen, Brandt, "Embezzler's Guide to the Computer," Harvard Business Review, July-August, 1975.

Army Regulation 190-5, Department of the Army, Washington, D.C., 1973.

Army Regulation 190-16, Department of the Army, Washington, D.C., 1984.

Baker, J. Stannard, Traffic Accident Investigation Manual, The Traffic Institute of Northwestern University, Chicago, IL, 1975.

Barnard, Robert L., Intrusion Detection Systems, Butterworth Publishers, Stoneham, MA, 1981.

Bequai, August, Computers + Business = Liabilities: A Preventive Guide for Management, Washington Legal Foundation, Washington, D.C., 1984.

Bologna, Jack, A Guideline for Fraud Auditing, Odiorne International, Inc., Plymouth, MI, 1984.

Bomb Incident Management, International Association of Chiefs of Police, Gaithersburg, MD, 1973.

Bombs and Explosives, Federal Law Enforcement Training Center, Department of the Treasury, Brunswick, GA, 1973.

Bomb Threats and Bomb Search Techniques, Federal Law Enforcement Training Center, Department of the Treasury, Brunswick, GA, 1971.

Brockett, W. Don, New Directions in Corporate Security, SRI International, Menlo Park, CA, 1984.

Broder, James F., Risk Analysis and the Security Survey, Butterworth Publishers, Stoneham, MA, 1984.

Brodie, Thomas G., Bombs and Bombings, Charles C. Thomas Publishers, Springfield, IL, 1972.

Buckwalter, Art, Interviews and Interrogations, Butterworth Publishers, Stoneham, MA, 1983.

Burke, John J., "Searches by Private Persons," FBI Law Enforcement Bulletin, October, 1972.

Carroll, John M., Computer Security, Butterworth Publishers, Stoneham, MA, 1977.

Carroll, John M., Confidential Information Sources: Public and Private, Butterworth Publishers, Stoneham, MA, 1975.

Clark, John P. and Hollinger, Richard C., Theft by Employees in Work Organizations, National Institute of Justice, Washington, D.C., 1983.

Conklin, John E., Illegal But Not Criminal, Prentice-Hall, Inc., Englewood Cliffs, NJ, 1977.

Corporate Aviation Security, National Business Aircraft Association, Inc., Washington, D.C., 1984.

Criminal Law Reference Handbook, Massachusetts Criminal Justice Training Council, Boston, MA, 1980.

Cunningham, William C. and Taylor, Todd H., Private Security and Police in America, Chancellor Press, Portland, OR, 1985.

Daskam, Samuel W., Eavesdropping Attacks and Countermeasures, International Security Associates, Inc., Stamford, CT.

Dean, William and Evans, David S., Terms of the Trade, Random Lengths Publications, Inc., Eugene, OR, 1980.

DeSola, Ralph, Crime Dictionary, Facts on File, San Diego, CA, 1982.

Department of Defense Industrial Security Program Manual, Defense Investigative Service, Washington, D.C., 1984.

Dienstein, William, Technics for the Crime Investigator, Charles C. Thomas Publishers, Springfield, IL, 1970.

Donelan, Charles A., Principles of Criminal Law for Law Enforcement Officers, Federal Bureau of Investigation, Washington, D.C.

Drug Atlas, Midwest Research Institute, Kansas City, MO, 1971.

Fay, John, Approaches to Criminal Justice Training, The University of Georgia Press, Athens, GA, 1979.

Fay, John, "Collection of Gunpowder Residue," Military Police Journal, April, 1973.

Fay, John, The Police Instructor's Guide, The Georgia Peace Officer Standards and Training Council, Atlanta, GA, 1978.

Fay, John, Security Officer Manual, The Charter Company, Jacksonville, FL, 1981.

Federal Rules: Criminal Procedure, Evidence and Appellate Procedure, West Publishing Company, Saint Paul, MN, 1982.

Fennelly Lawrence J., Handbook of Loss Prevention and Crime Prevention, Butterworth Publishers, Stoneham, MA, 1982.

Fisher Royal P., Information Systems Security, Prentice-Hall, Inc., Englewood Cliffs, NJ, 1984.

Fitzgerald, Jerry, Designing Controls into Computerized Systems, Jerry Fitzgerald and Associates, Redwood City, CA, 1981.

French, William B., et al., Guide to Real Estate Licensing Examinations, Warren, Gorham and Lamont, Boston, MA, 1978.

Fuqua, Paul and Wilson, Jerry V., Terrorism: The

Executive's Guide to Survival, Gulf Publishing Company, Houston, TX, 1978.

Gallati, Robert R. J., Introduction to Private Security, Prentice-Hall, Inc., Englewood Cliffs, NJ, 1983.

Gaynor, Frank, Concise Dictionary of Science, Philosophical Library, New York, NY, 1959.

Gigliotti, Richard and Jason, Ronald, Security Design for Maximum Protection, Butterworth Publishers, Stoneham, MA, 1984.

Green, Gion, Introduction to Security, Butterworth Publishers, Stoneham, MA, 1987.

Green, Thomas, et al., Glossary of Insurance Terms, The Merritt Company, Santa Monica, CA, 1980.

A Guide to Security Investigations, American Society for Industrial Security, Arlington, VA, 1975.

Handbook of Forensic Science, Federal Bureau of Investigation, Washington, D.C., 1979.

Haynes, Richard A., "Drugs in the Workplace," Security Management, December, 1983.

Hemphill, Charles F., Security for Business and Industry, Dow Jones-Irwin, Inc., Homewood, IL, 1971.

Hernon, Frederick E., The White Collar Ripoff, Management, Inc., Akron, OH, 1975.

Hofmeister, Richard A. and Prince, David J., Security Dictionary, Howard W. Sams and Company, Inc., Indianapolis, IN, 1985.

Inbau, Fred, et al., Protective Security Law, Butterworth Publishers, Stoneham, MA, 1983.

Jeffrey, C. Ray, Crime Prevention Through Environmental Design, Sage Publications, Beverly Hills, CA, 1977.

Kadish, Sanford H., Encyclopedia of Crime and Justice, The Free Press, New York, NY, 1983.

Kelley, Woody Anderson, Kelley's Security Thesaussory, Concept VIII, Inc., Gurley, AL, 1977.

Kingsbury, Arthur A., Introduction to Security and Crime Prevention Surveys, Charles C. Thomas Publishers, Springfield, IL, 1973.

Kionka, Edward J., Torts: Injuries to Persons and Property, West Publishing Company, Saint Paul, MN, 1983.

Kolodny, Leonard, Outwitting Bad Check Passers, Small Business Administration, Washington, D.C., 1976.

Law Enforcement and Private Security Sources and Areas of Conflict, Department of Justice, Washington, D.C., 1976.

Law Enforcement Investigations, FM 19-20, Department of the Army, Washington, D.C., 1977.

Lesko, Matthew, Information USA, Viking Press, New York, NY, 1983.

"Life Safety Glossary," Security Systems Administration, July, 1985.

Littlejohn, Robert F., Crisis Management: A Team Approach, American Management Association, New York, NY, 1983.

Loewy, Arnold H., Criminal Law, West Publishing Company, Saint Paul, MN, 1984.

Long Range Planning for Service Organizations, American Management Association Extension Institute, New York, NY, 1982.

McGowan, Kevin J., "Computer Power Protection," Data Processing and Communications Security, May-June, 1985.

Middaugh, J. Kendall, Transmission Security Threats and Countermeasures, Georgia State University, Atlanta, GA, 1984.

Montana, Patrick J. and Roukis, George S., Managing Terrorism, Quorum Books, Westport, CT, 1983.

National Criminal Justice Thesaurus, National Institute of Justice, Washington, D.C., 1984.

National Strategy for Prevention of Drug Abuse and Drug Trafficking, The White House, Washington, D.C., 1984.

Novitt, Mitchell S., Employer Liability for Employee Misconduct, Amacom, New York, NY, 1982.

O'Hara, Charles E., Fundamentals of Criminal Investigation, Charles C. Thomas, Springfield, IL, 1980.

"The Olympics: Terrorism and Disruption Potentials," Information Digest, June, 1984.

Opiates, Alcohol, Drug Abuse and Mental Health Administration, Washington, D.C., 1983.

Parker, Donn B., Fighting Computer Crime, Author's Copy Book Company, Los Altos, CA, 1981.

Part 179 of 27 CFR, Federal Laws and Regulations, Firearms, Department of the Treasury, Washington, D.C., 1983.

Patin, Harold C. and Egan, Raymond R., Industrial Drug Abuse, Drug Education Associates, Metairie, LA, 1981.

Patterns of Global Terrorism, Department of State, Washington, D.C., 1984.

Physical Security, FM 19-30, Department of the Army, Washington, D.C., 1979.

Physical Security of Window Assemblies, National Institute of Law Enforcement and Criminal Justice, Washington, D.C., 1976.

The Police Reference Notebook, International Association of Chiefs of Police, Gaithersburg, MD, 1970.

Purpura, Philip P., Security and Loss Prevention, Butterworth Publishers, Stoneham, MA, 1984.

Recognizing Bombs and Explosives, Federal Law Enforcement and Training Center, Department of the Treasury, Brunswick, GA, 1974.

Regulation of Private Security Services, Department of Justice, Washington, D.C., 1976.

"Report 695," Business Intelligence Program, SRI, International, Menlo Park, CA, 1984.

Report of a Panel Discussion on Drugs in Industry, Burns Security Institute, Briarcliff Manor, NY, 1975.

Ricks, Truett A., et al., Principles of Security, Anderson Publishing Company, Cincinnati, OH, 1981.

Reber, Jan and Shaw, Paul, Executive Protection

Manual, MTI Teleprograms, Inc., Schiller Park, IL, 1980.

Romig, Clarence H. A., The Physical Evidence Technician, Police Training Institute, Champaign, IL, 1975.

Rothstein, Paul F., Evidence: State and Federal Rules, West Publishing Company, Saint Paul, MN, 1983.

Safeguarding Your Business Against Theft and Vandalism, Research Institute of America, New York, NY, 1983.

Sanger, John, The Alarm Dealer's Guide, Butterworth Publishers, Stoneham, MA, 1985.

Schabeck, Tim A., Emergency Planning Guide for Data Processing Centers, Assets Protection, Madison, WI, 1979.

Schultz, Donald O., Principles of Physical Security, Gulf Publishing Company, Houston, TX, 1978.

The Science of Fingerprints, Federal Bureau of Investigation, Washington, D.C.

Scope of Legal Authority of Private Security Personnel, Department of Justice, Washington, D.C., 1976.

Sennewald, Charles A., Effective Security Management, Butterworth Publishers, Stoneham, MA, 1986.

Swint, J. Michael and Lairson, David R., "Employee Assistance Programs," Alcohol Health and Research World, Winter, 1983/84.

Terrorist Attacks Against US Business, Department of State, Washington, D.C., 1982.

Terrorist Bombings, Department of State, Washington, D.C., 1983.

Terrorist Incidents Involving Diplomats, Department of State, Washington, D.C., 1983.

Topical Bibliography: Security Officer/Investigator Training and Management, National Institute of Justice, Washington, D.C., 1985.

Understanding Crime Prevention, National Crime Prevention Institute, Butterworth Publishers, Stoneham, MA, 1986.

Van Meter, C. H., Principles of Police Interrogation, Charles C. Thomas Publishers, Springfield, IL, 1973.

Vandiver, James V., Criminal Investigation: A Guide to Techniques and Solutions, Scarecrow Press, Inc., Metuchen, NJ, 1983.

Walsh, Timothy J. and Healy, Richard J., The Protection of Assets Manual, The Merritt Company, Santa Monica, CA, 1983.

Weber, Thad L., Alarms Systems and Theft Prevention, Butterworth Publishers, Stoneham, MA, 1986.

Webster's Ninth New Collegiate Dictionary, Merriam-Webster, Inc., Springfield, MA, 1984.

White Collar Crime, Chamber of Commerce of the United States, Washington, D.C., 1974.

Woodman, Duane J., Shoplifting: An Illustrated Study, Security Data Services, Redlands, CA.